Cla...
His M...

A convenient, but steamy affair…

Praise for three bestselling authors –
Helen Bianchin, Sharon Kendrick,
Lucy Gordon

About MISTRESS BY ARRANGEMENT:
'Helen Bianchin pens a passionate tale with
spicy scenes, remarkable characters and
excellent story development.'
—*Romantic Times*

About MISTRESS MATERIAL:
'Sharon Kendrick delivers a gripping story
with sensual scenes, dominant characters
and an entertaining premise.'
—*Romantic Times*

About Lucy Gordon:
'Lucy Gordon charms readers as she masterfully
blends humour, dazzling characters and a
brilliant premise.'
—*Romantic Times*

Claiming His Mistress

MISTRESS BY ARRANGEMENT
by
Helen Bianchin

MISTRESS MATERIAL
by
Sharon Kendrick

TYCOON FOR HIRE
by
Lucy Gordon

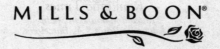

MILLS & BOON®

*MILLS & BOON and MILLS & BOON with the Rose Device
are registered trademarks of the publisher.*
*Harlequin Mills & Boon Limited,
Eton House, 18-24 Paradise Road, Richmond, Surrey, TW9 1SR*

CLAIMING HIS MISTRESS
© by Harlequin Enterprises II B.V., 2004

Mistress by Arrangement, Mistress Material and *Tycoon for Hire*
were first published in Great Britain by Harlequin Mills & Boon
Limited in separate, single volumes.

Mistress by Arrangement © Helen Bianchin 1999
Mistress Material © Sharon Kendrick 1996
Tycoon for Hire © Lucy Gordon 1999

ISBN 0 263 84067 0

05-0204

*Printed and bound in Spain
by Litografia Rosés S.A., Barcelona*

Helen Bianchin was born in New Zealand and travelled to Australia before marrying her Italian-born husband. After three years they moved, returned to New Zealand with their daughter, had two sons then resettled in Australia. Encouraged by friends to recount anecdotes of her years as a tobacco sharefarmer's wife living in an Italian community, Helen began setting words on paper and her first novel was published in 1975. An animal lover, she says her terrier and Persian cat regard her study as as much theirs as hers.

**Watch out for Helen Bianchin's
latest sizzling read:
The Spaniard's Baby Bargain.
On sale July 2004, in Modern Romance™!**

MISTRESS BY
ARRANGEMENT
by
Helen Bianchin

For Alex and Angie Kidas
with gratitude and affection

CHAPTER ONE

MICHELLE sipped superb Chardonnay from a crystal wineglass and cast an idle glance at the room's occupants.

The men were resplendent in black dinner suits, white dress shirts and black bow ties, while the women vied with each other in designer gowns.

This evening's occasion was a simple dinner party for ten guests held in the beautiful home of their hosts, Antonia and Emerson Bateson-Burrows, whose reputation for providing fine wine, excellent food, and scintillating company was almost unequalled in Queensland's Gold Coast society.

'Another drink, darling?'

She felt the proprietorial clasp of Jeremy's arm along the back of her waist.

Mine, the action seemed to shriek. The fond glance of his parents, *hers,* merely served to endorse their approval.

Did they think she was unaware of the subtle manipulative matchmaking attempts of late? It was too much of a coincidence that Jeremy had been a fellow guest at several social events she'd attended in the past four weeks.

Marriage wasn't on her agenda, nor was she willing to drift into a meaningless relationship. Thanks to an annuity from her maternal grandmother, her life

5

was good. At twenty-five, she owned her own apartment, ran a successful art gallery in partnership with a friend, and she had no inclination to change the status quo.

She felt the faint pressure of Jeremy's hand at her waist and she summoned a polite smile. 'Thanks, but I'll wait until dinner.'

Which would be when? Were all the guests not accounted for? Speculation rose as she glimpsed Jeremy's mother spare her wristwatch a surreptitious glance.

Who would dare to be late for a Bateson-Burrows soiree?

'Mother is becoming a tad anxious,' Jeremy revealed, sotto voce. 'Nikos warned he might be unavoidably late.'

Curiosity sparked Michelle's interest. 'Nikos?'

Jeremy cast her an amused look. 'Alessandros. Greek origin, relatively new money, respectably earned,' he added. 'Electronics. Bases in Athens, Rome, Paris, London, Vancouver, Sydney.'

'If his Australian base is in Sydney, what's he doing on the Gold Coast?'

'He has a penthouse in Main Beach,' Jeremy enlightened. 'The man is a consummate strategist. Word has it he's about to close an enviable deal.' His mouth formed a cynical twist. 'Instead of flying directly to Sydney, he's chosen to negotiate from the Gold Coast.'

'Impressive,' she acknowledged, summoning a mental image of a short, paunchy, balding middle-aged Greek with a stylish much younger wife.

'Very,' Jeremy declared succinctly. 'Father covets his patronage and his business account.'

'And his friendship?'

'It's at an adequate level.'

Adequate presumably wasn't good enough, and Emerson Bateson-Burrows' extended invitation to dine was merely part of a larger plan.

Politics, business and social, involved an intricate strategy of a kind that occasionally sickened her altruistic mind.

'Two hours to dine and socialise over coffee,' Jeremy inclined. 'Then we can escape and go on to a nightclub.'

It irked her that he took her acquiescence for granted. She was on the point of telling him so, when some sixth sense alerted her attention.

Curious, she lifted her head and felt the breath catch in her throat.

'Nikos,' Jeremy informed her, although she barely registered the verbal identification as her interest was captured by the tall male figure who had just entered the room.

He possessed broad-boned features, a strong jaw, and his mouth was chiselled perfection.

A man, Michelle perceived with instinctive insight, who wore the fine clothes of a gentleman, possessed the requisite good manners...and had the heart of a predatory warrior.

It was evident in his stance, the cool assessing quality in those dark slate-grey eyes as they roamed the room and its occupants.

They flicked towards her, paused, then settled in a

slow appraisal of her dark honey-blond hair, green eyes, and the slender feminine curves encased in a black designer dress.

There was no power on earth that could suppress the faint shivery sensation feathering its way down her spine at the intensity of that look. She felt as if it stripped away the conventional barrier of clothes, lingerie, and stroked her skin.

It took considerable effort to match his appraisal, but she was damned if she'd concede him any sort of victory by glancing away.

Dark hair, well-groomed. Broad shoulders beneath expensive tailoring, and his shoes were hand-tooled leather. In his mid-thirties, he was the antithesis of the middle-aged paunchy balding man Michelle had envisaged.

She watched as he worked the room during an introductory circuit, noting the undoubted charm, the easy smile, an easy grace of movement that implied a high level of physical fitness.

'Michelle Gerard,' Antonia announced by way of introduction, reaching their side. 'Jeremy's girl-friend.'

Nikos Alessandros reached forward, took hold of her hand, and raised it to his lips.

Michelle's eyes flew wide with shock as he placed a brief open-mouthed kiss to her palm, then he curled her fingers as if to seal in the flagrant action. Heat flooded her veins, coursing through her body as each nerve-end sprang into vibrant life.

'Michelle.' His voice held a faint inflection, an

accent that was more international than indicative of
his own nationality.

Primitive alchemy, potent and incredibly lethal,
was a compelling force, and her skin burned where
his lips had touched.

'We meet again.'

Again? She'd never met him in this lifetime. If she
had, she'd remember. No woman alive could possibly forget someone of Nikos Alessandros' calibre!

Michelle was at once conscious of Antonia's surprised gaze coupled with Jeremy's sharp attention.

'You've already met?'

'While Michelle was studying at the Sorbonne in
Paris,' Nikos declared with knowledgeable ease.

A calculated guess? Somehow she doubted it.
Which immediately drew the question as to how he
came by the information.

'Really?' Antonia queried lightly after a few seconds silence.

Michelle watched in fascination as he directed her
a blatantly sensual smile. 'How could I forget?'

She should refute they'd ever set eyes on each
other, and accuse him of being a sexist opportunist.

'Your capacity to remember surprises me.' That
much was true, yet as soon as the words left her lips
she wondered at the wisdom of playing his game.

Midsummer madness? An attempt to alleviate the
matchmaking techniques employed by two sets of
parents? Or just plain devilry.

Nikos' eyes never left her own, and she experienced the uncanny sensation he could read her mind.

Worse, that he could dissect the conventional barriers she'd learnt to erect and divine the path to her soul.

It wasn't a comfortable feeling. But then, she doubted there was anything *comfortable* about this man.

Dangerous, occasionally merciless, powerful. And rarely predictable. A tiny imp added, incredibly sexual. An earthy, uninhibited lover who would seek every liberty, and encourage a similar response. Demand, she amended with instinctive knowledge.

Just the thought of what he could do to a woman, and how he would do it was enough to raise all her fine body hairs in a gesture of…what? Self-preservation? *Anticipation?*

Her eyes dilated at a highly erotic image, one that was so evocative she was unable to subdue the flare of heat from her innermost core.

'Indeed?' That deep drawl held a wealth of meaning she didn't even want to explore.

Antonia sensed it, and immediately launched into an attempt at damage control. 'Nikos, you must allow Emerson to get you a drink.' She placed a hand on his sleeve, and for a moment Michelle held her breath at the possibility he might detach Antonia's hand and opt to stay where he was.

Something moved in his expression, then he smiled, inclining his head in mocking acquiescence as he allowed his hostess to steer him away.

The electric force-field evident didn't diminish, and it took considerable effort to lift the glass to her lips and take a sip of wine.

'You know him.'

Michelle's lips parted to deny it, only to pause fractionally too long.

'And to think I've been playing the gentleman,' Jeremy drawled silkily, raising his glass in a silent mocking salute as he conducted a slow encompassing survey from the top of her head to the tip of her toes and back again.

Indignation heightened the dark golden sparks in her green eyes, and anyone who knew her well would have heeded the silent warning.

'One has only to look at Nikos to know his *friend-ship* with women is inevitably of an intimate nature.'

'Really?' Michelle tempered the query with a deceptive smile. She wanted to hit him. 'You'd dare to accuse me on the strength of another man's reputation?'

Antonia Bateson-Burrows' announcement that dinner was ready proved opportune.

'Can you blame me for being jealous?' Jeremy offered as they crossed to the dining room.

Nikos Alessandros had a lot to answer for, she determined wryly.

Unbidden, her gaze shifted to the tall male Greek a few feet distant, and she watched in fascinated surprise as he turned briefly towards her.

Those dark slate-grey eyes held an expression she couldn't fathom, and for one infinitesimal second everything faded to the periphery of her vision. There was only *him*. The subdued chatter, the other guests, were no longer apparent.

A slight smile curved his lips, but his eyes remained steady, almost as if he withheld a knowledge of something she couldn't even begin to presume.

The breath caught in her throat, and she deliberately broke the silent spell by transferring her attention to the proposed seating arrangements.

With any luck, Nikos Alessandros would be at the opposite end of the table, precluding the necessity to indulge in polite conversation.

An accomplished hostess, Antonia skilfully manoeuvred her guests into chairs, shuffling them so there were six on one side with five on the other, while she and Emerson took their position at the head of the table.

Oh *hell*. Thirteen at the dinner table on Friday the thirteenth. Could it get any worse?

Don't tempt Fate by even *thinking* about it, a tiny voice taunted, only to discover she faced Nikos across a decorative floral centrepiece.

Emerson poured the wine while Antonia organised the serving of the first course.

'*Salute.*' Nikos' accent was flawless as he lifted his glass, and although his smile encompassed everyone seated at the table, his eyes remained fixed on Michelle.

The soup was delicious vichyssoise, although after the first spoonful Michelle's tastebuds seemed to go on strike.

Succulent prawns in a piquant sauce were served on a bed of mesclan lettuce, and she sipped the excellent white wine, then opted for chilled water in the need for a clear head.

The conversation encompassed a broad spectrum

as it touched briefly on the state of the country's financial budget, the possibility of tax reform and its effect on the economy.

'What is your view, Michelle?'

The sound of that faintly accented drawl stirred her senses. Her hand paused midway in its passage from the table to her lips, and her fingers tightened fractionally on the goblet's slim stem.

'Inconsequential, I imagine. Given that whatever my opinion, it will have little effect in the scheme of things.'

Jeremy's silent offer to refill Nikos' glass was met with an equally silent refusal.

The fact that Nikos declined didn't halt Jeremy's inclination to fill his own glass.

'Nevertheless, I would be interested to hear it.'

Having set the cat among the pigeons, it's a source of amusement for you to watch the outcome, she surmised silently. But what if one of the pigeons was unafraid of the cat? Two could play this game.

'As I recall, you were never particularly interested in my mind.'

His eyes held hers, mesmeric in their intensity. She watched as his lips parted to reveal even white teeth, and noticed the movement deepened the vertical slash on each cheek.

'Could anyone blame me, *pedhi mou?*'

His drawled endearment curled round her nerve-ends and sent them spiralling out of control.

'I'll serve the main course.'

Michelle heard Antonia's words, and watched absently as the hired help cleared plates and cutlery and replaced them.

'Some more wine, Nikos?'

Emerson, ever the genial host, merely warranted the briefest glance. 'Thank you, no.' He returned his attention to Michelle. 'I haven't the need for further stimulation.'

This was getting out of hand. It was also gaining the interest of everyone seated at the table.

Chicken in a lemon sauce accompanied by a selection of braised vegetables did little to tempt Michelle's flagging appetite, and she sampled a few mouthfuls of chicken, took a delicate bite of each vegetable, then set down her cutlery.

Water, not wine, was something she sipped at infrequent intervals as she wished fervently for the evening to end.

Yet there was dessert and the cheeseboard to complete the meal, followed by coffee. It would be at least another hour before she could make some excuse to leave.

Jeremy leaned towards her and placed an arm along the back of her chair.

'Tell me, darling.' His voice was a conspiratorial murmur. 'Is he incredibly physical in bed?'

She didn't deign to answer, and deliberately avoided glancing in Nikos' direction as she conversed with the guest seated next to her. Afterwards she had little recollection of the topic or her contribution.

Dessert was an exotic creation of baklava, together with fresh fruit and brandied cream.

Michelle passed on both, and selected a few grapes to freshen her palate.

'Shall we adjourn to the lounge for coffee?' Antonia queried when it appeared everyone had had their fill.

They were the sweetest words Michelle had heard in hours, and she subdued her enthusiasm as she stood to her feet and joined her parents.

Chantelle Gerard cast her daughter a thoughtful glance. 'I had no idea you knew Nikos Alessandros.'

Money was important. Breeding, equally so. The Bateson-Burrows possessed both. But the Alessandros' fortune couldn't be ignored.

Michelle could almost see the wheels turning in her mother's brain. 'I intend leaving very soon.'

'You're going on somewhere with Jeremy, darling?'

'No.'

'I see,' Chantelle voiced sagely. 'We'll talk in the morning.'

'Believe me, *Maman,* there is absolutely nothing to tell,' Michelle assured with an edge of mockery, watching as her mother lifted one eyebrow in silent chastisement. 'Nothing,' she added quietly.

Twenty questions at dawn wasn't her favoured way to begin the day. However, Chantelle was well-practised in the art of subtle manipulation, and Michelle was able to interpret every nuance in her mother's voice.

'We can easily give you a lift home if you're prepared to wait awhile.'

She should have brought her own car. Except

Jeremy had insisted he collect her. Not a wise move, she decided wryly in retrospect.

The mild headache she'd thought to invent was no longer a figment of her imagination. And Jeremy was fast becoming a nuisance. Her apartment was less than a kilometre away, a distance she'd entertain no qualms in walking during the day. However, the night hours provided a totally different context for a woman alone.

'I'll call a taxi.'

Antonia offered a superb blend of coffee, together with liqueur, cream, milk, exotic bite-sized continental biscuits and a variety of Belgian chocolates.

Michelle added milk and sugar, and sipped it as quickly as etiquette allowed. Placing her cup and saucer down onto a nearby side-table, she turned towards her hosts, and her stomach executed a slow somersault as she discovered Antonia and Emerson deep in conversation with Nikos Alessandros.

Just pin a smile on your face, thank them for a pleasant evening, and then exit the room. Two or three minutes, five at the most.

Almost as if he sensed her hesitation, Nikos lifted his head and watched her approach.

Jeremy appeared at her side and draped an arm over her shoulder. His hand lingered a hair's-breadth from her breast, and she stepped sideways in an effort to avoid the familiarity, only to have Jeremy's hand close firmly over her arm.

'Finished doing the duty thing with your parents?'

She took exception to his tone, and his manner. 'I don't regard talking to my parents as a duty.'

'You obviously don't suffer parental suffocation as a result of being the only child,' he alluded cynically.

'No,' she responded evenly.

'Ready to leave?' Nikos queried smoothly as she joined Jeremy's parents. 'If you'll excuse us,' Nikos announced imperturbably to his hosts. 'Michelle and I have some catching up to do.' He caught hold of her hand and drew her forward, inclined his head towards a startled Jeremy, then led her from the lounge.

'What do you think you're doing?' she hissed as soon as they reached the foyer.

'Providing you with a lift to your apartment.'

'Michelle.' Jeremy drew level with them. '*I'll* take you home.'

She felt like hitting each of them. One for being overly possessive and childishly jealous. The Greek for his arrogance.

'There's no need to leave your parents' guests,' Nikos intoned pleasantly. 'Michelle's apartment building is almost opposite my own.'

How did he know that?

'She's *my* girlfriend,' Jeremy reiterated fiercely as he turned towards her.

This was getting worse by the second.

'Michelle?' Nikos' voice was silk-encased steel.

Jeremy's hand closed over her shoulder, as if staking a claim. 'Damn you, *tell him.*'

'There's nothing to tell,' she assured quietly, and winced as Jeremy's hold tightened.

'I don't think so, my friend,' Nikos drawled with

dangerous softness, and Jeremy turned towards him
with emboldened belligerence.

'This is none of your business!'

'I disagree.'

'Why would you do that?'

'Because Michelle is with me.'

'Damned if she is!' Jeremy's face contorted with
fury.

'You want proof?' Nikos demanded silkily.

Michelle didn't get the chance to say a word in
protest as Nikos drew her into his arms and covered
her mouth with his own.

Possessive and frankly sensual, he took advantage
of her surprise to taste and plunder at will, then before she could protest he gathered her close and
turned the kiss into something incredibly erotic.

Her heart jumped, then raced to a quickened beat
as one hand slid to hold fast her nape while the other
cupped her bottom and brought her into startling contact with hard male arousal.

Each and every one of her senses intensified as he
sought her response.

Passion…electric, magnetic, *shameless,* it tore
through all the conventional barriers to a primitive
base that was wholly sexual.

It was as if an instinctive knowledge existed between them, she registered dimly. Something that
sanctioned the way his mouth wreaked havoc with
her own.

She was supremely aware of him, everything about
him. The faint layers of texture and smell heightened

her senses…the subtle tang of his cologne, the texture of his skin, the fine fabric of his clothing.

There was a part of her that wanted to travel with him wherever this sensual path might lead, while the sensible *sane* part registered alarm.

With a groan of disgust she dragged her mouth away. Her breathing was ragged, and for the space of a few seconds she had no knowledge of where she was. There was only the man, and a mesmeric helpless hunger.

'What in hell do you think you're doing?'

Jeremy's voice seemed to come from a distance, and she struggled to focus on the immediate present.

'Right now, taking Michelle home,' Nikos declared with deceptive mildness. Without missing a beat he lifted one eyebrow in silent query. 'Michelle?'

Dammit, his breathing was even, steady, while hers seemed as wild and ragged as her heartbeat.

'Walk away from me,' Jeremy warned. 'And I won't have you back.'

She registered Jeremy's rage and felt vaguely sickened. 'You never *had* me in the first place.'

The sound of voices and the appearance in the foyer of two other guests had a diffusing effect, and Jeremy's expression underwent an abrupt change from anger to affability.

'Let's get the hell out of here,' Nikos instructed quietly, taking hold of her arm.

He led her down the few steps to the driveway, and she made a futile effort to wrench her arm free from his grasp as they drew abreast of a large BMW.

'Don't,' he warned silkily. 'You'll only hurt yourself.'

It was difficult to determine his expression in the dim half-light as he withdrew a set of keys, unlocked the door, then handed them to her. 'Drive, if it will make you feel safer to be with me.'

The soft crunch of gravel as footsteps approached intruded, and she stood stiffly as they drew close.

'Goodnight, Michelle. Nikos.'

Nikos returned the acknowledgement as the couple slid into the car immediately behind them, and in an unbidden gesture Michelle thrust the keys at him, then she unlatched the door and slid into the passenger seat.

Nikos took his position behind the wheel, fired the engine, then eased the car onto the road. Minutes later the powerful car entered the main northbound highway, traversed it for less than a kilometre, and took the next turnoff that led into suburban Main Beach.

She was supremely conscious of him, the slight flash of gold on his wrist as he handled the wheel.

'We'll stop at a café for coffee,' Nikos informed as they paused at a set of traffic lights. 'There's something I'd like to discuss with you.'

'The subtle "your apartment or mine?" spiel?' Michelle mocked with light sarcasm. 'Forget it. One-night stands aren't my thing.'

'I'm relieved to hear it.'

The lights changed, and within minutes the powerful engine purred down a notch as he decelerated and touched the brakes, then he eased the vehicle to a halt.

Michelle reached for the door-clasp, a word of thanks ready to emerge from her lips.

Then she froze.

The underground car park was similar to a multitude of beneath street-level concrete caverns. Except it wasn't *her* apartment car park.

CHAPTER TWO

'WHERE the hell are we?'

'My apartment building,' Nikos drawled. 'It happens to be in a block a short distance from your own.' He opened his door and slid out from behind the wheel.

Michelle copied his actions, and stood glaring at him across the roof of the BMW, then she turned and walked to the sweeping upgrade leading to the main entrance.

'The security gate is activated by a personally coded remote.' He paused a beat, then added with killing softness, 'Likewise, the lift is security coded.'

She swung back to face him, anger etched on every line of her body. 'Kidnapping is a criminal offense. If you don't want me to lay charges, I suggest you allow me free passage out of here. Now,' she added with deadly intent. If she'd been standing close enough, she'd have lashed out and hit him.

Nikos regarded her steadily, assessing her slim frame, the darkness of her eyes. There was no fear apparent, and the thought momentarily intrigued him. Self-defence skills? His own had been acquired and honed to a lethal degree.

'All I want is fifteen, maybe twenty minutes of your time.'

Her heartbeat thudded painfully against her ribs. The car park was well-lit, there were a number of

22

cars lining marked bays, but it was eerily quiet. There was no one to whom she could appeal for help.

Michelle extracted her mobile phone and prepared to punch in the requisite digit that would connect her with Emergency Services and alert the police.

'You have nothing to fear from me.'

His voice was even, and controlled. Too controlled. He emanated an indefinable leashed quality, a watchfulness that only a fool would disregard. And she didn't consider herself a fool.

'I don't find this—' she swept an arm in silent indication of her surroundings '—in the least amusing.'

'You were averse to joining me in more comfortable surroundings,' he posed silkily.

Anger meshed with indignation, colouring her features and lending her eyes a fiery sparkle. 'Forgive me.' Her voice dripped icy sarcasm. 'For declining your invitation.'

Her passion intrigued him. Dammit, *she* intrigued him. Most women of his acquaintance, aware of his social and financial status, would have willingly followed wherever he chose to lead.

Yet for all that Michelle Gerard felt like an angel in his arms and responded with uninhibited fervour, instinct relayed that it wasn't part of an act.

'By your own admission,' Michelle vented with restrained anger. 'You brought me here to talk.'

She needed to shift the balance of control. *Fear* wasn't an option. Although the word in itself was a misnomer. Nikos Alessandros didn't mean her any harm, at least not in the physical sense. Yet when it

came to her emotions... Now that was an entirely
different ball game, something which irked her unbearably, for how could she be emotionally spellbound by a man who, in a short few hours, had broken every conventional social nicety?

'I suggest you do so, *now*,' she continued forcefully. 'And condense whatever you have to say into
two minutes.' She indicated the mobile phone. 'One
wrong move and I'll summon the police.'

He leaned one hip against the smooth bonnet of
his car, and regarded her thoughtfully.

'I want you to be my social companion for a few
weeks,' he stated without preamble.

Michelle drew in a deep breath and released it
slowly. Whatever she'd expected, it hadn't been this.
He had only to beckon and women would beat a path
to his side. 'Surely you jest?'

His attention didn't falter. 'I'm quite serious.'

'Why?'

'For much the same reason it would suit you.'

She didn't pretend to misunderstand. 'What makes
you so sure?'

'Body language,' Nikos drawled.

Her eyes flashed golden fire. 'I can handle
Jeremy.'

'I don't doubt you can.' One eyebrow lifted. 'The
question is, do you want to?'

'I don't need anyone to fight my battles,' she said
dryly. 'Any more than you do. So why don't you cut
to the chase?'

'I thought I already had.'

Her head tilted to one side. 'You expect me to

believe there's a female you can't handle?' The prospect was almost laughable.

'The widow of a very close friend of mine,' Nikos enlightened her slowly. 'Her husband was killed several months ago in a skiing accident.'

'She is emotionally fragile, and genuinely misinterprets the friendship?' Michelle posed. 'Or has she become a calculating vixen intent on snaring another rich husband?'

His expression imperceptibly hardened, a subtle shifting of muscle over bone that reassembled his features into a compelling mask.

'You presume too much.'

So she'd struck a tender nerve. Interesting that he didn't answer her question.

'You feel honour-bound to spare—' She paused deliberately.

'Saska.'

'Saska,' she continued. 'Any embarrassment during what is a transitional grieving period?'

'Yes,' he declared succinctly.

'I see.' She regarded him thoughtfully. 'And on the basis of one meeting, an appraisal of *body language,* you virtually kidnap me and suggest I have nothing better to do with my time than act out a part for your benefit.'

'There would be a few advantages.'

Topaz flecks shone in the depths of her green eyes, a silent evidence of her anger. 'Name one.'

'All of the pleasure and none of the strings.'

'And a bonus, I imagine, if I'm sufficiently convincing?' The flippant query slipped from her lips, and she glimpsed the faint edge of humour tilt the corner of his mouth.

'I'm sure we can come to an amicable arrangement.'

The entire evening had been a complete farce, including Jeremy's behaviour. As for Nikos Alessandros… *Impossible* didn't come close!

'Just who the hell do you think you are?' she demanded fiercely.

His expression hardened slightly, and his eyes took on the quality of steel. 'A man who recognises an opportunity, and isn't afraid to seize it.'

She could still feel the touch of his mouth on hers, his taste…and the way her senses had flipped into a tailspin.

His indolent stance was deceptive. She had the instinctive feeling that if she turned away from him, he would simply reach out and haul her back.

'Go find some other female,' Michelle directed. 'I'm not willing to participate.'

She caught the dark glitter in his eyes, glimpsed a muscle tense at the edge of his jaw, and experienced momentary satisfaction at besting him.

'There's nothing I can do to change your mind?'

Her gaze didn't waver. 'No, not a thing.'

He examined her features with contemplative scrutiny. 'In that case, we'll take the lift to the ground floor and I'll escort you to your apartment.'

She wanted to argue with him, and almost did.

'Wise,' Nikos drawled.

Michelle felt her stomach twist as they stepped into the small electronic cubicle. She was incredibly aware of the emotional pull, the intangible meshing of the senses.

Seconds later she preceded him into the main lobby, passed reception, then emerged into the fresh evening air.

Less than a hundred metres distant lay several trendy restaurants and cafés, each with outdoor chairs and tables lending the area a cosmopolitan air.

Michelle's apartment building was situated fifty metres distant on the opposite side of the road, and when they reached its entrance she paused, a polite smile widening her lips as she turned towards him.

There was nothing to thank him for, and she didn't make a pretense of doing so. The polite smile was merely a concession.

'You forgot something.'

She caught the purposeful gleam in those dark eyes an instant before hands captured her face.

His head descended and his mouth covered hers in a kiss that plundered deep, savouring the inner sweetness without mercy, his tongue swift and incredibly clever as he took his fill.

This was skilled mastery, she registered dimly, and a silent gasp of outrage remained locked in her throat as he cupped her bottom and brought her close up against him so that she was in no doubt of his arousal.

Potent, shimmering heat sang through her veins and pooled at the centre of her feminine core. She could feel the thrust of her breasts as they swelled in anticipation of his touch, their tender peaks hardening into sensitive buds craving the tantalising succour of his mouth.

This was insane. A divine madness that had no place, no basis in *anything*.

Almost as if he sensed her withdrawal, he gradually lightened the kiss to a gentle brush of his lips against her own. Then he lifted his head, and released her.

'Pleasant dreams, *pedhi mou*,' he bade gently.

His eyes were warm, and deep enough to drown in. The flip response she sought never found voice, and she turned away from him, activated the security code on the external door, then hurried into the lobby without a backward glance.

Damn him. He was the most arrogant infuriating devastating man she'd ever met. Infinitely dangerous, she added as she jabbed the call button to summon one of two lifts.

As soon as the doors slid open she entered the cubicle, stabbed the appropriate panel button, and barely suppressed a shiver as the lift sped swiftly upward.

If she never saw him again, it would be too soon. Which was a total contradiction in terms, she grimaced as the lift came to a halt at her floor.

Seconds later she let herself into her apartment, hit the light switch, checked the locking mechanism was in place, then she moved through to the kitchen.

Caffeine would keep her awake, so she opted for a glass of chilled water, sipped the contents, then crossed to her bedroom.

It was several minutes this side of midnight, and

she divested her clothes, took a leisurely warm shower, then slid between cool percale sheets in an effort to cull sleep.

Without success. There were too many images crowding her mind. A tall dark-haired Greek whose eyes seemed to haunt her. His voice, with its slightly accented timbre that curled like silk round every sensitive nerve-end, invading without license as a vivid reminder of his touch. The feel of his hands on her body, their caressing warmth, and the taste of his mouth on hers as it devoured, savoured, and sought to imprint his brand.

It was almost as if she could still sense the exclusive tones of his cologne, the clean smell of fine tailoring and fresh laundered cotton. And a subtle masculine scent that was *his*…

Dammit. She didn't want to be this *disturbed* by a man. To have her senses invaded by a pervasive sexual alchemy.

She'd met scores of men, been charmed by several, discovered an affection for a few, and loved none. At least, not the *swept off my feet, melting bones* kind of emotion portrayed on the cinema screen and extolled between the pages of many a romance novel.

When it came to attraction, she was still waiting for the earth to move. Warm and fuzzy somehow didn't come close to hungry shattering sensual sexuality.

Yet tonight she'd experienced it in the arms of a stranger.

For the space of…how long? Two, three minutes?

She'd lost all sense of time and place. There was only the man, the moment, and raw unbridled passion.

Her body had curved into his, and clung, moulding in a perfect fit as his mouth had taken possession of her own.

And it had been *possession.* Demanding, compelling, and frankly sensual, his kiss was a promise. Primitive, raw, libidinous.

It should have frightened her. Instead, for the space of those few minutes she'd felt exhilarated, *alive,* and aware. Dear God, so aware of every pulse beat, the heat that flared from every erogenous zone as her whole body coalesced into a throbbing entity, almost totally beyond her control.

If he could initiate such an effect with just a kiss, what sort of lover would he be?

Intensely vital, passionate, and incredibly sensual. Hungry, wild…*shameless,* she added with certainty.

What was she thinking?

Nikos Alessandros was the last man on earth she would want to have anything to do with.

She lifted her head and thumped her pillow. Damn the hateful images invading her mind. They clouded her perspective, dulled commonsense, and played havoc with her nervous system.

All she had to do was fall asleep, and in the morning a fresh new day would dispense with the night's emotional turmoil.

CHAPTER THREE

THE insistent ring of the telephone penetrated Michelle's subconscious, and she reached out a hand, searched blindly for the handset, and succeeded in knocking the receiver onto the floor.

Oh hell. What a way to start the day.

She caught hold of the spiral cord and tugged until her fingers connected with the receiver.

'Michelle.'

Inches away from her ear she recognised the feminine voice, and she stifled an unladylike oath.

'Maman,' she acknowledged with resignation. Just what she needed.

'Are you still in bed, *cherie?*' There was a slight pause. 'Do you know what time it is?'

Seven, maybe eight, she hazarded, sparing a quick glance at the bedside clock before drawing a sharp breath. *Nine.*

'You are alone?'

Michelle closed her eyes, then opened them again. 'No, *Maman.* Two lovers have pleasured me all through the night.'

'There is no need to be facetious, darling,' Chantelle reproved, and Michelle sighed.

'I'm sorry. Blame it on lack of sleep.'

'I thought we might do lunch.' Chantelle named a trendy restaurant at Main Beach. 'Shall we say twelve?' And hung up before Michelle had a chance to confirm or refuse.

'Grrr.' The sound was a low-pitched growl that held a mixture of irritation and compliance. She could ring back and decline, except she knew almost word for word what Chantelle would say as a persuasive ploy.

Emotional blackmail of the nicest kind, she added mentally as she replaced the receiver and rolled onto her stomach.

Lunch for her mother inevitably meant a minuscule Caesar salad, followed by fresh fruit, a small glass of white wine and two glasses of water. Afterwards they would browse the trendy boutiques, drive the short distance to Marina Mirage, relax over a leisurely *latte*, then wander at will through the upmarket emporiums.

It was a mother-daughter thing they indulged in together on occasion. Michelle was under no illusion that today's invitation was a thinly-veiled guise to conduct an in-depth discussion about her association with Nikos Alessandros.

In which case she'd best rise, shine and meet the day. Routine chores and the weekly visit to the supermarket would occupy an hour and a half, and she'd need the remaining time to shower and change if she was to meet her mother at noon.

Chantelle ordered her favourite Caesar salad, and mineral water, while Michelle settled for something more substantial.

'Antonia and Emerson have insisted we join them on their boat for lunch tomorrow.'

Sunglasses shielded her mother's eyes, successfully hiding her expression. Although Michelle wasn't fooled in the slightest.

Chantelle had conversation down to a fine art. First there would be the pleasantries, some light humour in the form of an anecdote or two, followed by the main purpose of the meeting.

'That will be nice,' Michelle commented evenly.

'We will, of course, be back in time to attend the Gallery exhibition.'

This month's exhibition featured an up and coming local artist whose work had impressed both Gallery partners. Arrangements for each exhibition were made many months in advance, and it said much for the Gallery's reputation that they had bookings well into next year for future showings.

Emilio possessed an instinctive flair for what would succeed, and their combined talents and expertise had seen a fledging Gallery expand to become one of the most respected establishments on the coastal strip.

Invitations had been sent out to fifty patrons and their partners, the catering instructions had been given. All that remained were the final touches, and placement of the exhibits.

Something which both she and Emilio would attend to this afternoon and complete early tomorrow morning. 'Do you have any plans for tonight, darling?'

Michelle wound a portion of superb fettuccine

marinara onto her fork and held it poised halfway above her plate. 'An early night, *Maman.*'

'Oh, I see.'

Did she? 'You know how much effort Emilio and I put into each exhibition,' Michelle said lightly. 'There are so many things to check, and Emilio is particular with every detail.'

'I know, darling.'

Chantelle considered education as something important for Michelle to acquire. The private school, university, time abroad to study at the Sorbonne. Except she really wasn't expected to *do* anything as a result of such qualification and experience.

The Gallery had been viewed as a frivolous venture. Michelle's partnership with Emilio Bonanno was expected to be in name only, something she quickly dispelled as she steadfastly refused to join her mother on the social circuit, confining herself to the occasional charity dinner or gala, much to Chantelle's expressed disappointment.

You could say, Michelle mused, that for the past three years her mother had graciously accepted that her own social proclivities were not shared by her daughter. However, it didn't stop Chantelle from issuing frequent invitations, or, for the past year, indulging in subtle matchmaking attempts.

'I think you've succeeded in making Jeremy jealous.' Chantelle took a sip of mineral water, then set down the glass. 'He wasn't quite himself after you left last night. Has he telephoned you this morning?'

'No,' Michelle responded evenly. 'I don't particularly want to hear from him.'

'Because of Nikos Alessandros?'

'Nikos Alessandros has nothing whatsoever to do with it.'

'He's quite a catch, darling.'

She chose to be deliberately obtuse. 'Jeremy?'

'Nikos,' Chantelle corrected with a tolerant sigh.

'As I have no intention of indulging in a fishing expedition, whether or not he's a catch is totally irrelevant.'

'Do you have time to do a little window shopping?' Chantelle queried. 'I really think I could add something to my wardrobe.'

To give her mother credit, she knew when to withdraw. 'I promised Emilio I'd be at the Gallery at two-thirty.'

Chantelle savoured the last mouthful of cos lettuce, then replaced her fork. 'In that case, darling, do finish your pasta. We'll share a coffee later, shall we?'

Clothes, shoes, lingerie, perfume. Any one, or all four, could prove a guaranteed distraction, and Michelle accompanied her mother into one boutique after another in her quest to purchase.

An hour and a half later Chantelle held no less than three brightly emblazoned carry bags, and there was no time left to share coffee.

'See you tomorrow, darling. Don't work too hard.'

Michelle placed a light kiss on her mother's cheek, then watched as Chantelle stowed her purchases in the boot before crossing to slide in behind the wheel of her Mercedes.

It was almost two-thirty when Michelle entered the

Gallery. A converted house comprising three levels, it had been completely renovated. Polished wooden floors gleamed with a deep honey stain, and the walls were individually painted in several different pale colours providing a diverse background for carefully placed exhibits. Skylights threw angled shafts of sunlight, accenting subtle shadows as the sun moved from east to west throughout the day.

She experienced a degree of pride at the decor, and what she'd been able to achieve in the past three years.

'Emilio?'

She returned her keys to her bag and carefully closed the door behind her.

'Up here, *cara*,' an accented voice called from the mezzanine level. 'Brett is with me.'

A short flight of stairs led to the next level. Above that were Emilio's private rooms.

Michelle moved swiftly towards the upstairs studio where Brett's exhibition was to be held. 'Hi,' she greeted warmly as she joined them. Both men glanced up, gave her a penetrating look, then switched their attention to the stack of paintings propped carefully against one wall.

'*Cara*, stand over there, and tell us what you think,' Emilio commanded.

For the next four hours they worked side by side, then when the artist left they ordered in pizza, effected a few minor changes, satisfied themselves that every exhibit was strategically placed according to their original plan.

'He's nervous,' Michelle noted as she bit into a

slice of piping hot pizza. Melted cheese, pepperoni, capsicum…delicious.

'It's his first exhibition,' Emilio granted, following her action.

The light glinted in reflection from the ear-stud he wore. Designer stubble was at odds with his peroxided crew cut. A lean sinewy frame clothed in designer jeans and T-shirt, he bore the visual persona of an avant garde. His sexual preferences were the subject for conjecture, and he did nothing to dispel a certain image. However, it was part of the tease, the glamour associated with a role he chose to play, and the knowledge very few close friends knew he was straight and not at all what he appeared to be, only amused him.

Behind the image lay a very shrewd business brain, an almost infallible instinct for genuine talent, and an indefinable *nous* for what appealed to the buying public.

It was something Michelle also shared, and their friendship was platonic, based on mutual knowledge, affection and respect.

'You are pensive. Why?'

Forthright, even confrontational, Emilio possessed the ability to divine whenever anything bothered her. She delayed answering him by pulling the tab on a can of soft drink and taking a long swallow of the ice-cold liquid.

'A man, huh?' Emilio pronounced. 'Do I know him?'

She replaced the can onto the table, and took another bite of pizza. 'What makes you so sure it's a man?'

'You have soft shadows beneath those beautiful green eyes.' His smile was gentle, but far too discerning. 'Lack of sleep, sweetheart. And as you rarely party 'til dawn, I doubt a late night among the social elite was the cause.'

'I could merely be concerned about tomorrow's exhibition.'

'No,' he declared with certainty. 'If you don't want to talk about him, that's fine.'

Michelle cast him a level look. 'He was a guest at a dinner I attended.' She paused fractionally. 'And if I never see him again, it'll be too soon.'

'Trouble,' Emilio accorded softly. 'Definitely.'

'No,' she corrected. 'Because I won't allow him to be.'

'*Cara*, I don't think you'll have a choice.' His quiet laughter brought forth a vexed grimace.

'Why do you say that?'

'Because you're a beautiful young woman whose fierce protection of self lends you to eat lesser men for breakfast,' he mocked. 'The fact you haven't been able to succeed with this particular one is intriguing. I shall look forward to meeting him.'

'It won't happen,' Michelle vowed with certainty.

'You don't think so?'

'I know so,' she responded vehemently.

'OK.' Emilio lifted both hands in a conciliatory gesture, although his smile held humour. 'Eat your pizza.'

'I intend to.' She bit into the crisp crust, then

reached forward, caught up a paper napkin and wiped her fingers. 'I'll help you clean up, then I'm going home.'

'An empty pizza carton, a few glasses, soft drink cans. What's to clean?'

'In that case,' she inclined, standing to her feet in one fluid movement. 'I'm out of here.' She leaned forward and brushed her cheek to his. '*Cíao.*'

The Gallery opened at four, and an hour later the full complement of guests had gathered, mingling in small clutches, glass in hand. Taped baroque music flowed softly through strategically placed speakers, a soothing background to the muted buzz of conversation.

Michelle had selected a classic fitted dress in black with a lace overlay. Stiletto heels, sheer black hose, her hair swept high, and understated make-up with emphasis on her eyes completed a picture that portrayed elegance and style.

Hired staff proffered trays containing a selection of hors d'oeuvres, and already a number of Brett's paintings displayed a discreet *sold* sticker.

Success, Michelle reflected with a small sigh of relief. Everything was going splendidly. The finger food couldn't be faulted, the champagne was superb, and the ambience was *perfecto,* as Emilio would say.

She glanced across the room, caught his eye, and smiled.

'Another triumph, darling.'

Her stomach tightened fractionally as she recognised Jeremy's cynical voice, and she summoned a polite smile as she turned to face him. 'I didn't expect you to honour the invitation.'

'I wouldn't have missed it for the world.'

He leaned forward and she moved slightly so that his lips brushed her cheek. An action which resulted in a faint intake of breath, the momentary hardening of his eyes.

'The eminently eligible Nikos has yet to put in an appearance, I see.' He moved back a pace, and ran light fingers down her arm.

Michelle tilted her head a little and met his dark gaze. 'A little difficult, when he wasn't issued an invitation.'

'Dear sweet Michelle,' Jeremy chided with sarcastic gentleness. 'Nikos was an invited guest on the parents' cruiser today. The enchanting Chantelle issued the invitation to your Gallery soiree.' He paused for effect before delivering the punch line. 'As I recall, Nikos indicated he would grace us with his presence.'

Her heart tripped and raced to a quicker beat. 'Really?'

One eyebrow slanted in mockery. 'Am I mistaken, or is that not pleasurable anticipation I sense?' He primed a barb and aimed for the kill. 'Didn't he come up to scratch last night, darling?' His smile held thinly veiled humour. 'Jet lag can have that effect.'

Calm, just keep calm, she bade silently as she moved back a pace. He didn't release her arm, and she gave him a deliberately pointed look. 'This conversation is going nowhere, Jeremy.' She flexed her arm, felt his grip tighten for an instant before he released her. 'If you'll excuse me, I really must mingle.' Her voice assumed an icy formality. 'I hope you enjoy the exhibition. Emilio and I are confident of Brett's talent and potential.'

'Ah, the inimical Emilio,' Jeremy drawled. 'You do know he's bisexual?'

As well as being untrue, it was unkind. She didn't miss a beat. 'Slander isn't a pretty word. Watch you don't find yourself in court on a legal charge.'

'A mite too protective, darling.'

'And you,' she declared with quiet emphasis. 'Are a first-class—'

'Michelle.'

Her body quivered at the sound of that faintly accented voice, and her pulse went into overdrive. How much of her argument with Jeremy had Nikos Alessandros heard?

Everything came into sharp focus as she slowly turned to face him.

'Nikos,' she acknowledged, and imperceptibly stiffened as he placed a hand at the back of her waist.

His expression gave nothing away, but there was a hint of steel beneath the polite facade as he inclined his head.

'Jeremy.'

Michelle's nerves flared into sensitised life at his close proximity.

'Is there a problem?' Nikos asked smoothly, and she felt like screaming.

Yes. Jeremy for behaving badly, and *you* just for being here!

A determined sparkle darkened her eyes. 'If you'll excuse me? I really should mingle.'

She turned away, only to find that Nikos had joined her.

'Just what the hell do you think you're doing?' she queried with quiet vehemence the instant they were out of Jeremy's earshot. She made a concerted effort to shift out of his grasp without success.

'Rescuing you.'

'I didn't need rescuing!'

His smile held a hint of cynical humour. 'Especially not by me.'

'Look—'

'Save the indignation for a more suitable occasion.'

'Why?' Michelle vented with quiet fury. 'When I have no intention of seeing you again.'

'Considering your parents and the Bateson-Burrows have issued me with a few interesting invitations, that's most unlikely,' Nikos assured silkily.

She wanted to hit him. It was enough she had to deal with Jeremy, whose recalcitrance in the past twenty-four hours could be directly attributed to the man at her side.

Had Nikos not been a guest at the Bateson-Burrows' dinner table, she could have conducted a diplomatic discussion last night with Jeremy, and he wouldn't now be behaving quite inappropriately.

Or would he? Jeremy had displayed a side to his personality she'd never suspected might exist.

'Suppose we embark on a conducted tour of your protegé's work.'

'Why?' she demanded baldly, and found herself looking into a pair of amused dark grey eyes.

'I could be a potential buyer, and you do, Chantelle assures me, have an excellent eye for new talent.'

Did she realise just how beautiful she looked when she was angry?

'Mother has excelled herself in lauding my supposed talents,' she stated dryly.

'Cynicism doesn't suit you.'

In any other circumstance, she would have laughed. However, tonight she wasn't in the mood to see the humorous side of Chantelle's machinations.

They drew close to one exhibit, and she went into a professional spiel about light and colour and style, Brett's unusual technique, and indicated the painting's possible worth on the market in another five years.

Nikos dropped his arm from her waist, and she wondered why she suddenly felt cold, even vaguely bereft.

Crazy, she dismissed. Every instinct she possessed warned that Nikos Alessandros was a man she should have nothing to do with if she wanted to retain her emotional sanity.

CHAPTER FOUR

'WHICH of the collection is your personal favourite?' Nikos queried as they moved from one exhibit to another.

There were interruptions as she was greeted by a few guests, and on each occasion good manners demanded she introduce the man at her side.

She could sense their masked speculation, sense their curiosity, and she wasn't sure whether to feel angry or resigned.

Michelle's lips parted to make a flippant response, only to change her mind at the last second. 'The little boy standing on a sandhill looking out over the ocean.'

He lifted a hand and tucked a stray lock of hair back behind her ear. He watched her eyes dilate, and felt the slight shiver his touch evoked. 'Why that particular painting?'

'Because it seems as if the ocean represents his world, and he's curious to know where it ends and what's beyond the horizon. If you look at his features, there's wonderment, excitement.' Her voice softened. 'He's trying not to be afraid, but he is. You can see it in the aint thrust of his lower lip, the way his chin tucks in a little.' She raised her hand, then let it fall again to her side.

It was more than just a painting, it represented life.

The promise of what might be. Even though the logical mind relegated the image to the skilled use of
paint on canvas and artistic flair.

'Consider it sold.'

Michelle glanced up and examined the chiselled
perfection of his features. 'You haven't asked the
price.'

'It's listed on the programme.' His smile was
wholly sensual. 'What discount are you prepared to
offer me?'

She badly wanted to say *none,* except 'business'
was a separate category to 'personal,' and anyone
with sufficient *nous* ensured the two were kept apart.
'It depends on your method of payment.'

'I'll present you with a bank cheque at midday
tomorrow, and organise delivery.'

Michelle didn't hesitate. 'Five per cent.'

It shouldn't concern her where he intended to hang
it, in fact she told herself she didn't care.

'Something is bothering you?'

His light tone didn't fool her in the slightest. He
was too intuitive, and she loathed his ability to tune
into her thoughts. It made her feel vulnerable, and
too acutely sensitive.

'Why should anything bother me? I've just sold
the most expensive painting featured in this exhibition.'

'By your own admission, it's the one you admire
most,' Nikos pursued softly. 'I imagine you can offer
a suggestion how it should be displayed to its best
advantage?'

She could tell him to do what he liked with it, but professional etiquette got the better of her.

'It should occupy centre stage on a wide wall,' she opined slowly. 'Preferably painted a very pale shade of blue, so the colours mesh and there's a sense of continuity.'

Interesting, he perceived, that her love of art overcame her instinctive wariness of him.

'Now, if you'll excuse me,' Michelle said purposefully. 'There's something I need to check with my business partner.' She offered him a polite smile, then turned and went in search of Emilio.

'So he's the one,' Emilio said in a quiet aside several minutes later.

'I don't know what you're talking about.'

'Yes, you do.'

'I'd prefer not to discuss it.'

'As you wish.'

'Dammit, I don't even like him!'

'So… What's liking got to do with anything?' Emilio queried mildly.

'Grrr,' she vented softly, and incurred his soft laughter.

'Stephanie.' He was suddenly the businessman, the art entrepreneur, assuming the faintly affected manner he'd honed to perfection. 'How are you, darling?'

Michelle followed suit, according the wealthy widow due deference. The money Stephanie Whitcomb had spent in their Gallery over the past few years went close to six figures.

'Such a success, *cherie*,' Chantelle complimented

as Michelle crossed to her parents' side. 'We are very
proud of you.'

'Indeed. A stunning exhibition.'

'Thank you, *Papa.* Naturally you're prejudiced.'

Etienne smiled as he leaned forward to bestow a
light kiss to her cheek. 'Of course.'

'Tomorrow we're hosting a small cocktail evening. Just very close friends. Six o'clock. You'll join
us, won't you?'

Her mother's idea of a small gathering could number anything from twenty to thirty people. Drinks on
the terrace, a seemingly casual but carefully prepared
finger-food buffet.

'*Maman,* no,' Michelle voiced with regret. 'I have
plans.'

'What a shame. We included Saska in Nikos' invitation. I thought you might like to bring Emilio.'

There was a silent message evident which
Michelle chose to ignore. 'Another time, perhaps?'

'If you reconsider…' Chantelle trailed delicately.

'Thank you, *Maman.*'

Guests were beginning to drift towards the door,
and as always, it took a while for the Gallery to
empty.

Michelle organised the hired staff as they packed
glassware into containers. Much of the cleaning up
had already been done, and Emilio handed over a
cheque, then saw them off the premises.

'Go home,' he ordered without preamble. 'You're
tired, it shows, and I'll deal with everything in the
morning.'

'I had no idea I looked such a wreck,' Michelle said dryly.

'Darling, I am an old friend, and I can tell it like it is,' he said gently.

'It was a successful evening.'

All of Brett's paintings had sold, and they'd succeeded in confirming a tentative date in April to host another exhibition of his work.

'Very,' Emilio agreed, as she reached up and brushed his cheek with her lips. 'For what it's worth, I approve of the Greek.' He lifted a hand and smoothed back a stray tendril of hair that had escaped from the chignon at her nape. 'I enjoyed watching him watch you.'

Something inside Michelle's stomach curled into a tight ball. 'Since when did you become my protector?'

'Since I fell in love with you many years ago…as a sister,' he teased gently.

She smiled with genuine affection. 'In that case, *brother,* I'm going home and leaving you with all that remains of the clean-up chores.'

'Tomorrow morning, ten,' Emilio reminded. 'Take care.'

Her car was parked about twenty metres distant, the street was well-lit, and as the Gallery was situated off the main street housing numerous cafés and restaurants, there were several parked cars in the immediate vicinity.

Michelle gained the pavement and stepped in the direction of her car, only to pause at the sight of a male figure leaning against its bonnet.

The figure straightened and moved towards her. 'I thought you were never going to leave,' Jeremy complained.

She stepped forward to cross the grass verge, and felt his hand grasp her arm.

'It's been a long day, and I'm tired,' she said firmly. Her patience was getting thin, but she recognised a certain quality about him that made her very wary. 'Goodnight.'

'Dammit, Michelle, you can't just walk away from me.'

'Please let go of my arm. I want to get into my car.'

She was unprepared for his sudden movement as he twisted her close with vicious strength, then ground his mouth against her own.

Instinct and training combined to allow her to unbalance him, and one swiftly hooked foot sent him falling to the ground.

Michelle moved quickly round to the driver's side, unlocked the door, and was about to slide into the seat when Jeremy caught hold of her arm and dragged her out.

'I believe the lady said no,' a slightly accented male voice drawled hardily.

Jeremy's fingers tightened with painful intensity, and she could feel his palpable anger.

'Bitch!'

'Let her go,' Nikos commanded with dangerous softness. 'Or else I promise you won't walk easily for days.'

Michelle caught her breath as Jeremy's fingers bit

to the bone, then he flung her arm free, turned and crossed the road to his car, fired the engine with an ear-splitting roar, and sent the tyres spinning as he sped down the road.

Nikos said something vicious beneath his breath as she stiffened beneath his touch, and he swore briefly, pithily, in his own language.

Michelle edged the tip of her tongue over her lips and discovered several abrasions where her teeth had split the delicate tissues.

'I'll drive you home.'

'No.' She told herself she didn't need his concern. 'I'm fine.' To prove it, she slid in behind the wheel, only to have him lean into the car and bodily shift her into the passenger seat.

Seconds later he took her place and engaged the ignition.

'There's no need for you to do this,' Michelle asserted as he set the car in motion.

Three blocks and two minutes later he swept through the entrance to her apartment building and paused adjacent the security gate leading to the underground car park.

'Do you have your card?'

She handed it to him wordlessly, and when the gate was fully open she directed him to her allotted space.

'What about your own car?'

He directed her a dark glance as he led her towards the lift. 'I walked.' He jabbed the call button, and when the lift arrived, he accompanied her into it. 'Which floor?'

'There's no—'

'Which floor?' Nikos repeated with dangerous quietness.

He was icily calm. Too calm, she perceived, aware there was something apparent in his stance, the set of his features, that revealed anger held in tight control.

'I appreciate your driving me home. But I'm fine.'

She glimpsed the darkness in his eyes, the hard purpose evident, and was momentarily bereft of speech. 'Really,' she added seconds later.

One eyebrow rose slightly, and she met his silent scrutiny with unblinking equanimity.

'Look in the mirror,' Nikos bade quietly, and watched as she spared the decorative mirrored panel a glance.

Her hair was no longer confined in a neat chignon, her eyes were dark, dilated and seemed far too large in features that were pale, and her mouth was swollen.

'Now, which floor?' he queried with velvet softness, and she hesitated momentarily before capitulating.

'Fifteenth.'

They reached it in seconds, and she silently indicated the door leading to her apartment.

Once inside she had the compelling urge to remove Jeremy's touch from her skin, and she wanted to scrub her teeth, cleanse her mouth.

'I'm going to take a shower and change.' She no longer cared whether Nikos Alessandros was there or not, or whether he'd have gone when she returned.

Uppermost was the need to be alone, shed and dispense with her clothes.

Hell, she'd probably burn them, she determined as she reached the bedroom and began peeling each item from her body.

Michelle activated the shower dial and set it as hot as she could bear, then she lathered every inch of skin, rinsed, and repeated the process three times. Satisfied, she turned the dial to cold and let the needle spray revive and revitalise her before she reached for a towel.

Minutes later she donned clean underwear, then reached for jeans and a loose cotton top. She discounted make-up, and applied the hair dryer for as long as it took to remove most of the dampness, then she simply wound it into a knot and pinned it on top of her head.

Michelle walked into the kitchen and saw Nikos in the process of brewing coffee. He'd removed his jacket and his tie. He'd also loosened a few top buttons and folded back the cuffs of his shirt.

His appraisal was swift, yet all-encompassing. 'I've brewed some coffee.'

There were two cups and saucers on the countertop, sugar and milk, and she watched as he filled her cup.

He looked comfortably at ease, yet instinct warned that anger lurked just beneath the surface of his control.

'You don't have to do this.' She hugged her arms together across her midriff, and temporarily ignored the cup and saucer he pushed towards her.

'No,' Nikos responded evenly. 'I don't.' He added sugar to his cup, stirred, then lifted it to his mouth.

She should suggest the more formal surroundings of the lounge, but the last thing she wanted to do was indulge in meaningless conversation.

'Do you intend laying charges?'

Her eyes widened slightly. Oh God, that meant involving the police, filing a complaint. The facts becoming public knowledge. Jeremy's parents, her parents, their friends...

'I don't think so,' she said at last.

His piercing regard unsettled her, and after what seemed an age she averted her gaze to a point somewhere beyond his right shoulder.

'What about the next time he lays in wait for you?' Nikos queried relentlessly.

Michelle's eyes snapped back into focus. 'There won't *be* a next time.'

'You're so sure about that?'

'If there is, I can handle it,' she reiterated firmly.

'Such confidence.'

'I handled you.'

His smile lacked any pretense at humour. 'At no time did my motives stem from a desire to frighten or harm you.'

'I didn't know that.' Any more than she knew it now.

'No,' he qualified, and glimpsed the way her body jerked imperceptibly, and the defensive tightening of her arms as she sought to control it. He wasn't done, and he derived no satisfaction or pleasure in what he intended to say. 'Don't presume to judge the son by his parents.'

'Hidden messages, Nikos?' Her eyes were clear as they met his.

The unexpected peal of the telephone startled her.

'Aren't you going to answer that?'

She moved to the handset and picked up the receiver.

'Michelle.'

Jeremy. Her fingers tightened. 'I have nothing to say to you.' She hung up without giving him the opportunity to utter a further word.

A minute later it rang again, and she ignored it for several seconds before snatching the receiver.

'I'm sorry.' His voice was ragged, and came in quick bursts. 'I was jealous. I didn't mean to hurt you.'

She didn't bother answering, and simply replaced the receiver.

Within seconds the telephone rang again, and she caught up the receiver, only to have it taken out of her hand.

'Call once more, and I'll ensure Michelle notifies the police,' Nikos directed brusquely. The tirade of abuse that followed was ugly. 'What you're suggesting is anatomically impossible. However I'm quite prepared to get a legal opinion on it. Would you care for me to do that?'

It was obvious Jeremy didn't want anything of the kind, and she watched as Nikos replaced the receiver.

'Does he have a key to your apartment?'

'No.' Indignation rose to the fore, and erupted in angry speech. 'No, he doesn't. No one does.'

'I'm relieved to hear it.'

Michelle fixed him with a fulminating glare. 'What I do with my life and who I do it with is none of your business.'

He admired her spirit, and there was a part of him that wanted to pull her into his arms and hold her close. Except he knew if he so much as touched her, she'd scratch and claw like a cornered cat.

'Tonight I made it my business.'

'I didn't leave the Gallery until half an hour after everyone else,' Michelle flung at him. 'How come you happened to still be hanging around?'

'I was on foot, remember? I noticed Jeremy sitting in a car he made no attempt to start.'

Nikos didn't need to paint a word picture. She got it without any help at all, in technicolour.

'I should thank you.'

His mouth tilted fractionally. 'So—thank me.'

Her eyes met his. 'I thought I just did.'

'And now you want me to leave.'

'Please.'

She watched as he extracted his wallet, withdrew a card, scrawled a series of digits and placed it onto the countertop.

'My mobile number. You can reach me on it any-time.'

She followed him from the kitchen, paused as he caught up his jacket, then crossed the lounge to the front door.

Nikos lifted a hand and brushed his fingers down her cheek. 'Goodnight, *kyria.*'

He didn't linger, and she told herself she was glad. She closed the door, set the locking mechanism in place, and threw the bolt.

Then she crossed to a comfortable chair and activated the remote.

Cable television provided endless choices, and she stared resolutely at the screen in an effort to block out what had transpired in the past hour.

She focused on the Gallery, its success, Emilio, until it became increasingly difficult to keep her eyes open, then she simply closed them, uncaring where she slept.

CHAPTER FIVE

MICHELLE woke at dawn to the sound of male voices and lifted her head in alarm, only to subside as realisation affirmed the television was on and the voice belonged to actor Don Johnson as Sonny in a rerun of 'Miami Vice.'

Her limbs felt stiff, and she stretched in an effort to ease them, then she checked her watch.

There was time for a swim in the indoor pool, then she'd shower and change, grab some breakfast, and drive to the Gallery.

It was almost nine when she swung the Porsche into a parking bay, and she used her key to unlock the outer Gallery door.

'Buon giorno.'

'Hi,' she greeted, and cast Emilio an appreciative smile as she saw the fruits of his labour in highly polished floors and everything restored to immaculate order. 'You're an angel.'

'Ah, from you that is indeed a compliment.'

'I mean it.'

The corners of his eyes crinkled with humour, and his smile was warm and generous. 'I know you do.'

'As you've cleaned up, I'll do the book work, enter the accounts, make the phone calls.'

'But first, the coffee.' He moved towards her and caught hold of her shoulders, then frowned as he saw

her wince. His eyes narrowed as he glimpsed the
shadows beneath her eyes. 'Headache, no sleep,
what?'

'A bit of all three.'

She bore his scrutiny with equanimity. 'Elaborate
on the *what*, Michelle.'

Emilio called her *darling, honey, cara,* but rarely
Michelle.

'It was such a successful evening,' she prevari-
cated.

'Uh-huh,' he disclaimed. 'We've achieved other
successful evenings, none of which have seen you
pale, wan, and hollow-eyed the next morning.'

She opted to go for the truth. Or as much of it as
he needed to know. 'I watched a film on cable, then
fell asleep in the lounge.' She arched her neck, and
rolled her head a little. 'I'm a little stiff, that's all.'

He didn't say anything for several long seconds.
'Nice try, *cara.*'

'You mentioned coffee?'

Michelle took hers into the office, and set to work
entering details from yesterday's sales into the computer. She double-checked the receipts and entries
before printing out the accounts, then stacked them
in alphabetical order. A few of their regular clientele
had paid by personal cheque, and she organised the
banking deposit sheet.

She made telephone calls and arranged packing
and delivery, then checked with the clientele to ascertain if the times quoted were convenient.

When the intercom beeped, she activated it. 'Yes,
Emilio?'

'Jeremy Bateson-Burrows is here. Shall I send him in?'

'No.' Her refusal was swift, and she breathed in deeply before qualifying, 'I don't want to see him.'

A minute later the intercom beeped again. 'He says it's of vital importance.'

Michelle cursed beneath her breath. 'Tell him I'll be down in a minute.'

Her stiletto heels made a clicking noise on the polished floor, and she saw Jeremy turn towards her as she drew close.

Emilio was within sight some distance away arranging a display of decorative ceramic urns.

'Jeremy,' she greeted with cool formality.

'I wanted to apologise in person.'

Careful, an inner voice cautioned. 'It's a little too late for that,' she said evenly. 'If you'll excuse me, I have a considerable amount of work to get through.'

'I need to talk to you, to explain. Have lunch with me. Please?' He was very convincing. Too convincing. 'I don't know what came over me last night,' he said desperately.

'I'd like you to leave. Now,' Michelle said quietly.

He reached out a hand as if to touch her arm, and she stepped back a few paces.

'Michelle.'

Emilio's intrusion was heaven-sent, and she turned towards him in silent query.

'I'm in the middle of an international call,' Emilio announced smoothly. 'Nikos Alessandros has arrived to arrange delivery and payment. Can you attend to him?'

He held the mobile phone, and she almost believed him until she glimpsed the dark stillness apparent in his expression.

'Yes, of course.'

Nikos watched as she walked towards him, and controlled the brief surge of anger as she drew close. She looked as fragile as the finest glass.

'Good morning.' Or was it afternoon? Hell, she'd lost track of whether it was one or the other.

His eyes met hers, dark, analytical, unwavering, and her eyes widened slightly as he leaned forward and cupped her face with both hands.

His mouth covered hers with a gentleness that made the breath catch in her throat, and she was unable to suppress the shivery sensation scudding down her spine as his tongue softly explored the delicate tissues, slowly traced each abrasion, then tangled briefly with her tongue before withdrawing.

He let both hands drop to his side, then he circled her waist and drew her close.

'What's going on? Michelle?' Jeremy's voice was hard and filled with querulous anger.

Nikos' arm tightened fractionally in silent warning, and the look he cast down at her was warm and incredibly intimate. 'I don't see the need to keep it a secret, do you?' He shifted his attention to Emilio. 'Michelle and I have decided to resume our relationship.'

She heard the words, assimilated them, and didn't

have a chance to draw breath as Nikos soundly kissed her.

Why did she have the feeling she was one of three players on a stage, with an audience of only one? Because that was the precise scenario, and it came as no surprise when Jeremy brushed past them and exited the Gallery.

Emilio locked the door after him and turned the ''open'' sign round to read ''closed.''

'You can't do that,' Michelle protested.

'I just did. So what are you going to do about it?' Emilio queried lightly, adding in jest—'Sue me?'

She looked from one to the other, then fixed her gaze on Nikos. 'You've really put the fat in the fire now.' Reaction began to rear its head. 'Do you realise the news will probably reach my parents? What will they think?' She closed her eyes, then opened them again in the knowledge that her darling *maman* would undoubtedly be delighted. Another thought rose to the fore, and her expression became fierce. 'This situation plays right into your hands with Saska, doesn't it?'

'Who is Saska?' Emilio asked with interest, and Nikos informed him urbanely.

'The recently widowed wife of a very close friend.'

'Whom Nikos suggested I collaborate with him to deceive,' Michelle added.

'Ah,' Emilio commented with a shrug in comprehension. 'But you wouldn't play, huh?'

'No, she wouldn't,' Nikos said smoothly.

A wide smile showed white teeth and lent dark

eyes a lively sparkle. 'I think you should, *cara*. Play,' Emilio added quizzically. 'It would do you good.'

'Emilio,' Michelle warned. 'I don't find this in the least amusing.'

'No, darling, I don't expect you do.' His expression sobered slightly. Jeremy was the catalyst, and Nikos, unless he was mistaken, was a man with a hidden agenda. 'You'll forgive me if I say I shall enjoy the show?' He didn't give her the opportunity to respond.

'I don't need to tell you that your secret is safe with me. Now, why don't you go have lunch together, and fine tune your strategy?'

'Yes,' Nikos agreed. 'Why don't we do that?'

She cast him a discerning look, opened her mouth to argue, then closed it again. 'I'll get my bag.' She crossed to the office, retrieved it, then swung back to the entrance.

Emilio was talking into the mobile phone, and she fluttered her fingers at him, checked her watch, and silently indicated she'd be back at two.

'I suggest somewhere close by in air-conditioned comfort,' Nikos indicated silkily as they walked into the midsummer sunshine.

Michelle slid down her sunglasses, and was aware he mirrored her actions. 'Fine. You choose.'

Ten minutes later they were seated in seclusion at a table overlooking an outdoor courtyard filled with potted flowers and greenery plants of numerous description.

'Your parents have invited Saska to their home this evening.'

Michelle looked at him over the rim of her glass. He looked relaxed and at ease, and far too compelling for his own good. '*Maman* is the consummate hostess,' she said evenly. 'I'm sure you'll both enjoy yourselves.'

She replaced the glass as the waiter delivered their order.

'I'll collect you at five to six.'

'I have other plans.'

'Change them.'

'Those plans involve other people. I don't want to let them down at such short notice.'

His eyes speared hers. 'I'm sure they'll understand if you explain.'

Yes they would, but that wasn't the point.

Michelle picked up her fork and stabbed a crouton, some cos lettuce, and regarded the poised fork with apparent interest. She was bargaining for time, and it irked that he knew. 'Surely the charade can wait a few days?'

'Antonia and Emerson Bateson-Burrows are fellow guests,' Nikos intimated. 'Won't they think it a little strange if you're not there?' He waited a beat. 'And Saska is seen to be my partner?'

She had to concede he had a point. 'I guess you're right.'

Why did she feel like she'd just made a lifechanging decision? How long would this pretense need to last? A few weeks? A month? It wasn't as if they had to attend every party and dinner in town. It was likely she'd only have to see him a couple of nights a week.

Just keep your emotions intact, a tiny voice taunted.

Michelle took a sip of mineral water, then speared another morsel of food. The salad was delicious, but her appetite diminished with every mouthful.

What about the chemistry? The way she felt when he touched her? Each time he kissed her, whether in sensual exploration or passion, she'd just wanted to die.

Dear heaven, she'd experienced more emotional upheaval in the past two days than she had in…a long time, she admitted.

Nikos observed each fleeting expression, and wondered if she realised how expressive her features were? Or how easily he was able to define them?

'I guess we should set down some ground rules.' That sounded fair, she determined. How had Emilio put it? *Fine tune your strategy.*

'What did you have in mind?'

Michelle looked at him carefully, and was unable to see beyond the sophisticated mask he presented. Oh God, was she *mad?* She wasn't even in the same league, let alone the same game. So why was she choosing to play?

'You don't make decisions for me, and vice versa,' she began. 'We consult on anything that involves the both of us.'

'That's reasonable.'

So far, so good. 'No unnecessary—' She was going to say *intimacy,* but that sounded too personal. 'Touching,' she amended, and missed the faint gleam in those dark eyes.

'I'll try to restrain myself, if you will.'

He was amused, damn him! 'This isn't funny,' she reproved, and he proffered a crooked smile.

'My sense of humour got the better of me.'

'Do you want to put a time limit on this?'

One eyebrow slanted. 'Lunch?'

'Our supposed relationship!'

'Ah—that.' He expertly wound the last of his fettuccine onto his fork and savoured it. 'How about…as long as it takes?'

Of course. That was the entire object of the exercise. She'd had enough salad, and she pushed the bowl forward, then sank back in her chair.

'I'm intrigued,' she ventured. 'To discover how you knew I'd studied at the Sorbonne?'

He looked at her carefully. 'I endeavour to discover background details of the people who claim to want to do business with me. It's a precautionary measure.'

Michelle's eyes narrowed slightly. That meant being able to access confidential data on file. Although with the right contacts and connections, it wouldn't be difficult.

'Emerson Bateson-Burrows has been vigilant in baiting the figurative hook,' Nikos revealed with wry cynicism.

As her parents mixed socially with Jeremy's parents, they, too, had come beneath Nikos' scrutiny. It didn't leave her with a comfortable feeling.

'We didn't meet in Paris.'

'Yes, we did,' he corrected.

'Where?' she demanded. 'I would have remembered.'

'At a party.'

It was possible. She'd attended several parties during her Paris sojourn. Although she was positive she'd never seen Nikos Alessandros at any one of them. 'We weren't introduced,' she said with certainty.

'No,' Nikos agreed. 'It was a case of too many people, and I was with someone else.'

Now why did that suddenly make her feel jealous? It didn't make sense.

'You'd better let me have your phone number in case I need to contact you,' he said smoothly, and she lifted one eyebrow in mocking query.

'You mean you don't already have it?'

His gaze was steady. 'I'd prefer you to give it to me willingly.'

She looked at him for a second, then she reached into her bag, extracted a card and handed it to him.

'Would you like something else to eat?' When she shook her head, he indicated, 'Dessert? Coffee?'

How long had they been here? Half an hour? Longer? 'No. Thanks,' she added. 'I have a few things to do before I go back to the Gallery.' She didn't, but Nikos wasn't to know that. 'Would you excuse me?'

He lifted one hand, gained the attention of the waiter, and rose to his feet. 'I'll walk back with you.'

She opened her mouth to say 'there's no need,' saw his expression, and decided to refrain from saying anything at all.

Nikos signed the proffered credit slip, pocketed the duplicate, then accompanied her onto the street.

Finding 'things to do' didn't stretch her imagination, and she made the bakery first on her list, where she selected bread rolls, a couple of Danish pastries. For Emilio, she justified. To lend credence, she entered the small local post office and stood in line to buy stamps.

Did Nikos suspect her mission was a sham? Possibly. But she didn't care.

'Are you done?'

The sound of that soft slightly accented drawl merely added encouragement, and she stepped into the pharmacy, picked up some antiseptic liquid, paid for it, then emerged onto the pavement.

The fruit shop was next, and she selected some grapes, an apple, a banana, and two tomatoes, justifying her purchases, 'I won't have time to get anything after work.'

It took only minutes to reach the Gallery, but they were long minutes during which she was acutely conscious of his height and breadth as he walked at her side.

Twice she thought of something to say by way of conversation only to dismiss the words as being inane.

At the Gallery entrance she paused and thanked him for lunch, then looked askance as he followed her inside.

'If you remember there was a distraction,' Nikos reminded indolently. 'I need to give you a cheque, and have you arrange delivery.'

Michelle tended to it with professional efficiency, then accompanied him to the door.

'What have we here?' Emilio queried, indicating her purchases shortly after Nikos' departure.

'Things.' She selected the bakery bag and handed it to him. 'For you.'

His soft laughter was almost her undoing. 'You initiated a small diversion?'

'Minor,' she agreed, and he shook his head in silent chastisement.

'Tonight could prove interesting.'

Michelle merely smiled and headed towards the office.

It was after five when she parked her car in its allotted space and rode the lift to her apartment.

The message light was blinking on the answering machine, and she activated the 'message' button, listened to Jeremy's voice as he issued an impassioned plea to call him, deliberated all of five seconds, then hit 'erase.'

His increasingly obsessive behaviour disturbed her, and she stood in reflective silence, aware that at no time had she given him reason to believe they could share anything more than friendship.

A quick glance at her watch revealed she had half an hour in which to shower and dress before she was due to meet Nikos downstairs.

Michelle entered the lobby as Nikos' BMW swept into the bricked apron immediately adjacent the main entrance, and she reached the car just as he emerged from behind the wheel.

Nikos noted the slight thrust of her chin, the cool expressive features, and suppressed a faint smile at the sleek upswept hairstyle. The make-up was perfection with clever emphasis on her eyes, the generous curve of her mouth.

The classic "little black dress" had a scooped neckline, very short sleeves and a hemline that stopped mid-thigh, with high stiletto-heeled black pumps accenting the length of her legs.

Everything about her enhanced the sophisticated image of a young woman in total control.

Michelle slid into the passenger seat and offered him a faint smile in greeting.

He looked relaxed, and she wished she could feel comfortable about deceiving her parents.

The car gained clear passage onto the road, and Nikos headed towards the main arterial road leading into Surfers Paradise.

'Ten minutes to countdown.'

'Less,' Nikos declared. 'It begins when we collect Saska from her hotel.'

Within minutes he drew the car to a halt adjacent the Marriott. 'I won't be long.'

She watched as he disappeared through the automatic glass doors, crossed to one of several armchairs in the large lobby, and greeted a tall elegantly dressed woman.

Beautiful wasn't an adequate description, Michelle decided as Nikos escorted the brunette to the car.

The mental image Michelle had drawn of a depressed and desperately unhappy widow didn't fit the vital young woman who conversed with ease during the ten-minute drive to Sovereign Islands, a group of seven manmade residential islands situated three kilometres north, and reached by an overbridge from the mainland.

Chantelle and Etienne Gerard's home was a modern architectural tri-level home, with two levels given over entirely to entertaining.

There were several cars lining the driveway, and Michelle experienced a vague sense of uneasiness as she entered the house at Nikos' side. She was all too aware of the role she'd committed herself to play and the deceit involved.

Almost on cue, Nikos caught hold of her hand and linked his fingers through her own, and the smile he cast her was intimately warm.

It stirred her senses and made her acutely aware of each breath she took. The blood seemed to race through her veins, quickening her pulse.

Oh God. What had she let herself in for?

CHAPTER SIX

'NIKOS, Saska, how nice to see you.' Chantelle, ever the gracious hostess, greeted them with pleasant enthusiasm, then she leaned forward and touched her daughter's cheek with her own. 'Darling, I'm so pleased you could come.'

Her mother's 'just a few friends' extended to more than thirty, Michelle estimated as Chantelle led them through the house and out onto the large terrace overlooking a wide canal.

Hired staff were in evidence to ensure trays of finger food and drinks were constantly on offer.

Introductions and greetings were exchanged with the ease of long practice as they mingled with fellow guests.

Every now and then she felt the pressure of Nikos' fingers on her own, and several times she made a furtive attempt to free them without success.

Antonia and Emerson Bateson-Burrows were among the guests, and Michelle's stomach twisted a little at the thought that Jeremy might put in an appearance.

'Have you known Nikos for long?'

Was this a trick question? Surely Nikos had already provided Saska with *some* basic information?

'We met while Michelle was studying in Paris,'

71

Nikos answered for her, and Michelle wrinkled her nose at him.

'Really, darling,' she chastised teasingly. 'I'm quite capable of answering for myself.' She turned towards Saska and rolled her eyes. 'At a party.' Surely it would do no harm to elaborate a little? 'Five years ago.' That fit in well. 'I was a student with a very new Arts degree, which my parents agreed should be followed by a year at the Sorbonne.' She lifted her shoulders in a typically Gaelic shrug. 'Intense study, you know how it is. I was dragged off to a party with friends. Nikos was there.'

Saska's eyes assumed a faintly quizzical gleam. 'Alone?'

'Of course not.' This could almost be fun, meshing fact with fiction. 'His companion for the evening was a stunning blonde.'

'He was obviously attracted to you.'

'Very much so,' Nikos admitted as he carried Michelle's hand to his lips, and she felt the graze of teeth against her knuckles in silent warning.

Which she took delight in ignoring. 'He played the gentleman, and was very circumspect in his interest.' She met his gaze and openly dared him to refute her words. 'Weren't you, darling?'

'Until the next time.'

The *knowledge* was there, apparent, and acted as a subtle reminder that when it came to game-playing, he was more than her equal.

'Michelle. Nikos.'

It was a relief to have Emilio join them, and she cast him a generous smile as Nikos introduced Saska.

'Pleasant evening,' Emilio commented, switching his attention to the widowed brunette. 'You're here on holiday?'

'Yes. Nikos suggested I take a break for a few weeks.'

'Perhaps we could have dinner together one night soon? Tuesday?'

My, Emilio was moving quickly, Michelle acknowledged silently, watching as Saska effected a slight lift of her shoulders.

'If that is acceptable to Nikos and Michelle?'

Whoa. A foursome? *Tomorrow?*

'We'll be delighted, won't we, *pedhi mou?*'

The endearment was deliberate, and she was tempted to say *no,* but knew it would sound churlish. 'Delighted,' she agreed. At the first opportunity, she decided, she would have words with Nikos about the frequency of such 'dates.'

Michelle took another sip of excellent champagne and removed a seafood savoury from a proffered tray. It seemed hours since she'd picked at a salad over lunch.

'What a magnificent view,' Saska enthused as she gazed out over the water. 'Nikos, you must tell me the history behind the design of these islands.'

'Take Saska down onto the jetty,' Michelle directed, and felt a tingle of pleasure at thwarting him. 'It's possible to obtain a more effective view from there.'

This was not part of the plan. It was evident from the faint warning flare in the depths of those eyes.

'Michelle is more knowledgeable,' he responded smoothly.

It was a very neat manoeuvre, and one she couldn't really extricate herself from without appearing impolite.

The ground was landscaped on three terraced levels from the outdoor pool down to the water's edge. Lavish landscaping included concrete steps, a decorative rockery, a large fountain, flower-edged paths, and expanses of lush green lawn.

Michelle led the way, and when they reached the jetty she stepped out to its furthest point as she directed Saska's attention towards the Broadwater.

'The stretch of land immediately in front of us is known as south Stradbroke Island. Beyond it lays the Pacific Ocean.'

Saska leaned forward. 'And these islands?'

'Manmade. Each small island is connected to the other by a series of bridges. It's very effective, don't you think?'

Saska didn't speak for several minutes. 'Nikos is a special friend,' she relayed conversationally. 'We've known each other a long time.'

Michelle didn't pretend not to understand. 'I imagine there's a purpose to you telling me this?'

'I find it unusual he has never mentioned you.'

Why did she suddenly feel as if she'd just stepped into a minefield? 'As you know, Nikos has diverse business interests in many European cities.' She was plucking reasons out of nowhere. 'We met not long before I was due to return to Australia to discover my niche in the art world.' A small elaboration, but much of it had its base in truth.

'And now?' Saska persisted. 'I understand you've only recently rediscovered each other?'

'Yes.'

'Do you love him?'

Think, she directed mentally. You can hardly say *no.* 'I care,' she said simply, and added for good measure, 'Very much.' May the heavens not descend on her head for such a transgression!

'So do I,' the brunette declared.

'What are you advocating? Swords drawn at dawn, and a fight to the death?'

Saska smiled, then began to laugh, and the effect transformed her features into something of rare beauty. 'I like you.'

'Well now,' Michelle drawled. 'That's a bonus.'

'In fact,' Saska deliberated. 'I think you'd be very good for Nikos.' The smile widened. 'But then, so would I. We share the same heritage, the same interests, the same friends. As much as I grieve for my dead husband, I have discovered I do not like being alone. Do we understand one another?'

'Yes. But haven't you neglected the most important factor?'

Saska lifted a finely arched eyebrow. 'I don't think so.'

'Nikos. The choice is his to make, don't you think?'

'Of course.'

Confidence was a fine thing. 'Now we've had this

little chat,' Michelle said evenly, 'shall we rejoin the other guests?'

'By all means.'

The evening air was still, and although light, there was a hint of impending dusk as shadows began to lengthen. The water lost its deep blue and began to acquire a shade of grey as the colours lost their sharp intensity.

Numerous garden lights sprang on, together with lit columns around the pool, illuminating the terrace and surrounding area.

Nikos moved forward to meet them, and although his smile encompassed both women, his hand settled in the small of Michelle's back for an instant before his fingers began a soothing movement up and down the indentations of her spine.

It felt warm, electric, and did crazy things to her composure. A sensation that was heightened when he leaned towards her and brushed his lips close to her ear before proffering her a plate of food.

It was then she caught sight of Jeremy, and her appetite became non-existent.

'I thought you might be hungry.'

'Not really.'

He picked up a savoury and held it temptingly close to her mouth. 'Try this.' When she shook her head, he took a small bite and offered her the rest.

What was he doing, for heaven's sake? She took the savoury from his fingers and ate it, then looked at him in exasperation when he followed it with another. 'Isn't this overkill?'

'You could at least look as if you're enjoying it.'

His voice was pure silk, and she retaliated by biting more deeply than necessary, caught his finger with her teeth as she intended, then managed to look incredibly contrite. 'Oh darling, did I bite you? I'm so sorry.'

'I think I'll live.'

'Perhaps you could get me a drink?'

'Champagne?'

She deliberated for all of five seconds. 'Of course.' Not a wise choice, but she'd sip it slowly for a while, then discard it in favour of mineral water.

'Saska?'

All he had to do was catch the waiter's attention, and seconds later their drinks were delivered. Nikos possessed a certain air of command that drew notice. Add a compelling degree of power with sophisticated élan, and the combination was lethal.

Her eyes were drawn to those strong sculpted features, the broad facial bone structure, the well-defined jaw, and the firm lines of his mouth.

What would he be like if ever he lost control? A faint shiver slithered its way over the surface of her skin. Devastating, a tiny voice prompted. Unbridled, flagrant, *primitive*.

At that moment his eyes met hers, and held. Her own dilated, and she felt as if her breath became suspended. Then his lips curved to form a lazy smile that held knowledge and a sense of pleasurable anticipation.

He couldn't *see* what she was thinking...could he? And it wasn't as if she *wanted* to go to bed with him. Heaven forbid! That would be akin to selling her soul. Besides, you might never recover, a secret inner voice taunted.

She'd seen women who never experienced their sexual equal prowl the party circuit in search of an adequate replacement. They tended to possess few scruples, dressed to kill, and drank a little too much.

She needed to get away for a few minutes, and the powder room provided an excellent reason. 'If you'll excuse me?' She handed her champagne flute to Nikos. 'I won't be long.'

Michelle paused several times en route to extend a greeting to a number of her parents' friends. Indoors there were two guests lingering adjacent the powder room, and she by-passed them and headed for the curved flight of stairs leading to the upper floor which housed her parents' suite and no less than five guest rooms with en suite facilities.

She chose one, then lingered to tidy her hair and retouch her lipstick.

Michelle emerged into the bedroom, and came to a shocked standstill at the sight of Jeremy leaning against the doorjamb.

'These are my parents' private quarters,' she managed evenly.

She kept walking, hoping he would move aside and allow her to pass. He didn't, and she paused a few feet in front of him. 'Jeremy, you're blocking my way.'

Her instincts were on alert. However, the upper floor was well insulated from the people and noise on the terrace out back of the house. Even if she screamed, it was doubtful anyone would hear a thing.

She took a step forward only to have him catch
hold of her arm.

'Wasn't I good enough?' Jeremy demanded softly.

'Your father and mine are business associates,' she
said carefully. 'Our parents share a similar social circle. We were friends,' she added.

'You're saying that's all it was?'

'For me, yes.' She looked at him, glimpsed the
darkness apparent in his eyes, and knew she'd need
to tread carefully. 'I'm sorry if you thought it was
more than friendship.'

'If Nikos hadn't put in an appearance that night...'
He trailed to a halt.

She was silent for several long seconds. 'It
wouldn't have made any difference.'

'That's not true,' he said fiercely. 'You have to
give me another chance.'

Not in this lifetime. She chose not to say a word.

'Michelle!' The plea was impassioned, and desperate. Too desperate.

'What do you hope to achieve by holding me
here?' She had to keep talking. And pray someone,
Nikos, would think it curious she'd been away so
long and investigate.

His face contorted. 'Have you slept with him yet?'

'You don't have the right to ask that.'

'Damn you. I'm making it my right.' He yanked
her close up against him, twisted her arm behind her
back and thrust a hand between her thighs. His fingers were a vicious instrument for all of ten seconds
before she went for the bridge of his nose, but he

ducked and the side of her palm connected with his cheekbone.

'I doubt Nikos will want you when he knows I've had you first.'

All of a sudden she was free, and Jeremy lay groaning on the carpet.

'You won't have the opportunity.' Nikos' voice held the chill of an arctic floe. 'A restraining order will be put into effect immediately. If you violate it, you'll be arrested and charged.'

Nikos swept her a swift encompassing glance, and his eyes darkened as he took in her waxen features, the way her fingers shook as they smoothed over her hair.

'You can't have me arrested,' Jeremy flung wildly as he scrambled to his feet, and Michelle almost quaked at the controlled savagery evident in Nikos' response.

'Watch me.'

'My father—'

'Doesn't have enough money to get you out of this one. Attempted rape is a serious charge.'

Jeremy's face reddened, and he blustered—'I didn't touch her.'

Nikos reached out a hand and sought purchase on Jeremy's jacket.

'What are you doing?'

'Detaining you while Michelle fetches your parents.'

'Everything comes with a price. My father will pay yours.'

'As he has in the past?' Nikos queried silkily. 'Not

this time,' he stated with a finality that moved Jeremy close to hysteria as Michelle stepped through the doorway.

'Don't bring my mother. She'd never understand.'

'Then perhaps it's time she did,' Nikos said pitilessly.

'Michelle, don't,' Jeremy begged. 'I'll do anything you want. I promise.'

'We can do this one of two ways. Michelle fetches your parents and you're removed from these premises without fuss. Or I force you downstairs and onto the terrace for a very public denouncement. Choose,' he commanded hardily.

Michelle smoothed a shaky hand over her hair in a purely reflex action as she descended the stairs. Reaction was beginning to set in, and she drew a deep breath in an effort to regain a measure of composure.

What followed wasn't something she would choose to experience again in a long time. Parental love was one thing. Blind maternal devotion was something else.

Nikos dismissed Emerson's bribe, and suggested the Bateson-Burrows remove their son as quickly as possible.

At which point Chantelle arrived on the scene, took everything in with a glance, and demanded an explanation.

'Jeremy has had a little too much to drink,' Emerson indicated smoothly. 'We're taking him home.'

As soon as they were alone Chantelle looked from

Michelle to Nikos. 'Would one of you care to tell me what really happened here?'

Michelle didn't say a word.

'Nikos?'

'Jeremy failed to accept Michelle and I have a relationship.' His eyes were hard, his expression equally so. 'He hassled her last night when she left the Gallery, and tonight he went one step further.'

Chantelle looked suitably horrified. '*Cherie*, this is terrible. Are you all right?'

'I'm fine, *Maman*,' Michelle reassured her quietly.

'I'll see to it that Michelle initiates a restraining order. Jeremy has a history of violence,' Nikos informed grimly. 'One recorded offense in Sydney three years ago.'

'The Bateson-Burrows moved to the Coast almost three years ago,' Chantelle reflected slowly.

'He was expelled from two private schools, and kicked out of University,' Nikos continued. 'In Perth, Adelaide, and Melbourne.'

Chantelle straightened her shoulders. She didn't ask how he acquired the information. It was enough that he had. 'It's to be hoped they soon leave the Coast.'

'It appears to be a familiar pattern.'

'Meanwhile, Michelle—'

'Will stay with me.'

'Now just a minute,' Michelle intervened, and met his dark gaze.

'It's not negotiable, *pedhi mou*.'

'The hell it's not!'

'*Cherie,* for my sake, as well as your own, do as Nikos suggests. Please.'

'I'll tell Saska we're leaving early,' Nikos declared. 'If she wants to stay, she can get a taxi back to the hotel.'

'Can I get you something, darling?' Chantelle queried as soon as Nikos disappeared down the hallway. 'A drink? Some coffee? A brandy?'

'I'm OK. Really,' she assured in a bid to lessen her mother's anxiety. 'Just a bit shaken, that's all.'

'Antonia and Emerson—Jeremy. I had no idea,' she said wretchedly. 'Thank heavens Nikos was here.'

All this has happened *because* of Nikos, she felt like saying. Yet that wasn't entirely true. Nikos' presence had only accelerated Jeremy's irrational jealousy.

'*Maman.*' She paused, then changed her mind against confiding that her purported relationship with the powerful Greek was just a sham.

'Yes, darling?'

'I'll just go tidy up.' She felt the need to remove Jeremy's touch, preferably with a long very thorough soaping in the shower. But for now, she'd settle for pressing a cold flannel to her face and redoing her hair.

Nikos had returned by the time she emerged, and she met his swift gaze, held it, then she crossed to brush her lips to her mother's cheek.

'I'll ring you in the morning.'

Chantelle hugged her close, then reluctantly released her. 'Please. Take care.'

Minutes later Nikos eased the powerful BMW onto the road, and she didn't offer a word as he drove to Main Beach.

'I'll be fine on my own,' Michelle stated as he parked the car outside her apartment building and slid out from behind the wheel.

'Nice try.'

She faced him across the car roof, glimpsed the dark glittery look he cast her, and felt like stamping her foot in frustrated anger. 'Look—'

'Do you want to walk, or have me carry you?' Nikos' voice was hard, his intention inflexible.

'Go to hell!'

'I've been there. Twice in the past twenty-four hours. It's not something I plan to repeat.' He moved round the car to her side. 'Now, which way is it going to be?'

'If you dare—' Whatever else she planned to say was lost in a muffled sound as he simply hoisted her over one shoulder, walked to the entrance, activated the door with her security card, then strode towards the bank of lifts at the far end of the lobby.

'Put me down, dammit!' She beat fists against his back, aimed for his kidneys, and groaned in frustration when he shifted her out of range. A mean-intentioned kick failed to connect, and she growled as fiercely as a feline under attack as he gained the lift, punched the appropriate panel button, then when the lift stopped, he walked calmly to her apartment, unlocked the door, and only when they were inside did he let her slide down to her feet.

'You want to fight?' he challenged silkily. 'Go ahead.'

She wanted to, badly, and right at this precise moment she didn't care that she couldn't win.

'You,' she vented with ill-concealed fury. 'Are the most arrogant, egotistical man I've ever met. I want you to leave, now.'

'It's here,' Nikos stated ruthlessly. 'Or my apartment. Choose.'

Something about his stance, the stillness of his features slowly leeched most of the anger from her system.

'Don't you think you're taking the *hero* role too far?'

'No.'

Succinct, and clearly unmoveable. Maybe she should just concede defeat now and save her emotional and physical energy. It would be a whole lot easier than continuing to rage against him.

'I could ring the police and have them evict you.' It was a last-ditch effort, and she knew it.

'Go ahead.'

She badly wanted to call his bluff. Except she had no trouble visualising how such a scene would evolve, and how it would inevitably prove to be an exercise in futility.

Occasionally there could be success in conceding defeat. 'You can sleep in the spare room.'

She turned away from him and crossed the lounge to her bedroom and carefully closed the door.

If he insisted on staying—*fine*. She was going to have a long hot bath with bath oil and bubbles...the whole bit. Then when she was done, she'd dry off and climb into bed, hopefully to sleep until the alarm went off in the morning.

Michelle stayed in the scented water for a long time. It was bliss, absolute bliss to lay there and let the perfumed heat seep into her bones and soothe her mind.

It had a soporific effect, and she closed her eyes. For only a minute, she was prepared to swear, when a rapid knock on the door caused her to jackknife into a sitting position.

Seconds later the door opened and Nikos walked calmly into the bathroom.

'What the hell are you doing in here?'

She looked like a child, was his first thought, with her hair piled on top of her head, and all but buried beneath a layer of frothy foam.

'Checking you hadn't fallen asleep and drowned.'

Her eyes were huge, the pupils dilated with anger.

Most women would have sank back displaying most if not all of their breasts, and behaved like a sultry temptress by inviting him to join them.

'You could have waited for me to answer!'

'You didn't,' he relayed coolly. 'That's why I came in.'

'Well, you can just turn around and go out again!' Indignation brought pink colour to her cheeks, and she looked at him through stormy eyes. Then, in a totally unprecedented action, she did the unforgivable. She scooped up water and foam and threw it at him in a spontaneous action that surprised her almost as much as it did him.

Her aim was good, it drenched the front part of his shirt, and she watched in fascination as a patch of foam began to dissipate. Then she lifted her gaze to lock with his. And wished fervently that she hadn't, for what she glimpsed there made her feel terribly afraid.

There was strength of purpose, a knowledge that was entirely primitive. For a moment she thought he was going to reach forward and drag her out of the bath and into his arms.

It was uncanny, but she could almost feel his mouth on hers, savour the taste of him as he invaded the soft inner tissues and explored them with his tongue. Staking a possession that could only have one ending.

The breath caught in her throat, and for seemingly long seconds she wasn't capable of saying a word.

'You provoked me,' she managed at last.

'Is that an apology?' Nikos demanded silkily.

'An explanation.'

His eyes speared hers. 'Pull the plug, and get out of the bath.'

She looked at him incredulously. 'While you're still here? Not on your life!'

He reached out, collected a large bath towel, unfolded it and held it out.

Nikos saw the anger drain out of her. Her eyes slowly welled, leaving them looking like drenched pools. It twisted his gut, and undid him more than anything she could have said. Without a word he replaced the towel, then he turned and walked from the en suite.

Michelle released the bath water, towelled herself dry, then she pulled on a huge cotton T-shirt and slid into bed to sit hugging her knees as she stared sightlessly at a print positioned on the opposite wall.

The events of the past few hours played and replayed through her mind until she made a concerted effort to dismiss them.

Where was Nikos? Ensconced in the spare bedroom, or had he left the apartment?

She had no way of knowing, and told herself she didn't care. Except she had a vivid memory of the way her body reacted to his; the protective splay of his hand at her back; the intense warmth in his eyes when he looked at her. The feel of his mouth on hers, the way he invaded her senses and stirred them as no man had ever done before.

Michelle shifted position, picked up a book from the pedestal and read for a while. Three nights ago she'd been so engrossed in the plot she hadn't been able to put the book down. Now, she skimmed sentences and turned pages, only to discard it with disgust at her inability to focus on the plot.

All she needed, she determined as she switched off the light, was a good night's sleep.

CHAPTER SEVEN

MICHELLE woke with a start, the images so vivid for the space of a few seconds that she was prepared to swear they were real.

Jeremy, maniacal. Nikos, dark and threatening.

It was as if she was a disembodied spectator, watching the clash of steel as they fought, the thrust and parry as they each meshed their skill with physical prowess.

Then there was darkness, and she heard a cry of pain, followed by silence. She tried to ascertain who was the victor, but his features eluded her.

'Dear heaven,' Michelle whispered as she shifted into a sitting position and switched on the bedlamp. Light flooded the room, and she relished the reality of familiar surroundings. Then she lifted her hands to her cheeks and discovered they were wet.

She scrubbed them dry, then she slid out of bed, pulled on a wrap, and walked quietly out to the kitchen. The digital display on the microwave relayed the time as one-o-five.

A cold drink would quench her thirst, and she selected a can, popped the top, and carried it into the lounge.

The night was warm, and she had an urge to slide open the wide glass doors and let the fresh sea air blow away the cares of the past few days.

Michelle stepped out onto the terrace and felt the coolness wash over her face. There was the tang of salt, a clean sweetness that drifted in from the ocean, and she breathed deeply as she took in the sweeping coastal view.

Street lamps, bright splashes of neon, pinpricks of light that diminished with distance from enumerable high-rise apartment buildings lining the coastal strip.

It resembled a fairyland of light against the velvet backdrop of an indigo night sky and ocean.

She lifted the can and took a long swallow of cool liquid. The breeze teased loose a few stray tendrils of hair and pulled at the hem of her wrap.

It could have been ten minutes or twenty before she returned indoors, and the sight of a tall male figure framed in the lounge brought her to a shocked standstill.

Her rational mind assured it was Nikos, but just for a split second with the reflected hall light behind him, her imagination went into overdrive.

'How long have you been standing there?' Was that her voice, sounding slightly high and vaguely breathless?

'Only a few minutes,' Nikos ventured quietly.

A towel was draped low on his hips, his chest and legs bare. It occurred that she hadn't even bothered to consider he wouldn't have anything to change into.

'I noticed the hall light go on half an hour ago.'

'So you decided to investigate.' She didn't mean to sound defensive. Except he could have no idea how vulnerable she was feeling right now, or be aware of the image he presented.

For one crazy moment she wanted to walk up to him and take comfort from the warmth of his embrace. Yet that was a madness she couldn't afford.

'I didn't mean to frighten you.'

Hadn't he been able to sleep? Or did he simply wake at the slightest sound? His features were dark, and in this half-light it was difficult to read his expression.

Her senses leapt at the electric energy apparent. It was almost as if all her fine body hairs rose up in anticipation of his touch, and she felt her heart quicken to a faster beat.

Get out of here, *now,* a tiny voice urged. Except her legs wouldn't obey the dictates of her brain.

The slow ache of desire flared deep inside, and she was aware of her shallow breathing, the pulse throbbing at the base of her throat.

Nikos didn't say a word as he took the few steps necessary to reach her, and his eyes held hers, compelling, dramatic, unwavering. Dark onyx fused with emerald, and she was unable to look away.

A hand closed over her shoulder, while the other slid beneath the heavy knot of her hair, loosened it, then when it fell to her shoulders he threaded his fingers through its length and smoothed a few stray tendrils behind her ear.

She felt him move imperceptibly, then sensed his lips brush over her hair and settle at the edge of one temple.

Unbidden she linked her arms round his waist and

sank into him. She didn't want to think, she just wanted to feel. To become lost in sensation, transported to a place where there was only the moment, the man, and the passion.

She lifted her face to his, and felt the soft trail of kisses feather across her cheek, then descend to the generous curve of her mouth, tantalising, teasing, nibbling as he explored the soft fullness of her lower lip, tracing it with the tip of his tongue before delving in to make slow sweeping forays of the sweetness within.

It wasn't enough, not nearly enough, and she opened her mouth to him, angling her head in surrender as passion swept her to new heights.

Michelle dragged his mouth down to hers as his hand slid to her thigh and slowly crept up to her bottom, shaped it, then pressed her in close so she could be in no doubt of his arousal.

'Put your arms round my neck,' Nikos instructed, and she obeyed, only to catch her breath as he lifted her up against him and curved each thigh round his waist so that she straddled him.

Then he walked towards the bedroom, every step providing an erotic movement that heightened the ache deep inside.

She wanted, needed the physical joining, the hard thrusting primal rhythm as he took her with him to a place where there was only acute primitive sensation. Michelle was dimly aware they reached the bed. She felt him pause as he tossed back the bedcovers and drew her down onto the percale sheet, stilling as his eyes locked with hers.

He saw slumberous passion, desire, and something else that gave him pause. It would be so easy to take her, to sink into those moist depths and slake a mutual need until they reached satiation.

Instead he took the slow route, the long sensual tease that began with a sensory exploration of all her pleasure pulses, the sensitive crevices, as he used his lips, the soft pads of his fingers to touch and tantalise.

Michelle was unaware of the slight sounds she made deep in her throat as he took the tender peak of her breast into his mouth and began to shamelessly suckle until she cried out for him to desist. Then he merely shifted to its twin and brought her to the edge of pain.

Not content he caressed a path to her navel, explored it, then travelled low over her belly, teased the dark blonde curls with his tongue, then indulged in an intimacy that took her to the brink, then tipped her over the edge in a free fall that had her threshing against him, imploring him to stop…to never stop.

For one wild moment, she didn't think she could handle the intensity, then mercifully it began to ease, and she met his kiss hungrily, her hands eager, searching, wanting to bestow some of the pleasure he had gifted her.

She cried out as he caught her hands together and pressed them to his lips. There were a few emotive seconds as he paused to use prophylactic protection, then he positioned his length and eased into her, exulting in the gradual feeling of total enclosure as he slid deep. And stayed there for several long seconds before repeating the action. Longer and deeper, then harder and faster until she cried out and fell off the edge of the world.

What followed became a feast of the senses as he soothed her fevered flesh with a gentleness that brought her close to tears. He explored each sensitive pulse, felt her quivering response and savoured it in a long after-play that stirred her senses to a point where it no longer became possible to lay supine, a willing supplicant to everything he chose to bestow.

She wanted to stir him to passion, to render him mindless beneath her touch until he begged her to stop.

With one easy movement she dragged herself free, then she captured his head between her hands and kissed him, thoroughly, slaking a sensual thirst as she employed sufficient pressure to roll him onto his back.

His eyes were dark, slumberous, and intent as she straddled his waist, then she trailed an exploratory path along one collarbone with her lips, dipped into the faint hollows, using her teeth to tease the hair on his chest, nibbling, savouring, tasting, until she reached one hard brown male nipple.

With extreme delicacy she laved it with her tongue and slowly suckled until the peak began to swell, then she took it between her teeth and employed the lightest pressure.

She felt, rather that heard his slight intake of breath, and she rolled the slightly distended peak with her teeth, then suckled with greedy sensitivity, all too aware of his fingers lightly brushing the soft fullness of her breasts.

Not content, she trailed a path of lingering kisses across his chest to bestow a similar treatment to its twin, and was unprepared for the sharp arrow that was part pleasure part pain as he took her nipple between two fingers and rolled it.

She gently swatted his hand and slid slowly down his torso, caressing the line of dark hair until she reached his stomach, hovered there for long tantalising seconds, then descended with such painstaking slowness.

Nikos held his breath as she began to explore with such devastating gentleness, it took all his willpower not to haul her into his arms and take control.

Yet he'd tested the measure of her endurance with an equally lingering sensual torture.

Nevertheless when she touched him lightly with the tip of her tongue, the breath hissed between his teeth, and her tentative examination brought a surge of powerful emotion. Not for the degree of her expertise. It was her touch, the desire to please him as he had pleasured her that brought him to the brink of climax.

Did she know she had this effect on a man? On *him?* Somehow he doubted it.

When he was almost ready to take independent action, she rose up in one graceful movement, carefully positioned herself, then slid slowly down until he was buried deep inside her.

It felt good, so very good. As if every nerve fibre, every sensory cell heightened as she sheathed and held him tightly.

There was a part of her that didn't want to move,

simply to be. Yet there was a primal need for sensory stimulation, and she placed a hand on either side of his shoulders, then began to withdraw. Just a little, increasing the action until it became something primitive, and she cried out as his hands curved into her waist, held her still, then assumed the position of supremacy, lifting her high as his hips rose and fell endlessly until it was she who cried out, she who clutched hold of him.

Afterwards he held her, his fingers drifting a lazy pattern back and forth along her spine until her breathing quietened.

Michelle felt his lips graze her ear, then slip to the sensitive curve of her neck, linger there, before moving to the edge of her mouth.

His kiss was incredibly soft, the lightest touch as he savoured a path over the fullness of her lower lip.

'We're still—'

'Connected.'

She felt his mouth part in a humorous smile. 'Uncomfortable?'

'No.' The sound sighed from her lips. She felt as if she could lay here forever, absorbing the man, his texture and taste.

There were words she wanted to say. Words that would adequately express what she'd just experienced. How special it had been. Emotionally, spiritually, physically. For the first time she knew what it was like to be a part of someone on every level. To share, possess, and be possessed.

Frightening. For inevitably there would follow a sense of loss. *Don't think about it,* she bade silently.

Just enjoy the night, and forget about what the new day might bring.

It wasn't love. Love was a slow process, a gradual learning, appreciation, understanding. An attunement of the senses.

Yet what they'd just shared was more than lust. That much she knew. Lust didn't leave you caught up with introspective thought, wishing for something beyond reach, or cause you to wonder if what had just happened could irreparably change your life. Or if, she decided a trifle wildly, there would be any choice.

There was no magic wand she could wave to remove the past few hours. Tomorrow would be dealt with when it arrived. Now all she wanted to do, all she had the energy for, was sleep.

She was unaware of Nikos carefully shifting her to lay at his side, or that she instinctively curled into the curve of his body as he settled the bed-covering over her sleeping form.

Michelle felt something soft drift across her arm, and she burrowed her head more deeply into the pillow. It was early, her alarm hadn't sounded, and she was tired.

Minutes later there it was again, whispering along the curve of her waist. It had to be an early morning breeze teasing the sheet, and she kicked the tangle of soft percale, freeing it from her body.

This time there was no mistaking the brush of skin on skin, and her eyes swept open to see Nikos propped up on one elbow, watching her. His expression was slumberous and deceptively indolent, and he looked as sexy as hell with stubble darkening his jaw.

She'd experienced the entire gamut of emotions in his arms. Physical, emotional, spiritual had combined to make their coupling as good as she imagined it could possibly get.

Even thinking about what they'd shared brought a surge of heat flooding her body, and her eyes widened as he stroked gentle fingers over her breast. The sensitive peak hardened beneath his touch, and she drew in her breath as he rolled it gently between thumb and forefinger. Answering sensation flowered deep within, instantly so she ached with need, and her breathing hitched as he leaned forward and began teasing her breast with his lips.

His hand trailed low, conducting a seeking path with unerring accuracy, and within seconds she scaled the heights, begging as he held her there, then she tipped over the brink in a sensual free fall that left her breathing ragged, her voice an indistinguishable groan as she whispered his name.

He slid into her in one deep movement, nestled momentarily, then slowly withdrew, only to repeat the controlled thrust again and again. There was little of the hard passion of the night, just long and sweet and slow as she became consumed by a deep pulsing flame, intensely exquisite as it swirled and shimmered through her body like a treacherous heat haze.

She decided dreamily that it was a wonderful way to start the day.

'You have the most beautiful smile.'

'Mmm?'

His husky laughter curled round her nerve-ends and tugged just a little too much for comfort, activating a renewed spiral of sensation infinitely dangerous to an equilibrium already off balance.

Assertiveness was the key, she determined as she reached out and ran an idle forefinger down the slope of his nose. And humour.

'Time to begin all those mundane things like shower, breakfast, and don the business suit.' She traced the groove creasing his upper lip, then pressed down on the fullness beneath it, only to have him take her fingertip between his teeth. 'Ouch, that hurt.'

'It was meant to,' Nikos chided solemnly, although his eyes were darkly alight with amusement. 'We have an hour.'

Her heart lurched. 'I dislike being rushed.'

'I don't think you'll object.'

'Personal grooming,' Michelle said helplessly as he slid out of bed. 'A leisurely breakfast,' she intimated as he scooped her into his arms. 'And two cups of coffee. Where are you taking me?'

'The shower.' He reached the en suite bathroom in a few long strides. 'You can have that second coffee at the Gallery.'

With economy of movement he turned on the water dial, adjusted it, then stepped into the large glassed cubicle.

Nikos picked up the huge sponge, poured perfumed liquid soap onto it, then became intent on smoothing the sponge over every inch of her body.

It was an erotic experience, as he meant it to be,

and she balled her hand into a fist and playfully struck his shoulder.

'Is that a complaint?'

The thought of sharing this kind of morning experience on a regular basis made her mouth go dry.

'Yes. I think I'm going to miss breakfast.'

His eyes were impossibly dark with lambent emotion as he lowered his head down to hers. 'Then I guess tomorrow we'll just have to make an earlier start, hmm?'

She didn't answer. She couldn't. The words were locked in her throat as his mouth took possession of her own.

She became oblivious to the warm spray of water, for there was only the hard strength of his body. Strong muscle and sinew that bound her close, so impossibly close that all she had to do was wind her arms up around his neck and hang on as he parted her thighs.

His arousal was a potent force he withheld in a bid to heighten her desire, and she was almost crazy with need when he finally surged into her. She cried out as sensation washed through her body, taking her higher than she'd thought it was possible to climb.

His mouth ravaged hers as he reached the physical peak with her, and she exulted in the primitive shudder that shook his large frame as they clung to each other in mutual climactic rapture and its aftermath.

Michelle missed breakfast entirely. There wasn't even time to do more than take a few hurried sips of the coffee Nikos brewed while she put the finishing touches to her make-up.

'I'll book the restaurant,' Nikos intimated as she collected her shoulder bag and turned towards the door. 'We're dining with Emilio and Saska, remember?' he prompted as she swivelled to face him, 'By the way,' he gently teased, 'Cute butterfly tattoo.'

It was small, and positioned low on the soft curve of her right buttock.

His smile was slow, musing. 'A moment of madness, flouting of parental authority, or what?'

'A dare. Paris.' A mischievous gleam lit her eyes. 'It was the tattoo or a navel ring.'

The phone rang, and for a moment the humour drained away. If it was Jeremy— She crossed the room and picked up the receiver.

'Michelle? Everything OK?'

Relief poured through her. 'Emilio. Yes. I'm just leaving now.' She cut the connection, and looked at Nikos. 'Just—lock up when you leave.'

'I'll contact my lawyer and set the paperwork in motion for a restraining order, then ring you.'

She was already crossing the lounge. 'Thanks.'

A chill slithered down her spine as she rode the lift down to the underground car park. The thought of Jeremy and just how close she'd come to assault was the reason why Nikos had stayed overnight in her apartment.

Not part of the agenda had been their shared intimacy. Who had initiated it?

Dear heaven, did it matter?

Michelle discovered that it did, very much, for it made a farce of their charade, and provided an unexpected twist in that they no longer needed to pretend.

A paradox really, for the lines determining their supposed relationship had shifted. For the better, if one believed in a transitory affair. Sadly, she didn't. What had begun as a mutual arrangement, now took on a different context. Jeremy was an unknown quantity. And there was Saska.

How long would it take to effect a resolution? A week? Two? Then what? Would Nikos extricate himself, move base to wherever in the world he chose, and never seek to contact her again?

That surely was part of the master plan. It had to be.

Wasn't that what she'd wanted?

The Gallery was just up front, and she parked the car, locked it, then ran up the short flight of steps to the main door.

Work, she decided, was a panacea for many things. All she had to do was keep herself busy, her mind occupied, and deal with each day as it occurred.

A hollow bubble of laughter rose and died in her throat. In theory, the analogy was fine. The problem was reality.

CHAPTER EIGHT

THE mobile phone rang as Michelle eased the car onto the road, and she assured her mother she was fine, she'd slept well; and no, she hadn't forgotten the charity function at a city hotel scheduled for Thursday evening.

'Nikos can partner you, darling. You'll sit at our table, of course.'

Michelle parked outside the Gallery, and cut the connection as she reached the main entrance.

It proved to be a hectic morning. A shipment due to be unloaded from a dockside container in Sydney was caught up in a strike, and numerous phone calls were necessary to reschedule and put a contingency plan in place.

There was paperwork requiring attention, data to enter into the computer, and several phone calls to make confirming collection and delivery of items ordered on consignment.

The phone pealed, and she automatically reached for the receiver and intoned a professional greeting.

'Michelle. Nikos.'

His voice was deeper and slightly more accented over the phone, and the sound of it evoked a pulsing warmth flooding her veins.

'I've arranged an appointment with my lawyer at twelve-thirty.'

The restraining order. 'I'll reorganise my lunch hour.'

'I'll meet you at the Gallery and take you to Paul's office,' Nikos intimated, and she sank back in her chair, swivelled it to take in the view across the Nerang river.

'I don't think that's necessary.'

'Twelve-fifteen, Michelle.'

He hung up before she had the opportunity to argue.

'Problems?'

Michelle swung back to face Emilio, who had walked into the office during the conversation. 'Nothing I can't handle.' It was said more to convince herself than Emilio. Somehow she didn't think any woman could manipulate Nikos. Unless he permitted it.

'You left early last night.'

It was better she went with the fictional excuse. 'I had a headache.'

He placed both hands on the desk and leaned forward. 'This is Emilio, remember?'

She kept her gaze steady as he raked her pale features, then settled on the pulse at the base of her throat.

'So, do we play guessing games, or are you going to tell me?'

'OK.' She used facetiousness and shock value as a form of defence. 'Nikos took me home, and we made wild passionate love all night.'

His eyes lit with amusement, and something else she was unable to define. *'Brava,'* he said gently. 'I approve. Of the loving, and the Greek.' He straightened away from the desk. 'Jeremy was the catalyst, am I right? For someone who knew what to look for last night, it wasn't difficult to put two and two together. Your absence, Jeremy, then Nikos.' His expression hardened fractionally. 'I'll wring his neck.'

'Jeremy, or the Greek?'

'Don't jest, *cara*. If there's a problem, I want to know about it.' He waited a beat. 'We're more than just business partners, we're friends.'

She spent a major part of her waking hours at the Gallery. Emilio deserved to be on the alert if Jeremy continued to prove a nuisance.

'Nikos insists I file a restraining order.'

Emilio's eyes sharpened. 'Give,' he uttered in succinct command.

'Last night was the third— *Assault?* She settled for '—attack, in seventy-two hours.'

'Son of a bitch!' The words were uttered with such silky softness, it sent a shiver down her back. 'He won't get a foot inside the Gallery. Your apartment is secure.' His expression became ruthlessly hard. 'Don't go anywhere alone. *Comprende?*'

'I just love it when you lapse into Italian,' Michelle teased at his protective stance.

'I'm serious.'

She tilted her head to one side, her eyes solemn. 'I'm a big girl. And capable of defending myself, remember?'

She was good, he visited the same *dojo* and had witnessed a few of her training sessions. However, expertise in formal surroundings was a different kettle of fish to the reality of an unexpected attack with brutal intent in a dark deserted street.

'Stand up,' he instructed quietly. 'Turn with your back to me.'

'Emilio—'

'Do it, *cara.*'

'This really is unnecessary,' she protested, and caught his faint smile.

'Indulge me.'

The electronic buzzer attached to the main door sounded, heralding entrance of a customer, and Emilio spared a quick glance in the overhead monitor.

'Nikos.'

It was twelve-fifteen already? She should go powder her nose and ensure her hair was OK.

'We'll continue this later.'

'What will you continue later?' Nikos drawled from the open doorway.

His tall frame almost filled the aperture, and Michelle was positive the room seemed to shrink in size. He looked the epitome of an urbane sophisticate attired in impeccably cut trousers, a dark blue shirt unbuttoned at the neck and a jacket hooked casually over one shoulder.

'A test against a real attack attempt, as opposed to an orchestrated practised manoeuvre,' Emilio enlightened, meeting Nikos' steady gaze with one of his own.

'Michelle has filled you in.' It was a statement, not a question.

'Yes.'

'I take it you have no objection if she has an extended lunch hour?'

'As long as it takes.'

'I'm moving her into my apartment.'

Michelle thrust the swivel chair forward, and glared from one man to the other. 'Now, just wait a damn minute.' She settled on Nikos. '*Excuse me.* You're doing *what?*'

'Moving you temporarily into my apartment,' he reiterated calmly.

Her eyes flashed emerald fire. 'The hell you are.'

'Then I'll move into yours. Either way, it makes little difference.'

'It makes plenty of difference!'

'Then choose.'

'Just who has granted you the God-given right to take over my life and order me around?' She was so furious, her body was almost rigid with anger.

'I did,' Nikos relayed with deceptive ease. 'Your apartment, or mine, *pedhaki mou?*'

'I am *not* "your little one"!'

Nikos' eyes flared. 'Yes, you are.'

Emilio watched the by-play with interest. Intriguing the sparks that flew between these two. He smiled, despite the gravity of the situation at hand. Unless he was very wrong, Michelle had met her match in the forceful Greek.

'I'd rather move home.'

Nikos shook his head. 'Due to your parents' social commitments, they're rarely in residence except for a few requisite hours each night, and they don't have live-in help.'

'While you,' she vented with deliberate emphasis, 'intend to stand guard over me every minute of the day?'

'And night,' he added equably, although his tone was deceptive. The eyes had it. Inflexible, compelling. Invincible.

'No.' She refused to be ordered about like a child.

'No?' His voice was pure silk.

'I'll book into a hotel.'

'Where, without independent security, Jeremy could access your room in a minute?'

'Don't you think,' she inclined carefully, 'you're getting just a bit carried with all this?'

'I have your parents' approval.'

'That's a low trick.'

'They're just as concerned about your safety as I am.'

She was angry, so angry at the way he was taking control. 'I don't doubt that. But I can take care of myself. I don't need a minder, or a baby-sitter!'

He wanted to take hold of her shoulders and shake her. Instead, he used words to create a similar effect.

'Jeremy has a history of previous violence. In this instance, it's been activated by his jealousy of me and what he sees as my involvement with you. Which makes me responsible to a degree.'

He looked at her carefully. 'What if I hadn't been there when he accosted you outside the Gallery Sunday night?' It gave him little pleasure to see her eyes dilate at his implication. 'Or last night?' he pursued relentlessly. 'Was anyone else aware Jeremy might use any opportunity to get you alone? Was there anyone who became alarmed when you didn't return within a reasonable time?'

He paused, then slid home the final barb. 'Have you considered what would have happened had I not come in search of you when I did?'

She opened her mouth to refute what he'd said, then closed it again.

'Jeremy has attacked you three times,' Emilio stated inexorably. 'You want to try for four?'

Nikos' eyes pierced hers, their depths dark and inflexible. 'Don't you think you're protesting too much... after last night?'

He was too skilled a tactician not to choose his weapons well, she perceived, and silently cursed him for his temerity.

'Aren't we late for an appointment?' she posed stiffly, and heard his drawled response.

'I'll ring Paul and let him know we've been delayed.'

'If it's all right with you,' Michelle declared with deliberate mockery, 'I'll just go powder my nose.'

Nikos Alessandros, she decided, had a lot to answer for. At this very moment her feelings were definitely ambivalent.

Damn, damn, *damn*. Why was she objecting? The man was a lover to die for. Why not just go with the flow, enjoy the perks, and live for the day?

Last night had been *heaven*. Was it such a sin to enjoy responsible sex?

Without commitment? And what happens when it ends, as it inevitably will? a small imp taunted. What then? Do you think you'll be able to walk away, heart-whole, smile, and thank him for the memory?

'Give me a break,' she pleaded with the inimical imp, snapped on the lid of her lipstick, then she re-entered the office and shot Nikos a dark glance.

Which merely resulted in a raised eyebrow. 'Ready?'

'Take your time,' Emilio bade as Michelle preceded Nikos out onto the mezzanine balcony.

They traversed the short flight of stairs down to the main Gallery.

'Do what you need to do, and if you don't make it back by five, I'll see you at the restaurant at six.'

'I'll be back midafternoon,' she declared firmly, as she leant forward and brushed Emilio's cheek.

Nikos unlocked the BMW and she slid into the passenger seat, watched as he crossed round to slip in behind the wheel, then she sat in silence as he eased the large car into the flow of traffic heading towards the main highway.

'You're very quiet.'

'I'm saving it all for later,' she assured, and heard his husky laughter. 'If you weren't driving, I'd *hit* you,' she said fiercely.

Southport was merely a few kilometres distant, and within five minutes Nikos drove into a client car park adjacent a modern glassed building.

Nikos' lawyer led her through a series of questions as he compiled a detailed draft statement, informed what a restraining order entailed, perused a sheaf of faxed reports Nikos provided him with, then he advised her as to her personal safety, and requested she call into the office at four that afternoon to sign the statement.

It was one-thirty when they emerged from the building, and within minutes Nikos headed the car towards Main Beach.

'Where are you going?' Michelle queried sharply when he turned towards the Sheraton hotel and its adjacent marina shopping complex.

'Taking you to lunch.'

'I'm not hungry.'

'The seafood buffet should tempt your appetite.'

'Nikos—'

'I've never known a woman who argues the way you do,' he drawled with amusement.

'You,' she stated heatedly. 'Are the most domineering man I've ever met!'

He eased the BMW into an empty parking space and killed the engine. Then he released his seat belt and leaned towards her.

His mouth settled on hers, hard, as he shaped her jaw to his, and he employed a sensual ravishment that tore her anger to shreds and left her breathless and trembling.

She was incapable of uttering a word, and he brushed a gentle finger over her lower lip.

'You talk too much.' He reached for the clip of her seat belt, released it, then he slid out from behind the wheel and led her towards the restaurant.

It was peaceful to sit overlooking the huge pool with its lagoon bar, and the buffet offered a superb selection which proved too tempting for Michelle to resist.

'Feel better?' Nikos queried when she declined dessert and settled for coffee.

'Yes,' she answered simply.

'We need to discuss whose apartment we share.'

'I don't think—'

'Yours or mine?'

'Are you always this dictatorial?'

'It's an integral part of my personality.' The waiter presented the bill, and Nikos signed the credit slip, added a tip, then he drained the last of his coffee. 'Shall we leave?'

Within minutes Nikos turned the car into the street housing both their apartment buildings, and she opened her mouth to protest when he swept down into the car park beneath his building.

'Come up with me while I collect some clothes.'

She turned towards him. 'I don't like people making decisions for me.'

His expression assumed an inflexibility, accenting the vertical grooves down each cheek, and his mouth settled into a firm line. 'Get used to it, *pedhi mou.*'

Michelle rode the lift with him to the uppermost floor. 'We're going to have to draw a few ground rules,' she insisted as she entered his penthouse apartment.

It was beautiful, marble tiled floors, Oriental rugs, imported furniture and exquisite furnishings. Interior decorating at its finest.

'Make yourself comfortable,' Nikos bade. 'I won't be long.'

There were a few framed photographs positioned on a long mahogany table, and she crossed to examine them. Family, she perceived, noting an elderly couple pictured in one, while the others were presumably siblings with a number of young children.

She knew so little about him, his background. Why, when his family obviously resided in Europe, he chose to spend part of his time in Australia.

Which inevitably led to how long he intended to stay on this particular occasion. Weeks, or a month or two? With business interests on several different continents, he wouldn't remain in one place for very long at a time.

Nikos returned to the lounge with a garment bag hooked over one shoulder, and a hold-all in his hand.

'Two sisters,' he revealed, anticipating her question. 'Both married. One lives in Athens, the other in London. My parents reside on Santorini.'

'While you wander the world.' She could imagine the high-powered existence he led. International flights, board meetings, wheeling and dealing.

'I have houses in several countries.'

'And a woman in each city?'

'I have many women friends,' he said with dry mockery.

Now why did that suddenly make her feel bereft? Did she really think *she* was different? Special? Get real, an inner voice mercilessly taunted. You're simply a momentary diversion.

With determined effort she spared her watch a glance and turned towards the door. 'Shall we leave?' She needed some space and time away from him. 'You can drop me off at the Gallery. I'll give you a key to my apartment.'

Minutes later he drew the car to a halt outside the Gallery. 'I'll pick you up at five.'

She was about to argue, but one look at his implacable expression was sufficient to change her mind, and she refrained from saying a word as she handed him her keys, then she slid out, closed the door, and trod the bricked path to the Gallery's main entrance without so much as a backward glance.

If Emilio was surprised to see her, he didn't say so, and she went straight through to the office and booted up the computer.

With determined resolve she set her mind on work, and refused to give Nikos Alessandros a second thought.

Until he appeared with Emilio in the doorway a few minutes after five.

'Time to close down for the day, *cara*.'

Michelle saved the data, closed the programme and shut down the machine. Without a word she collected her bag and preceded Nikos out to the car.

It was a bright summer's evening, the sun was still warm, and she could easily have walked. She wasn't sure whether it bothered her more that her freedom of choice had been endangered, or that Nikos had nominated himself as her protector.

Or perhaps she was more shaken at the thought of sharing her apartment with him. Last night... Hell, she didn't even want to think about last night!

Nikos parked in the bay next to hers, and they rode the lift to the fifteenth floor in silence.

Nikos unlocked her apartment, and she swept in ahead of him.

'Fix yourself a drink if you want one,' Michelle suggested politely as she tossed her bag down onto the coffee table. 'I'm going to shower and change.'

She entered her bedroom and went straight to the walk-in wardrobe. If he'd *dared* invade her space by hanging his clothes here...

He hadn't, and she told herself she was glad as she entered the shower.

Half an hour later she caught up an evening purse and paused in front of the cheval mirror to briefly examine her appearance.

The emerald-coloured evening pantsuit complemented her slim frame and highlighted her eyes. Minimum jewellery and an upswept hairstyle presented an essential sophisticated image, given that Saska would undoubtedly appear at her stunning best.

Michelle took a deep breath, released it, then joined Nikos in the lounge.

His appraisal was swift, encompassing, and caused a shivery sensation to scud across the surface of her skin.

She offered him a brilliant smile. 'Do you think Saska will be impressed?'

He didn't offer a word as he crossed the short distance to her side, and her eyes widened as he cradled her face, then settled his mouth on hers in passionate possession.

When he lifted his head she wasn't capable of saying so much as a word.

'Better,' he drawled. He touched the pad of one finger to her lips. 'Lipstick repair.' The edge of his mouth curved. 'Although personally, I prefer the natural look.'

'Don't overdo the play-acting,' she managed evenly. 'I doubt Saska will be fooled.'

It was just after six when they reached the nominated restaurant, and within minutes Emilio and Saska joined them in the lounge bar.

As Michelle predicted, Saska could have stepped from one of the fashion pages of *Vogue*. In classic black, the style was deceptively demure…a total contradiction when Saska removed the fitted bolero top to reveal the dress was virtually strapless, with a thin shoestring strap over each shoulder.

'It's a little warm in here, don't you think?'

Oh my. Were those generous curves for real? They just begged to be shaped and caressed by a man's hand.

She caught Emilio's eye, saw the faint glimmer of amusement apparent, and prepared to shift gears into 'compete' mode.

This was, Michelle accorded silently, going to be quite an evening!

'Michelle,' Saska almost purred. 'One hopes you no longer suffer from your headache?'

The faint emphasis gave the malady quite a different interpretation. 'Nikos took good care of me.'

How was that for an understatement? If Saska were to guess the manner in which he'd cared for her, the sparks would surely fly!

It was fortuitous the maître d' chose that moment to indicate their table was ready, and within minutes the wine steward appeared to take their order.

CHAPTER NINE

'CHAMPAGNE?' Saska suggested. 'We should drink to our continuing friendship.'

'Yes,' Michelle agreed with a winsome smile. 'Why don't we do that?'

'Nikos and I go back a long way.'

'So he told me.'

Saska's eyebrow arched. 'I imagine you know I was married to his best friend?'

'You must miss him very much,' she said gently. Saska deserved some compassion. It would be devastating to be widowed at any age, but for someone so young, the loss must be terrible.

Eyes dark and faintly cloudy regarded Michelle with contrived steadiness. 'Dreadfully. But life moves on, and so must I.'

With Nikos, Michelle deduced. She could hardly blame Saska for pursuing the possibility. Nikos was a man among men, irrespective of his wealth, status and social position. As a lover... Just the thought of what she'd shared with him was enough to melt her bones.

Nikos ordered a bottle of Dom Pérignon, and together they perused the menu, their choices varied as they deliberated over a starter, main and dessert.

The waiter presented the champagne with a flourish, eased off the cork, then part-filled each flute before setting the bottle in the ice bucket and retreating.

'To old friends,' Saska said gently, touching the rim of her flute to that of Nikos'.

His answering smile was equally gentle, then he silently saluted Emilio and turned to Michelle.

'To us.'

His eyes were dark, and so incredibly sensual, she had to consciously prevent her eyes dilating with shock.

Her mouth shook slightly as he caught her hand and linked her fingers with his.

He'd missed his vocation as an actor. If she hadn't known better, she could almost believe he meant the light touch on her arm, the slight brush of his fingers against her cheek. The warmth of his smile, the way his eyes gleamed with latent emotion.

Together, they decided on a selection from each course, gave their order, then discussed a range of topics from art to travel as they sipped champagne.

Emilio added authenticity to Nikos and Michelle's 'romance' with anecdotes from his years as an art student in France.

'Remember, *cara?* That little café on the Left Bank, where the waiter plied you with coffee and pledged his undying love?'

Saska looked from one to the other, her fork poised as she posed a question. 'You studied together and shared accommodation?'

Michelle wrinkled her nose, then laughed, a faint husky sound that was unintentionally sexy. 'Yes, with four other students. Communal kitchen, bath-room. Tiny rooms. It was little more than a garret.'

'But you adored it,' Emilio endorsed. 'Too much coffee, too little food, and too much discussion on how to change the world.'

'You lived in a garret?' Saska queried in disbelief. 'With little money? Didn't your parents help you?'

'Of course. Except I didn't want a nice apartment in the right quarter, with smoked salmon and caviar in the fridge.'

'She gave all that up for the baguettes, sardines, and cheese.'

'And wine,' Michelle added with an impish smile. 'It was fun.'

'Pretending to be poor?'

'Dispensing with the trappings of the rich,' she corrected with quiet sincerity. 'Had I not done that, my time in Paris would have been very different.'

'Yet you managed to meet Nikos.' Saska gave a faint disbelieving laugh. 'I cannot imagine him slum-ming it.'

'We met at the home of mutual friends,' Nikos drawled, embellishing the original fabrication.

'It was one of those rare occasions when we ven-tured into the sophisticated arena of the rich Parisians,' Emilio revealed with droll cynicism.

'So you were at the party, too?'

'As Michelle's bodyguard,' he declared solemnly. 'She rarely left home without me. And no,' he added quietly at Saska's deliberately raised eyebrows. 'We were never more than just very good friends.'

'And now you're business partners.'

Emilio inclined his head in mocking acquiescence. 'Our friendship is based on trust. What better foundation to establish a business?'

'How—quaint,' Saska acknowledged. 'Pretending to be impoverished students, then returning home to open a Gallery.'

You don't get it, do you? Michelle queried silently. We needed the struggle, the very essence that combines naked ambition with the perspicacity to survive and succeed. A nebulous element that shows in the art as something more than talent. We wanted to be able to recognise that flair through personal experience, not as judgmental eclectics.

It was perhaps as well the waiter delivered the starter. Although she wasn't so sure as Nikos played the part of attentive lover by tempting her with a morsel of food from his plate.

It was relatively easy to take up his challenge by spearing a succulent prawn from its bed of lettuce and offering it to him from the edge of her fork. She even managed to adopt the role of temptress with a melting smile, which brought an answering gleam and a flash of white teeth as he took a bite of the fleshy seafood.

Michelle daren't glance in Emilio's direction, for if he acknowledged her performance with a surreptitious wink she would be in danger of subsiding into laughter, and that would totally destroy the illusion.

Saska was not about to be outdone. Although her attempts to gain Nikos' attention were infinitely more subtle with the light touch of her hand on his arm, the few 'remember' anecdotes that served to endorse a long friendship.

Michelle had to concede it was a fun evening, for she enjoyed the nuances, the interplay, and the elusive rivalry, albeit that on her part it was contrived.

Or was it? There was nothing false about her reaction to Nikos' touch. Or the warmth that radiated through her body when he smiled. The brush of his lips caused a spiral of sensation encompassing every nerve cell.

It provided a vivid reminder of the exquisite orgasmic experience they'd shared, and the need to recapture it again.

Which would be the height of foolishness. Sexual gratification was no substitute for lovemaking. It was something she'd vowed to uphold. Selective sex with someone she cared for, and who she believed cared for her. It didn't sit well that last night she'd broken her own rule.

They chose to decline dessert in favour of the cheeseboard, and lingered over excellent coffee.

Michelle was surprised to see it was after eleven when they parted outside the restaurant, and she offered her cheek for Emilio's kiss.

'*Brava,* darling,' he murmured close to her ear, then offered, 'Your performance was incredible. See you in the morning.'

Saska followed suit by pressing her lips to Nikos' cheek, then lightly, briefly on his mouth. 'We must do this again soon.'

Nikos' smile held warmth. 'We'll look forward to it.' He caught Michelle's hand and threaded her fingers through his own, then brought it to his lips. 'Won't, we?'

Oh my, he was good. She offered him a melting smile. 'Of course. Thursday evening there's a charity ball being held at the Marriott. *Maman* is on the committee. I can arrange a ticket if Saska would like to join us.'

Saska didn't hesitate. 'I'd love to.'

Nikos waited until they were seated in the car before venturing with silky amusement, 'Do you delight in setting the cat among the pigeons?'

Michelle turned towards him and offered a stunning smile. 'Why, *darling*, *Maman* will be gratified at the sale of another ticket, and Saska will enjoy the evening.'

'And you, *pedhaki mou*,' he drawled. 'What will you enjoy?'

'Watching you,' she responded sweetly.

'Playing the part? Isn't that what we all do on occasion? In business, socially?'

'You do it exceptionally well.'

'Let me return the compliment.'

'In the interest of establishing our pseudo relationship, the evening was a success.'

He didn't answer as he negotiated an intersection, and she lapsed into a silence that stretched the several minutes it took to reach her apartment building.

'There's no need for you to stay,' Michelle declared firmly as he rode the lift with her to the fifteenth floor.

'We've already settled this issue.'

'Last night was different.' The lift came to a halt and she retrieved her key in readiness.

'No.'

She crossed the carpeted lobby to her apartment and unlocked the door.

'What do you mean—*no?*'

'Your apartment or mine,' Nikos reiterated hardily. 'It's irrelevant. But we share.'

'I doubt Jeremy will attempt to enter the building, and even if he did, he'd never get past my front door.'

He thrust a hand into each trouser pocket, and looked at her with open cynicism. 'You don't think he's sufficiently devious to disguise himself as a delivery messenger?' He continued before she had a chance to answer. 'Or utilise some plausible ploy to get past reception?'

A week ago none of these possibilities would have entered her head. Now, she had good reason to pause for thought. And she didn't like any of the answers.

'You're not prepared to give in, are you?' she queried wearily.

'No.'

She didn't say a further word, and simply turned and walked through to the kitchen. She needed a drink. Hot sweet tea to take the edge off the champagne and an excellent meal.

Michelle filled the electric kettle and switched it on, then she extracted a cup, teabag, sugar and milk, and stood waiting for the water to boil.

She was conscious of Nikos' presence, and all too aware of him silently watching her actions as she poured hot water into the cup, sweetened it and added milk.

If he stayed there much longer, she'd be tempted to throw something at him.

She discarded the spoon into the sink, and looked at him. Then wished she hadn't.

Eyes that were dark and frighteningly still held her own captive, and she felt like an animal caught in a trap.

Everything faded into the background, and there was only a mesmeric quality apparent as he closed the distance between them.

'Fight me, argue with me,' Nikos berated silkily. 'But don't turn your back and walk away.' He lifted a hand and caught hold of her chin between thumb and forefinger, then tilted it. 'Ever.'

It was impossible to escape that deep assessing gaze, and her own anger lent an edge of defiance.

'Don't say a word,' he warned with deceptive mildness, as she opened her mouth to give vent to his actions.

'Why?'

His mouth angled over hers, then took possession in a kiss which tore the breath from her throat as he plundered at will.

Then the pressure eased, and she almost cried out as he began an evocative tasting with such sensual mastery it was almost all she could do not to respond.

A flame deep within ignited and flared into vibrant life, until her whole body was consumed with it, and she wound her arms up around his neck, leaned into him, and simply went with whatever he dictated.

It was a long time before he gradually broke contact, and she could only look at him in stunned silence as he lightly traced the swollen contours of her mouth.

'There's no one here to observe the pretense,' Michelle said shakily, and his smile held musing warmth.

'Who says it's a pretense?'

His hand brushed across her collarbone, back and forth in a hypnotic movement, and she bit back a gasp as he settled his lips at the base of her throat.

'Let's not do this,' she pleaded fruitlessly, and felt his mouth part in a soundless smile.

'Frightened?'

'Scared witless,' she admitted.

He savoured the sweet valley between her breasts, then slowly nibbled his way back to her lips. 'Don't be.'

She had to stop him now, or she'd never find the willpower to break away.

'Last night was a mistake,' she said desperately, and almost died at the force of his arousal.

'Something which felt so good could never be a mistake.'

Michelle made a last-ditch effort. 'Foolish, then,' she amended.

'What makes you say that?'

Self-preservation and remorse reared its head. 'I don't do this sort of thing,' she assured, then attempted to clarify. 'We haven't even known each other a week.'

His eyes held hers, and there was wry humour,

sensuality, and something else she couldn't define.
'A lifetime,' he mocked lightly.

'It has to mean something,' she protested.

'And this doesn't?'

'No—yes. Oh hell. I don't know.' She was supremely conscious of the sensual warmth stealing
through her veins, heating her body until her bones
seemed to liquify and dissolve beneath the flood of
sensation.

She felt bare, exposed, and frighteningly vulnerable, and she needed to explain why. 'I like to plan
things, have a reason for everything. Not dive off the
deep end with—'

'Someone you've known less than a week?'

'Yes!' She was out of her depth, and flailing.
'Where can this—this farce, possibly lead? In a few
weeks it'll all be over. Then what?'

Nikos brushed gentle fingers down her cheek and
let them rest at the edge of her mouth.

'Why not wait and see?'

Because I don't want to be hurt, she cried silently.
Too late, a tiny gremlin taunted. You're already in
this up to your neck, and in a one-sided love, pain
is part of the deal.

Love? She didn't love him. Lust, maybe.
Definitely lust, she amended as he hoisted her high
up against him and walked towards the bedroom.

Michelle wound her legs around his waist and held
on, exulting in the feel of him, the broad expanse of
his chest, the tight waist, the strength of his arms.

In the bedroom he switched on the lamp, then let
her slide down to her feet.

For a moment she just looked at him, then he lowered his head and took her mouth, gently this time, employing such acute sensitivity she felt she might cry.

Together, they slowly divested their clothes, pausing every now and again to brush a tantalising path over bare flesh in a teasing discovery.

She adored the texture of his skin, the hard ridges of muscle and sinew, the clean faint musky aroma. There was the faint tightening of muscle, the soft intake of breath as she caressed him, and she groaned out loud when he wreaked havoc with one sensitive peak, then the other as he suckled at each breast.

There were no questions asked, no answers given, as they embarked on a sensual feast that was alternately gentle and slow, then so hard and fast sweat beaded their skin and their breath became tortured and ragged.

It was a long night, with little sleep, only the mutual sharing of something infinitely special. Wholly sexual, blissfully sensual, and to Michelle, incredibly unique.

On the edge of exhaustion she wondered if it all wasn't a figment of her fervent imagination. Except there was a hard male body to which she clung, and something terribly *real* to the scent and feel of him.

'Orange juice, shower, breakfast, work,' a husky male voice tormented. 'Rise and shine, *pedhi mou.* You have forty minutes.'

Michelle lifted a hand, then let it fall back onto the bed. 'It's the middle of the night.'

'Eight-fifteen on a bright and warm Wednesday morning,' Nikos assured, and pulled the sheet from her supine form.

He could, he thought regretfully, get very interested in the slender lines of her back. The twin slopes of her bottom were firm mounds his hands itched to shape. And as for that daring little butterfly tattoo... It just begged to be kissed, tasted, and savoured. Like the cute dimple on each side of her lower spine.

'Five seconds,' he warned musingly. 'Or I'll join you, and you won't surface until midday.'

That had the desired effect, for she rolled onto her back and opened her eyes. 'Five?'

'Three, and counting,' Nikos assured, laughing softly as she swung her feet to the floor.

'Orange juice.' He handed her the glass and watched her drain half the contents before handing it back to him.

'Shower,' Michelle said obediently, and searched for her wrap.

'Nice view,' he complimented gently, and glimpsed the tinge of pink colour her cheeks.

'You're dressed,' she observed as she pushed a tumbled swathe of hair behind one ear.

'Showered, shaved, and I've just cooked breakfast.'

'A gem among men.' She found the wrap and shrugged her arms into it. 'I hope you've made coffee?'

'It's percolating.'

'Are you usually so energetic at this hour of the

morning?' She caught his gleaming smile, and her mouth formed a wry grimace. 'Don't answer that.'

Michelle crossed to the en suite, and adjusted the water dial in the shower to hot. Afterwards she'd turn it to cold in the hope it would encourage her blood to circulate more quickly and force her into bright-eyed wakefulness.

A fifty per cent improvement was better than none, she perceived half an hour later as she sipped ruin-ously strong coffee and sliced banana onto cereal.

By the time she finished both, she felt almost hu-man.

Five minutes remained to take the lift down, slip into her car and drive the short distance to the Gallery.

'I have meetings scheduled for most of the day,' Nikos informed as they took the lift together. 'I should be back about six. If there's any delay, I'll phone you.'

'Oh hell,' Michelle said inelegantly as they crossed to where their cars were parked.

'Problems?'

'A flat tyre.' Disbelief coloured her voice, and Nikos swore softly beneath his breath.

'I'll drop you off at the Gallery. Give me your car keys, and I'll arrange to have someone fix it.'

Closer examination revealed the tyre had been very neatly slashed.

'You don't think—'

'This is Jeremy's handiwork?' He was certain of it. 'Possibly.' Just as he was sure there would be no evidence.

He unlocked the BMW and Michelle slid into the passenger seat. Within seconds he fired the engine and eased the large car up the ramp and out onto the road.

Two blocks down he pulled into the kerb, let the engine idle, and reached across to unlatch her door. 'I'll ring you through the day.' He kissed her, hard, briefly, then straightened as she released the seat belt and stepped out from the car.

It was a hectic morning as Michelle caught up on a batch of invoices, liaised with the framing firm, and made countless phone calls.

Lunch was something she ate at her desk, and it came as something of a shock when Nikos rang at three-thirty.

'I've had your car delivered to the Gallery. Don't forget your four o'clock appointment with the lawyer. I'll collect you in fifteen minutes.'

Oh hell, she hadn't forgotten, she simply hadn't expected the time to come around so fast. 'Thanks.'

There was a sense of satisfaction in attaching her signature to the legal statement, and a degree of relief the matter was now in official hands.

It was almost five when Nikos drew the BMW to a halt outside the Gallery, and it was a simple matter to slip behind the wheel of her Porsche and followed him the few blocks to her apartment.

The message light was blinking on her answering machine, and she activated the button and listened to the recorded message.

''Eloise, Michelle. You haven't called. So this is

a reminder. Don't forget Philippe's party tonight. Six-thirty.''

'Philippe?' Nikos queried.

'My godson,' she explained. 'He's three years old, and tonight is his day-care Christmas party.' She lifted a hand and pushed a stray lock of hair behind one ear. 'I can't believe I didn't remember.' She checked her watch. 'I'll have to shower, change and leave.'

'I'll come with you.'

Michelle cast him a wry glance. 'To a children's party?'

'To a children's party,' he repeated mockingly.

It was fun. Parents, family, gathered in front of a large open-air stage at the day-care centre, young children dressed in costume as the teachers led them through their practised paces. Taped music, and childish voices singing out of tune and synch. Smiles and laughter when some of the children forgot they were supposed to act and waved to their parents.

Michelle stood among the crowd, with Nikos positioned behind her, secure within the light circle of his arms.

Afterwards she searched for and found Eloise and her husband, and spent time with Philippe, who displayed his delight at her being there, as well as curiosity for the man at her side. She whispered in his ear in French, and made him giggle.

'I am a bon tot,' Philippe repeated in English to his parents. 'Tante Michelle says so.'

It was almost nine when the pageant concluded,

and after bidding Philippe an affectionate goodnight she walked with Nikos to the car.

Minutes later she leaned back against the headrest and closed her eyes. It had been an eventful day, following on from a very eventful night.

When they stepped inside her apartment Nikos took one look at her pale features, the dark shadows beneath her eyes, and gently pushed her in the direction of her bedroom.

'Go to bed, *pedhaki mou*.'

She needed no second bidding, and within minutes she'd divested her clothes, cleansed her face of make-up and was laying supine beneath the bed-covers.

Sleep came almost instantly, and she woke in the morning, alone. Except the pillow beside hers held an indentation, and there was the soft musky aroma of male cologne as a vivid reminder that Nikos had shared her bed.

Michelle took a hurried shower, then she dressed ready for work and emerged into the kitchen to discover Nikos dressed and speaking into his mobile phone in a language she could only surmise as being his own.

One glance at the countertop was sufficient to determine he'd already eaten, and she finished a small plate of cereal with fruit before he'd completed his conversation.

'Good morning.' He crossed to her side, brushed her lips with his own, then he picked up a cup and drained his coffee. 'Almost ready? I'll drop you at the Gallery.'

CHAPTER TEN

IT HADN'T been the best of days, Michelle reflected as she entered her apartment just after five. Whatever could have gone wrong, had.

Nikos had called to say he'd be late, and while she told herself she was pleased to have the apartment to herself for more than an hour, that wasn't strictly true.

She craved the warmth of his arms, the feel of his mouth on hers, the heat that pulsed through her veins at the mere thought of him.

The light on her answering machine blinked, and she ran the message tape, only to hear three hang-ups, which she considered mildly disturbing, given that her mobile number was recorded for contact.

Jeremy? Would he revert to nuisance hang-up calls?

A shower would do much to ease the tension, and ten minutes later she donned denim cut-offs, a fitted rib-knit top, left her hair loose, and applied minimum make-up. It was way too early to begin dressing for the charity ball, and she didn't fancy floating around the apartment for more than an hour in a wrap.

The intercom buzzed, and she crossed to activate it.

There was silence for a few seconds. 'Having fun with your live-in lover, Michelle?'

A sickening feeling twisted her stomach at the sound of Jeremy's voice, and she released the intercom, only to hear it buzz again almost immediately. She hugged her arms together, hesitated, then picked up the receiver.

Her fingers clenched, and her voice assumed an unaccustomed hardness. 'Don't be a fool, Jeremy.'

'Wisdom isn't my forte.'

'What do you hope to achieve by harassing me?'

'Haven't you worked it out yet? I find it a challenge to skate close to the law and remain unscathed.'

She hung up on him, and almost didn't answer the phone when it rang twenty minutes later.

'Michelle? We have a delivery of flowers for you at reception.'

Michelle's lips curved into a smile. 'I'll be right down.' She caught up her key and went out to summon the lift.

A beautiful bouquet of carnations in delicate pastels encased in clear cellophane greeted her, and she reached for the attached envelope.

A single word was slashed in black, and showed starkly against the white embossed card. *Bitch*.

She didn't need to question who'd sent them.

'Will you dump these for me?'

'Excuse me?'

'Dump them,' Michelle repeated firmly.

'But they're beautiful,' the receptionist declared with shocked surprise.

'Unfortunately the intention behind them isn't.'

A fleeting movement on the bricked apron beyond

the automatic glass entrance doors caught her eye, and she recognised Jeremy execute an elaborate bow before he moved quickly out of sight.

It was a deliberate taunt. A reminder that he was choosing to play a dangerous game by his own rules.

'It seems a shame to waste them.'

Michelle merely shrugged her shoulders and headed towards the double bank of lifts.

She had an hour in which to change, apply make-up and do something with her hair.

The thought of attending a pre-Christmas ball to aid a prominent charity held little appeal. Women spent days preparing for this particular annual event. Chantelle, she knew, would have gone from the masseuse to the beautician, had her nails lacquered, then spent hours with the hairdresser.

Ten minutes later she'd stripped down to briefs, added a silky wrap, then she crossed to the vanity to begin applying make-up.

It was there that Nikos found her, and he wondered at the faint shadows beneath her eyes, the slightly too bright smile.

'Bad day?' He felt his loins tighten as she leaned close to the mirror.

'So-so,' Michelle answered cautiously.

'Are you wearing anything beneath that wrap?' he queried conversationally.

She glimpsed the purposeful gleam apparent in those dark eyes, and shook her head in silent mockery. 'There's not enough time.'

His smile tugged at her heart and did strange

things to the nerves in her stomach. 'We could always arrive late.'

'No,' she declared. 'We couldn't.'

He moved to stand behind her, and her eyes dilated at their mirrored image. One so tall and dark-haired, while the top of her blond head barely reached his shoulder.

His hands slid round her waist, released the belted tie, then moved to cup each breast.

Liquid warmth spilled through her veins, heating her body as desire, raw and primitive, activated each nerve cell.

Michelle watched with almost detached fascination as her skin quivered beneath the sweet sorcery of his touch, and she felt her breath catch as one hand splayed low over her abdomen, seeking, teasing the soft curling hair at the apex of her thighs.

The lacy bikini briefs were soon dispensed with, and when she would have turned into his arms he held her still, then he lowered his mouth to the curve of her neck and gently savoured the delicate pulse beating there.

Her bones melted, and she sank back against him, wanting more, much more.

'You're not playing fair.' The words emerged as a sibilant groan as he pressed her close in against him.

His arousal was a potent force, and the need to have him deep inside her was almost unbearable.

Michelle caught a glimpse of herself in the mirror, and almost gasped at the reflected image. She looked like a shameless wanton experiencing a witching ravishment.

Her eyes were large, the pupils dilated, and her lips had parted to emit a soundless sigh. Pink coloured her cheeks, and her body arched against his in silent invitation.

'Nikos, please.'

Without a word he grasped hold of her waist and lifted her to sit on the wide marbled vanity top, then he lowered his head to her breast and caressed one pale globe.

It was an erotic tasting that held her spellbound as she became consumed with treacherous sensation, and when she could bear it no longer she caught hold of his head and forced it up, then angled her mouth to his in a kiss that was urgent, hungry, and passionately intense.

How long before they slowly drew apart? Five minutes, ten? She had no idea. All she knew was that the slightest touch, the faintest sound, would tip them both past the point of no return.

It was Nikos who rested his forehead against her own as he effected a soothing circular movement over her shoulders.

'I guess we should take a raincheck, hmm?'

She wasn't capable of saying a word, and she looked faintly stricken as she inclined her head in silent acquiescence.

He cupped her face and kissed her gently, then he drew her down onto her feet. 'I'll go shower, shave and change.'

When he left she leaned both hands on the vanity

and closed her eyes. She felt as if all her nerves had stretched to breaking point, and then shredded into a thousand pieces.

No man had ever had this effect on her before. Not once had she felt so *consumed,* so helpless. Or so deeply *involved.* It was frightening. For what happened when it ended, as it inevitably would? Could she walk away, and say, Thanks, it was great while it lasted?

The thought of a life without him in it seemed horribly empty.

You're bound to him, a tiny voice taunted. Until Saska relinquishes her widow's hold, and Jeremy has been removed, voluntarily or forcibly, from the picture.

So what do you suggest? she demanded silently. Love and live each day as if it's the last? That's the fiction. Reality will be a broken heart and empty dreams.

The sound of water running in the adjacent en suite acted as an incentive to gather herself together. She was a mess. Hair, make-up... She'd have to begin from scratch.

Michelle forced herself to work quickly, and after a shaky start she used expert touches to heighten her delicate bone structure, highlight her eyes, and outline her mouth.

Her hair was thick, and it wasn't difficult to add extra thickness with the skilful use of a brush and hair dryer.

The gown she'd chosen to wear was an ankle-length slinky black silk sheath with a softly draped bodice and slim shoestring shoulder straps. Black stiletto-heeled shoes completed the outfit, and she caught up a matching black stole, a small beaded evening bag, then walked out to the lounge.

Nikos was waiting for her, looking resplendent in a dark evening suit, white cotton pin-pleated shirt and black bow tie.

Michelle felt her heart stop, then quicken to a rapid beat. His broad facial bone structure lent him a primitive air, the chiselled cheekbones, dark eyes, the perfectly moulded nose, and a well-shaped mouth that could wreak such sensual havoc.

He was an impressive man, in a way that had little to do with the physical. There was a ruthlessness apparent that boded ill for anyone who dared to cross his path. There was also a gentleness that was totally in variance with his projected persona.

If he were to gift his heart to a woman, it would be a gift beyond price. A wise woman would treasure and treat it with care.

Such wayward thoughts were dangerous. She couldn't afford them, daren't even pause to give them a second of her time.

'Shall we leave?' She couldn't believe her voice sounded so steady, so cool.

The lift descended nonstop to the ground floor, the doors slid open to admit the receptionist before resuming its descent to the car park.

'Michelle. I put the flowers in a vase on the lobby side-table. It seemed such a pity to waste them. I hope you don't mind?' The lift slid to a halt and they emerged into the concrete cavern. 'Have a great evening.'

'What flowers?' Nikos queried as he led Michelle in the opposite direction towards his car.

'A bouquet of carnations.'

One eyebrow rose slightly. 'I'll rephrase that. Who sent you flowers?' He caught hold of her elbow and drew her to a halt when she didn't answer. 'Michelle?'

There didn't seem any advantage in prevaricating. 'Jeremy.'

Nikos' eyes hardened measurably. 'He delivered them personally?'

'Yes.'

'He spoke to you?' he demanded sharply.

'No. He merely stood outside and choreographed an elaborate bow.'

Nikos bit off a pithy oath. 'That young man seems to choose to dance with danger.'

She could almost feel the palpable anger emanate from his powerful frame as he unlocked the BMW, saw her seated, then he crossed round the car and slid in behind the wheel.

'Has he rung you at any time today?' He fired the engine, then eased the car towards the ramp.

'This evening, shortly after I arrived home.'

There was something primitive in his expression as he turned briefly towards her. 'Tomorrow morning we transfer to my apartment. And don't,' he warned bleakly. 'Argue. The penthouse can only be accessed by using a specially coded security key to operate the lift. Even the emergency stairwell is inaccessible from the floor below.' His eyes became hard and implacable. 'At least I know you'll be safe there.'

This was all getting a bit too much! 'Look—'

'It's not negotiable,' Nikos decreed with pitiless disregard.

'The hell it isn't!'

'We're almost there.'

He was right, she saw with amazement. It was less than two kilometres to the Marriott hotel, and they'd traversed the distance in record time.

'We'll discuss this later,' Michelle indicated as he cruised the car park for an empty space.

'You can count on it,' Nikos agreed with chilling bleakness.

Anger at his highhandedness tinged her mood, and her back was stiff as she walked at his side to the lift. There was a group of fellow guests already waiting to be transported to the ballroom, and she forced her facial muscles to relax as they rode the necessary two flights.

From that moment on it was strictly smile-time as they mixed and mingled in the adjoining foyer. Uniformed waiters circulated with trays loaded with champagne-filled flutes, and she accepted one, sipped the sparkling liquid, and endeavoured to visually locate her parents.

'There you are.'

Michelle heard Saska's slightly accented voice, summoned a smile, then she turned to face the tall brunette.

'Saska,' she acknowledged politely. 'It's nice to see you.' How many mistruths did people utter beneath the guise of exchanging social pleasantries? Too many, she perceived cynically as she tilted her cheek to accept Emilio's kiss.

The guests began to dissipate as staff opened up the ballroom, and Michelle was supremely conscious of Nikos' arm along the back of her waist, the close proximity of his body as they moved slowly into the large room.

Circular tables seating ten were beautifully assembled with white linen, gleaming cutlery and glassware, beautiful floral centrepieces. Each table bore a number, and they gravitated as a foursome towards their designated seats.

Saska deliberately positioned herself next to Nikos, and Michelle was intensely irritated by the widow's deliberate action.

There was, unfortunately, very little she could do about it without causing a scene. A fact Saska had already calculated, and her smile was akin to that of a cat who'd just lapped a saucer of cream.

The evening's entertainment was to be broken into segments during the elaborate four-course meal, with a fashion parade as the conclusion.

Chantelle and Etienne Gerard joined them, together with two young couples. There was time for a brief round of introductions before the obligatory speech by the charity's fundraising chairman, which was followed by a delicious French onion soup.

A magician dressed in elegant black, grey and white fatigues, white-painted face and black-painted lips demonstrated a brief repertoire with a multitude of different coloured scarves, silver rings, and a small bejewelled box.

A seafood starter was served, and Michelle nibbled at a succulent prawn, forked a few mouthfuls of dressed lettuce, then reached for the iced water.

Saska held Nikos' attention in what appeared to be a deep and meaningful conversation. Michelle caught Emilio's eye, saw his almost imperceptible wink, and felt her lips twitch.

He held no fewer illusions that she did. Emilio enjoyed the social scene, deriving cynical amusement from the many games of pretense the various guests played for the benefit of others. He was rarely mistaken in his assessment.

The starter dishes were collected by staff as the lights dimmed and a gifted soprano gave an exquisite solo performance from a popular opera.

Michelle sipped champagne and endeavoured to ignore the spread of Saska's beautifully lacquered nails on Nikos' thigh. The slight movement of those nails didn't escape her attention, and she felt the slow build of anger. And jealousy. Although she refused to acknowledge it as that emotion.

'Oh well done,' Saska accorded as the guests burst into applause.

Michelle watched her turn towards Nikos, say something in Greek, laugh, and touch the sleeve of his jacket.

Perhaps, she decided, it was time to play. The young man seated next to her was about her own age, and had partnered his sister to the function.

Michelle leaned towards him. 'I would say it's going to be a very successful evening.'

Two spots of colour hit his cheekbones. 'Yes. Yes, it is.' He indicated the soprano accepting a second round of applause. 'She's really quite something, isn't she?'

'Quite something,' Michelle agreed solemnly.

'The food is good, don't you think?' he rushed on earnestly. 'Can I help you to some wine? More champagne?'

She gave him a slow sweet smile. 'You could fill my water glass, if you don't mind.'

He didn't mind. In fact, he couldn't seem to believe his luck, given that the beautiful blonde who seemed to want to talk to him was in the company of a man whose power, looks and degree of sophistication were something he doubted he'd ever aspire to.

'Do you attend many of these charity functions?'

He was nice, pleasant and easy to talk to. 'My parents are very supportive of a few major charities,' she revealed. 'So yes, I attend a few each year.'

'Is—' he began awkwardly. 'Are you— Would you dance with me later?'

'I'd like that,' she said gently.

They were interrupted as the waitress deftly served the main course, and Michelle offered him a faint smile as she transferred her attention to the food.

She felt the light brush of fingers against her cheek, and she turned towards Nikos in silent query.

'He's just a boy,' he chided softly, and glimpsed

the brilliant flare of gold in the depths of those beautiful green eyes.

'Are you saying,' she said with extreme care, 'that I shouldn't talk to him?'

'I doubt he's equipped to cope with your flirting.'

She met his gaze with composed tolerance. 'While you, of course, are well able to cope with Saska.'

'You noticed.' It was a statement, not a query, and she wanted to say she noticed everything about him. Except to acknowledge it would be tantamount to an admission of sorts, and she didn't want to betray her emotions.

He took hold of her hand and lifted it to his lips, then kissed each finger in turn. 'Eat, *pedhaki mou.*'

Dynamic masculinity at its most lethal, she accorded silently. All she had to do was look at him, and she became lost. It was if every cell in her body wanted to fuse with his, generating a sensual chemistry so vibrant and volatile, it was a wonder it didn't burst into flame.

'In that case, you'd better let me have my hand back,' she managed calmly, and glimpsed the musing gleam evident in those dark eyes so close to her own.

'Don't be too sassy,' Nikos drawled softly. 'Remember, we eventually get to go home together.'

'I'm trembling.'

'It will be my pleasure to ensure that you do.'

'Then I suggest you eat,' Michelle said demurely. 'You'll need the energy.'

One eyebrow slanted in visible amusement, and his eyes gleamed darkly.

'Darling,' she added, sotto voce, and pulled her

hand free. She glanced up, caught Emilio's wicked expression, and widened her eyes in a deliberately facetious gesture.

Chicken and fish were served alternately, and she picked at the fish, speared the exotically presented vegetables, then pushed her plate forward. Dessert would follow, accompanied by a cheeseboard, and all she felt like was some fruit and cheese.

She picked up her glass and sipped the iced water, watching with detached fascination the precise movements as Nikos dealt with his food. He looked as if he took pleasure in the taste, the texture of each mouthful.

As he took pleasure in pleasing a woman. Just to see his mouth was to imagine it gliding slowly over her body, caressing soft skin, savouring each pulse beat. The sensual intimacy, the liberties he took, and her craven response.

Dear heaven, she could feel the blood course through her veins, heating her skin, just at the thought of what he could do to her.

Almost as if he sensed a subtle shift in the rhythm of her heart, he paused and slowly turned towards her.

For one millisecond, she was unable to mask the stark need, then it was gone, buried beneath the control of self-preservation, and his eyes darkened in recognition.

It felt as if there was no one else in the room, only them, and she could have sworn she swayed slightly, drawn towards him as if by some magnetic power.

Then he smiled. A soft widening of his mouth that held the hidden promise of what they would share.

She bit into the soft tissue of her lower lip, felt the slight stab of pain, and tasted blood. Her eyes flared, and the spell was broken. The room and its occupants reappeared, the sound of muted chatter, background music.

The waiters moved unobtrusively, removing dishes, plates, while a noted comedian took the microphone and wove jokes into stories with such flair and wit, it was impossible not to laugh.

Dessert comprised glazed strawberries in a chocolate basket decorated with fresh thickened cream. Sinful, Michelle accorded silently as she bit into the luscious fruit. She abandoned the chocolate and cream, and reached for the crackers and cheese as the compere announced the fashion parade.

Models took the stage in pairs, displaying an elegant selection of day wear, after five, and evening wear.

Coffee was served as the last pair of models disappeared from the stage, and it acted as a signal for the deejay to set up the music. It was also a moment when several guests chose to leave their respective tables to freshen up.

'Do you think—' a male voice inclined tentatively. 'Would you care to dance with me?'

Michelle turned towards him with a smile. 'Yes.' She placed her napkin on the table and rose to her feet.

He was good, very good, and she laughed as he led her into a set of steps she could only hope to follow. This was fun, *he* was fun, and for the next few minutes she went with the music.

'You do this very well,' she complimented as the music slowed to a more sedate beat.

'My sister and I are ballroom dancing competitors.'

'It shows,' she assured.

'I don't suppose—' He shook his head. 'No, of course not. Why would you?'

She looked at him and saw the enthusiasm of youth. 'Why would I *what?*' she queried gently.

'Agree to go out with me. The movies, a coffee. Anything.'

'If I wasn't with someone, I'd have loved to.'

'Really?' He could hardly believe it. 'You would?'

'Really,' she assured.

The track finished, and Michelle took the opportunity to thank him and indicate a return to their table.

CHAPTER ELEVEN

NIKOS met her eyes as she took the seat beside him, and he refilled her glass and handed it to her as the young man led his sister onto the floor.

'Did you let him down gently?'

'He asked me out.'

'Naturally you refused.'

She decided to tease him a little. Heaven knew he deserved it. 'I gave it considerable thought,' she said demurely. 'And I decided I would—' She paused deliberately, then offered an impish smile. 'Dance with him again.'

Nikos pressed a forefinger to the centre of her lips. 'Just so long as the last one is mine.'

'I'll try to remember,' she responded solemnly.

'Minx,' he accorded. 'Do you want some coffee?'

'I think so,' Michelle said solemnly. 'Any more champagne, and I might not be held responsible.'

His smile almost undid her. 'Responsible for what?'

'Doing Saska an unforgivable harm.'

'She's a friend.'

'I know, I know. It's just that the boundaries of her friendship with you seem to be expanding.'

'At the moment. Soon they'll shift back to their former position.'

'I admire your faith in human nature, but don't you think you're a little misguided?'

'No.'

A waitress appeared with a carafe of coffee and she poured them each a cup. Michelle reached for the sugar and stirred in two sachets.

'Nikos? Perhaps we could dance? Michelle, you don't mind, do you?'

She gave Saska a brilliant smile. 'Of course not. I intend to finish my coffee.'

'You and Nikos appear to be getting along together exceptionally well,' Chantelle inclined when Nikos and Saska had moved out of earshot.

She wanted to tell her mother the truth, but what was the truth? She wasn't sure any more. 'Yes,' she responded carefully. How would her mother react if she relayed they fought like hell on occasion and their lovemaking resembled heaven on earth?

Be amused, probably, offer a good argument cleared the air, and add the making up was always the best part.

'We're leaving soon, darling,' Chantelle relayed. 'It's quite late, and your father has an early flight to catch tomorrow. Maybe we could have lunch together? I'll call you, shall I?'

Nikos and Saska resumed their seats, and Michelle tried to ignore the arm he draped across the back of her chair. It brought him close and implied a deliberate intimacy.

'Please, *Maman*. I'll look forward to it.'

'Saturday, perhaps?'

'Not the weekend,' Nikos disputed. 'We'll be in Sydney.'

She cast him a challenging look. 'We will?'

'I have business there,' he enlightened with a mocking drawl that didn't fool her in the slightest.

'The break will do you good, *cherie*,' Chantelle enthused.

Since when had Nikos gained the God-given right to organise her life? Since he first walked into it, she acknowledged cynically.

Which didn't mean she'd simply give in without a struggle, and she said as much as he drew her on to the dance floor.

'I don't like being told what to do.'

'Especially by me, hmm?'

'Look—'

'No, *pedhi mou*,' Nikos stated with deceptive mildness. 'This is the way it is.' His eyes were at variance with his voice. 'Tomorrow I have a two o'clock meeting in Sydney, which will conclude with a social dinner. I plan to fly back to the Coast on Sunday. You get to go with me.'

'And just how do you propose to indicate my presence?'

His appraisal was swift, calculating, and brought a tinge of soft colour to her cheeks. 'I am answerable to no one.'

Michelle closed her eyes, then slowly opened them again. 'Well, now there's the thing. Neither am I.'

'Yes,' he refuted with silky tolerance. 'You are. To me. Until the situation with Jeremy is resolved.'

Anger and resentment surged to the surface, lending her eyes a brilliant sparkle. 'Let's not forget Saska in this scheme of things.'

An indolent smile curved the generous lines of his mouth. 'No,' he drawled with an edge of mockery. 'We can't dismiss Saska.'

Her back stiffened in silent anger. 'I don't think I want to dance with you.'

His lips brushed her temple, and his hands trailed a path up and down her lower spine in a soothing gesture.

'Yes, you do.'

Caught close in his arms wasn't conducive to conducting an argument, for she was far too conscious of the feel of that large body, the subtle nuances of sensation as her system went into overdrive.

'Always so sure of what I want, Nikos?'

His eyes held knowledge as he held her gaze. A knowledge that was infinitely sensual and alive with lambent passion. 'Yes.'

She was melting, subsiding into a thousand pieces, and there wasn't a sensible word she could frame in response.

His cologne combined with the scent of freshly laundered clothes and a barely detectable male muskiness. It proved a potent mix that attacked her senses, and she felt the need to be free of him, if only for the five or so minutes it would take to freshen up.

'I need to visit the powder room.'

It was late, and already the evening was beginning to wind down. In another hour the venue would close, and those inclined to do so would go on to a nightclub.

Michelle left the ballroom and entered the elegantly appointed powder room. After using the facilities, she crossed to the mirror to repair her make-up, and barely glanced up as the door swung in to admit another guest.

Saska. Coincidence, or design? Michelle opted for the latter.

'I have to hand it to you,' Saska complimented as she crossed to the mirror. 'You move quickly.'

No preamble, no niceties. Just straight to the heart of the matter.

'It's taken you less than a week to have Nikos delight in playing your knight in shining armour.'

Michelle capped her lipstick and placed it in her bag. 'I'm very grateful for his help.'

'Very convenient, these little episodes which have occurred with Jeremy.' She spared a glance at Michelle via the mirror, and one eyebrow arched in disbelief. 'You must agree it raises a few questions?'

'Are you accusing me of contriving a situation simply to manipulate Nikos' attention?'

'Darling, women are prepared to do anything to get Nikos' attention,' Saska declared with marked cynicism.

'Does that include you?'

'I would be lying if I said no,' Saska admitted.

Michelle drew in her breath and released it slowly. 'And the purpose of this little chat is?'

'Why, to let you know I'm in the race.'

'There is no race. Nikos isn't the prize.'

'You're neither naive nor stupid. So what game are you playing?'

'None,' Michelle said simply. 'Blame Nikos. He's the one intent on being the masterful hero, without any encouragement from me.' Without a further word she turned and left the room.

Nikos and Emilio were deep in conversation when she slid into her seat, and she met Nikos' swift glance with equanimity.

'More coffee?'

'Please.'

He signalled the waitress, and instructed her to re-fill both cups.

It was almost midnight when they left, and Michelle looked at the towering apartment buildings standing like sentinels against a dark sky. Lit windows provided a sprinkling of regimented light, and she wondered idly at the people residing there. A mix of residents and holiday-makers intent on enjoying the sun, surf and shopping available on this pictur-esque tourist strip.

Nikos paused at the lights, then turned into sub-urban Main Beach. Within minutes the car swept beneath her apartment building.

'I'm going to bed,' Michelle announced the instant Nikos closed the front door behind them.

'If you want to fight, then let's get it over and done with,' Nikos drawled with amusement.

She swung round to face him, and her chin tilted fractionally as she lifted one hand and began ticking off one finger after another. 'I'm not moving into your penthouse, and I'm not—' she paused and gave the word repetitive emphasis '—*not* spending the weekend in Sydney with you.'

'Yes, you are.'

She was on a roll, and unable to stop. 'Will you please do me a favour and inform Saska that I did not contrive to gain your attention by playing a *pretend assault* game with Jeremy!'

His eyes narrowed. 'She's—'

'Delusional,' Michelle accused fiercely.

'Temporarily obsessive,' Nikos amended.

'That, too!'

He crossed to where she stood and placed his hands on her shoulders, kneading them with a blissfully firm touch that eased the kinks.

Dear Lord, that felt good. Too good, she perceived. Any minute now she'd close her eyes, lean back, and give in to the magic of his touch.

His lips brushed against the sensitive hollow at the edge of her neck, and she stifled a faint groan in pleasure.

She felt his fingers slide the shoestring straps over her shoulders, and the trail of kisses that followed them.

'This isn't going to resolve a thing,' Michelle inclined huskily as she acknowledged the slow curl of passion that began building deep inside. Any second now she wouldn't possess the will to resist him.

'Nikos, please—don't,' she almost begged as he kissed a particularly vulnerable spot at her nape.

'You want me to stop?'

No, but I daren't allow you to continue. Not if I want to retain any vestige of sanity.

'Yes,' she answered bravely. The loss of his touch made her feel cold, bereft, as she slowly turned to face him. Self-preservation caused her to move back a pace.

'I don't see the necessity for me to move into your penthouse. Removing myself to Sydney for the weekend is tantamount to running away. You're not responsible for me. What has happened with Jeremy would have happened anyway.' It came out sounding wrong, and Nikos used it to his advantage.

'You're saying you want to stay here alone,' he began with chilling softness. 'And risk having Jeremy utilise devious means and front up to your door? Or maybe lay in wait in the underground car park for the time you return home alone?'

His words evoked stark images from which she mentally withdrew. 'Suffer probable trauma as well as possible injuries? For what reason? Simply to prove you can protect yourself from an emotionally unbalanced young man with a history of previous attacks?'

Put like that, it sounded crazy. But what about *her* emotions? With each passing day she became more tightly bound to him on every level. What had begun as an amusing conspiracy was now way out of hand.

'You expect me to go to Sydney for the weekend, and spend every waking moment worrying if you're all right? Forget it.'

'Dammit. Why should it matter to you?'

His eyes hardened to a bleak grey. 'It matters.'

It was too much. *He* was too much. Without a word she crossed the lounge and entered her bedroom.

She closed the door, and wished fervently it held

a lock and key. Although it would hardly prove an impenetrable barrier, for he possessed the brute strength to break the door down if he was so inclined.

With hands that shook she released the zip fastening at the back of her dress and slipped out of it. Next came her shoes, and she gathered up a cotton nightshirt and slipped it over her head.

It took only minutes to remove her make-up and brush her teeth, then she slid in between the sheets, snapped off the light to lay staring into the darkness.

Michelle had little knowledge of the passage of time as thoughts meshed with dreamlike images, and it was only when she stirred into wakefulness that she realised she must have fallen asleep.

She moved restlessly, and her hand encountered warm male flesh, hard bone and muscle. Her body went rigid with shock.

'Nikos?'

'Who else were you expecting, *melle mou?*' He brought her close and lowered his mouth to nuzzle the sweet hollows at the base of her throat, then trailed up to capture her mouth in a slow evocative kiss that stole her breath away.

It would be so easy to lose herself in his embrace, and she told herself she needed the warmth of his touch, the feel of him deep inside, and the mutual joy of lovemaking. At this precise moment she refused to label what they shared as *sex.*

Tomorrow she'd deal with when it dawned. But for now there was only the man and the wild sweet heat of his loving.

And the passion. Mesmeric, provocative, ravaging, until she went up in flames and took him with her.

Michelle rose early the next morning, then showered and dressed, she gathered together a selection of clothing suitable for a weekend in Sydney, added personal items and make-up, and packed them into a bag.

She'd considering making a final protest about the need to move into Nikos' penthouse, then dismissed it before she uttered a word. One look at his compelling features was sufficient to convince her that he intended to win any verbal battle she might choose to initiate.

'Leave your car here,' Nikos instructed as he stowed her bags in the boot of the BMW. The larger bag was destined to be deposited in the penthouse. 'I'll pick you up from the Gallery at ten.'

'OK.'

He shot her a musing glance. 'Such docility.'

'It's your forceful personality,' she assured sweetly. 'It has a cowering effect.'

His laughter was soft, husky, and sent renewed sensation spiralling through her body as she slid into the car beside him.

'No,' he mocked. 'It doesn't.' He fired the engine and sent the car up the ramp and onto the road.

It was at her insistence she spend an hour at the Gallery to dispense with some of the paperwork, rather than linger in her own or Nikos' apartment.

It was after midday when their flight touched down

in Sydney, and almost one when they registered at
an inner city Darling Harbour hotel.

'What do you plan to do this afternoon?' Nikos
queried as he unfastened his garment bag and slotted
it into the wardrobe.

'Shop,' Michelle declared succinctly as she followed his actions.

'I should be back by six. I'll make dinner reser-
vations for seven.'

'Fine,' she acknowledged blithely, then gasped as
he cradled her face and kissed her. Hard, and all too
briefly.

He trailed gentle fingers along the lower edge of
her jaw. 'I'll have my mobile if you need to contact
me.' He caught up his suit jacket and pulled it on.
'Take care.'

Five minutes later Michelle took the lift down to
reception, had the concierge summon a taxi, and she
gave instructions to be driven to Double Bay.

The exclusive suburb was known for its numerous
expensive boutiques housed in a delightful mix of
modern glass-fronted shops and converted terrace
cottages.

The sun shone, and the gentlest breeze stirred the
leaves of magnificent old trees lining the streets.

Boutique coffee shops and trendy cafés with outdoor seating beneath sun umbrellas created a cosmopolitan influence.

Michelle pulled down her sunglasses from atop her
head and prepared to do some serious shopping.

Two hours later she took a brief respite and ordered a cappuccino, then fortified, she caught up a

selection of brightly emblazoned carry-bags and wandered through the Ritz-Carlton shopping arcade, paused to admire a display of imported shoes, fell in love with a pair of stilettos and after declaring them a perfect fit, she added them to her purchases.

It was after five-thirty when a taxi deposited her at the door of the hotel, and on entering their suite she took pleasure in examining the contents of numerous bags before storing them in the wardrobe.

With quick movements she gathered fresh underwear and a wrap, then escaped into the adjoining bathroom.

Nikos found her there, in a cloud of steam, her body slick with water, so completely caught up with her ablutions that she didn't even hear him enter.

The first Michelle knew of his presence was the buzz of his electric shaver, followed minutes later by the rap of his knuckles against the glass door as he slid the door open and stepped in beside her.

'Communal bathing, hmm?' she teased, loving the feel of his hands on her waist. 'Sorry to disappoint you, but I've nearly finished.'

'No, you haven't.' He slid his hands up over her ribcage and cupped each breast.

His fingers conducted an erotic teasing of each sensitive peak, and she felt desire arrow through her body.

'No?'

He didn't answer. He merely reached forward and closed the water dial, and she was incapable of saying another word as his mouth touched her own, teased, tasted, nibbled, then hardened with possessive masterfulness.

His tongue laved hers, and encouraged participation in an erotic dance that eventually became an imitation of the sexual act itself.

She wasn't conscious of leaning into him, or lifting her hands to hold fast his head. There was only the need to meet and match his passion until the heat began to dissipate.

Her skin was acutely sensitive to his slightest touch as he trailed gentle fingers back and forth across each collarbone, then slowly traversed to the slopes of her breasts.

His lips found the sweet hollow at the edge of her neck, and nuzzled. One hand splayed low over her abdomen, and caressed her hip, her buttock, then teased the soft curling hair at the apex between her thighs.

Michelle felt as if she was dying. A very slow erotic and incredibly evocative death as he brought her close to orgasm with tactile skill. Unbidden, her neck arched and a soft almost tortured moan escaped her throat as her feminine core radiated heat and ignited into sensual flame.

It was almost more than she could bear, and she cried out as he lifted her up against him. With one easy movement she linked her arms around his neck and wound her legs over his hips, glorying in the feel of him, the surging power, his strength.

Pagan, electrifying, primeval.

Michelle sensed the moment he let go, the slight shudder that shook his body, then the stillness, and she kissed him with such exquisite gentleness her eyes ached from unshed tears.

With infinite care they indulged in a long after-play, the light brush of fingers over sensitised skin, kisses as soft as the touch of a butterfly's wing.

She touched his face with the pads of her fingers, and slowly traced the strong bone structure with the care of someone who needed to commit his features to memory.

The firm eyebrows, broad forehead, the slightly prominent cheekbones and the wide firm jaw-line. She explored his lips, the clean curves, the firm flesh that could wreak such havoc at will.

Then she gave a soft yelp as he drew the tip of her finger into his mouth and gently nipped it.

Without a word he reached forward and turned on the water dial, set it at warm, then palmed the soap and began to smooth it over her body.

When he finished, she took it from his extended hand and returned the favour.

'Food,' Michelle inclined in a voice that shook slightly as he closed the water dial.

Nikos' eyes gleamed dark and his lips parted to form a musing smile. 'Hungry?' He leant forward and extracted a towel, draped it over her shoulders, then collected another and wound it round his hips.

'Ravenous.'

'Now wouldn't be a good time to tell you I've put our reservation back to eight.' He lifted a hand and smoothed a damp tendril of hair behind her ear. 'Or that we're joining three of my associates and their partners for dinner.'

She reached up and kissed his chin. 'I forgive you.'

'Do you, indeed?'

'Uh-huh.' Her eyes sparkled with devilish humour. 'I bought a new dress to wear tonight. And shoes.' She began to laugh. 'You get to see what I'm not wearing beneath it.' She wrinkled her nose at him. 'And suffer,' she added in an impish drawl.

'We can always leave early.'

He watched beneath hooded eyes as she went through the deodorant and powder routine, then she stepped into lacy thong bikini briefs, and his loins stirred into damnably new life.

She activated the hair dryer and brushed the damp curling length until it bounced thick and dry about her shoulders, then she began applying make-up.

If he stayed any longer, they wouldn't make it out of the suite, he perceived wryly. And for all that the evening was social, the prime criterion was business.

With that in mind he walked into the bedroom and began to dress.

When Michelle emerged from the bathroom all he had to do was fasten his tie and don his jacket.

She crossed to the wardrobe, extracted the dress, then stepped into it and turned her back to him.

'Would you mind?'

He moved forward and slid the long fastener closed over her bare skin. Minuscule briefs, no bra. Throughout the course of the evening he was going to go crazy every time he looked at her.

Michelle swung round to face him. 'What do you think?'

The cream silky sheath with an overlay of lace fell to just above her knees. Its scooped neckline was saved from indecency by a swathe of lace, and a single shoestring strap extended over each shoulder. Very high stiletto-heeled shoes in matching cream completed the outfit.

'You were right,' he drawled with an edge of mockery, and she laughed, a soft throaty sound that was deliciously sexy.

'It works both ways,' she assured with sparkling humour, and spared him an encompassing look.

Dark tailored trousers, blue shirt, navy silk tie, hand-stitched shoes. Expensive, exclusive labels that showed in the cloth and the cut. But it was more than that, she perceived a trifle wryly. The man wore them well, but it was the man himself who attracted attention. His height, breadth of shoulder, tapered waist, slim hips and long muscular legs would intrigue most women to wonder or discover if the physique matched up to the promised reality. Michelle could assure that it did.

He pulled on his suit jacket and extended a hand. 'Let's go.'

They took a taxi, got held up in traffic, arrived late, and opted to go straight to the table rather than linger at the bar.

In retrospect it proved to be a pleasant evening. Beneath the social niceties, it was clear that a deal had been struck and cemented during the afternoon. In Nikos' favour, Michelle perceived.

She found it intriguing to witness him in the executive role. He was a skilled tactician. His strategy was hard-edged, and she was reminded of the iron fist in a velvet glove analogy.

Tenacity, integrity. He possessed them both. His associates admired those qualities and lauded him for them. They also coveted his success.

It was after eleven when the bill was settled and they converged briefly outside the entrance.

Nikos went to hail a taxi, only to pause when Michelle caught hold of his hand.

'Our hotel is just across the causeway,' she indicated, pointing it out. There were people enjoying the warm summer evening. 'It's a beautiful night. Why don't we walk?'

Nikos cast her a wry glance. 'In those heels?'

'They're comfortable,' she assured. 'Besides, after that sumptuous meal we need the exercise.'

'I think I prefer a ten-minute taxi ride to a ten-minute walk.'

Her laughter was infectious. 'Conserving energy, huh?'

'Something like that.' His drawl held musing mockery.

'And I thought you were at the peak of physical fitness,' she teased unmercifully, and laughed at his answering growl. 'We walk?'

It took fifteen minutes because they paused midway to admire the city-scape. Myriad lights reflected in the dappled surface of the water, gunmetal in colour beneath the night sky. The air was fresh, tinged with the tang of the sea, and she felt the warmth of his arm as it curved along the back of her waist.

There was a part of her that wished this was real.

That the sexual chemistry they shared was more, much more than libidinous passion.

How could you care deeply for someone in the space of a week? More than care, a tiny voice prompted. With each passing day she found it more difficult to separate the fantasy and the reality.

How much was pretense? Could a man kiss a woman so deeply, and not care? Make love with her so beautifully, and feel nothing more than sexual gratification?

And even if there is affection, is that all it would be?

Worse, when this is all over, what then?

What do you want? A convenient relationship for as long as it lasts? Then heartache? Don't kid yourself, she silently derided. Nikos doesn't want the *forever* kind, with a marriage certificate and children. Nor do you. Or at least, you didn't think you did until now.

Her life had been good until Nikos Alessandros walked into it. She'd been satisfied with the status quo. Content to run the Gallery jointly with Emilio. Happy in her own apartment, and with her social life.

Now, it didn't seem to mean as much.

Apprehension seeded and took root. How could she bear to live without him?

'Shall we continue?'

Michelle brought her attention back to the present and she tucked her hand into the crook of his elbow. 'Yes, let's go back.'

There was a sadness in the depths of her heart as they undressed each other and made love in the late hours of the night.

CHAPTER TWELVE

'Do you want to go down to breakfast, or shall we order in?'

'The restaurant,' Michelle said at once. 'Staying in could prove dangerous.'

'For whom, *melle mou?*'

'I might ravish you,' she teased mercilessly, and heard his soft mocking laughter.

'I tremble at the mere thought.'

'Well you might,' she threatened as she slipped from the bed, aware that he followed her actions.

'Today you have plans, hmm?'

Nikos sounded amused, and she picked up a pillow and threw it at him, then watched in fascination as he neatly fielded it. 'If you don't want to play, *pedhaki mou,*' he drawled, 'I suggest you go shower and dress.'

She escaped, only because he let her, and re-emerged into the bedroom to quickly don elegantly tailored trousers and a deep emerald singlet top.

Nikos followed her actions, and after a superb breakfast they spent almost two hours in the Aquarium viewing the many varieties of fish displayed in numerous tanks before walking across the causeway to Darling Harbour to explore the many shops.

It was a beautiful summer's day, the sun shone,

167

there was just the barest drift of cloud, and a gentle breeze to temper the heat.

They had lunch at a delightful restaurant overlooking the water, then they boarded a large superbly appointed catamaran for a cruise of Sydney harbour.

Mansions built on the many sloping cliff-faces commanded splendid city views, and the cruise director pointed out a few of the exceptionally notable residences nestling between trees and foliage.

Coves and inlets provided picturesque scenery, and there were craft of every size and description moored close to shore.

Sydney was famous for its Opera House, a brilliant architectural masterpiece instantly recognisable throughout the world, and its Harbour Bridge.

Of all the cities she'd visited, this one represented *home* in a vast continent with so many varying facets in its terrain. It tugged a special chord in the heart that had everything to do with the country of one's birth, patriotism and pride.

Nikos rarely moved from her side, and he appeared relaxed and at ease. The suit had been replaced by tailored trousers and a casual polo shirt which emphasised his breadth of shoulder, the strong muscle structure of his chest.

Michelle was supremely conscious of him, the light brush of his hand when they touched, the warmth of his smile.

Here, they were a thousand miles away from the Gold Coast, and Jeremy. Let's not forget Saska, she added wryly.

There was no need to maintain any pretense. So

why hadn't Nikos abandoned the facade the moment they touched down in Sydney?

Because the sex is good? an inner voice taunted.

She should, she reflected, have insisted on separate suites. They could have each gone their separate ways for the entire weekend, then simply travelled to the airport together and caught the same flight to the Gold Coast.

So why didn't you? a silent voice demanded.

The answer was simple…she wanted to be with him.

Oh great, she mentally derided. Not only was she conducting a silent conversation, she was answering herself, as well.

It was almost five when the cruise boat returned to the pier, and afterwards they wandered at leisure along the broadwalk at Darling Harbour, and sat in one of many sidewalk cafés with a cool drink.

'Let's eat here,' Michelle suggested. The area projected a lively almost carnival ambience, and she loved the feel of a sea breeze on her face, the faint tang of salt in the air.

'You don't want to go back to the hotel, change, and dine *a deux* in some terribly sophisticated restaurant?' Nikos queried.

He looked relaxed, although only a fool would fail to detect the harnessed energy exigent beneath the surface.

'No,' she declared solemnly.

They ate seafood, sharing a huge platter containing a mixture of king-size prawns, mussels, oysters, lobster and Queensland crustaceans cooked in a variety of different ways, accompanied by several sauces and a large bowl of salad greens.

Dusk began to fall, and the city buildings took on a subtle change, providing a delightful night tapestry of light, shadow and increasing darkness.

'We could take in a movie, a show, visit the casino,' Nikos suggested as they emerged from the restaurant.

Michelle offered him a sparkling glance. 'You mean, I get to choose?'

'Last night was business,' he drawled, and she bit back a laugh.

'Not all of it.'

He took hold of her hand and linked his fingers between her own. 'Behave.'

'I shall,' she said demurely. 'Impeccably, for the next few hours. At the casino. Then,' she added with wicked humour, 'I plan to ravish you.'

'Two hours?'

'Uh-huh. It's called *anticipation*.'

It was worth the wait, Nikos accorded a long time later as he gathered her close on the edge of sleep. She'd made love with generosity and a sense of delight in his pleasure. And fun, before the intensity of passion had swept them both to a place that was theirs alone.

His arm tightened over her slender back, and she made a protesting murmur as she burrowed her cheek more deeply against his chest.

He soothed her with a gentle drift of his fingers, and brushed his lips against her hair, listening, feeling, as her breathing steadied into a deep even pattern.

'The Rocks,' Michelle chose without question when Nikos queried over breakfast what she would like to do with the day. Their flight to the Gold Coast was scheduled for midafternoon.

'Trendy cafés, shops, and—'

'Ambience,' she intercepted with a wicked smile.

They took a taxi, and spent a few pleasant hours wandering the promenade, examining the various market stalls, chose a café where they enjoyed a leisurely meal, then it was time to return to the hotel, collect their bags and head for the airport.

With each passing hour she felt an increasing degree of tension. And sadness the weekend was fast approaching a close.

'Thank you,' she said quietly as they waited for their bags to arrive on the carousel from the flight. 'It was a lovely break away.'

Nikos glimpsed the subtle edge of apprehension apparent, and divined its cause. A muscle hardened along the edge of his jaw. Jeremy's behaviour pattern was predictably unpredictable. His parents' method of dealing with their son's recurring problem, however, was not.

For the past week he'd deliberately scaled down his business commitments to an essential few, and chosen to work via the computer link-up in his apartment, instead of his company office overlooking the Southport Broadwater.

Nikos sighted their bags and lifted them off the

carousel. Five minutes later he was easing the large BMW out from the security car park.

'Do you mind if I make a phone call?' Michelle queried soon after they entered the penthouse.

'Go ahead. I'll be in the study for an hour.'

She rang her mother, put a call through to Emilio, then she retreated to the bedroom to unpack.

Michelle left early the next morning for the Gallery, and by midday she'd managed to catch up with most of the paperwork. Lunch was a sandwich washed down with mineral water and eaten at her desk.

Preliminary festive season parties were already under way, and tonight they were to join her parents and several of her father's associates for dinner at the Sheraton.

It was after five when she entered Nikos' penthouse, and after a quick shower she tended to her make-up, swept her hair into a smooth French pleat, then she donned a cobalt blue fitted dress with a sheer printed overlay, slid her feet into stiletto-heeled shoes, and collected her evening purse.

'OK, let's go.'

'There's something you should know before we leave.'

Her smile faltered slightly. 'Bad news?'

'Jeremy and his parents left the country early this morning. Their home is up for sale, and Emerson's office is closed.'

'Thank God,' she breathed shakily, as surprise mingled with relief.

'Rumour has it they intend settling in Majorca.'

It was over! She could hardly believe it. No longer would she have to look over her shoulder, suspect every shadow, or be apprehensive each time the phone rang. She could resume a relatively carefree life, move back into her apartment...

Nikos caught each fleeting expression and successfully divined every one of them.

A weight sank low in her stomach as comprehension dawned. Nikos' protection was no longer necessary. Which meant—*what?* Did she thank him, then walk out of his life? *Would he let her?*

'The news has already leaked and speculation is rife,' Nikos said quietly. 'I wanted you to hear it from me, rather than an exaggerated version from someone else.'

'Thank you.'

He could sense her tentative withdrawal, see the hidden uncertainty, and he wanted to shake her.

'We'd better leave,' Michelle said brightly. '*Maman* said six-thirty.' It was almost that now.

It was a beautiful evening. Except she didn't really *see* the azure blue of the sky as Nikos drove the short distance to the Sheraton hotel.

Michelle drew in a deep breath, then slowly released it as he slid from the car and consigned it to the concierge's care for valet parking.

She'd have to go inside and act her socks off in an attempt to portray an air of conviviality.

It didn't help to discover Saska was present in the company of one of her father's business associates. Although it was hardly surprising given the associate had been a guest on the same night as Saska at her parents' home the previous week.

Champagne on an empty stomach was not a wise move, and her appetite diminished despite the superb seafood buffet. While everyone else filled their plates and returned for more, all she could manage to eat was a few mouthfuls of salad and two prawns.

Michelle conversed with apparent attentiveness to the subject, but within minutes she retained only a hazy recollection of what had been said.

Her mind was consumed with Nikos as she reflected on every detail, each sequence of events that had brought and kept them together.

She reached out and absently fingered the stem of her champagne flute.

'Michelle?'

Oh Lord, she really would have to concentrate! She looked across the table and saw Saska's bemused expression. 'I'm sorry,' she apologised. 'What did you say?'

'I'm leaving for Sydney tomorrow to spend a few weeks with friends before flying home to Athens.'

Sydney, *Athens?* Saska was leaving the Gold Coast *tomorrow?* Her brain whirled. Did that mean Saska had given up any hope of turning Nikos' affection into something stronger, more permanent?

'I'm sure you'll enjoy Sydney,' she managed politely. 'There are so many things to see and do there.'

'I'm looking forward to it.'

Michelle wasn't sure how she managed to get through the rest of the evening. She even managed to pretend to eat, and followed mineral water with two cups of very strong coffee.

It was after eleven when Etienne settled the bill and brought the evening to a close. Some of the guests had taken advantage of valet parking, others had chosen to park in the underground car park. Consequently farewells and festive wishes were exchanged in the main lobby.

Within minutes of emerging from the main entrance the concierge had organised Nikos' car, and Michelle sat in silence during the short drive.

The penthouse had been a haven, now it seemed as if she was viewing it for the last time. Dammit, she daren't submit to the ache of silent tears.

She was breaking up, fragmenting into countless pieces. Tomorrow... Dear heaven, she didn't want to think about tomorrow.

Nikos lifted a hand and tilted her chin, then held fast her nape as he angled his mouth over hers in a kiss that tore at the very depths of her soul.

It became a bewitching seduction of all her senses, magical, mesmeric, and infinitely flagrant as he led her deeper and deeper into a well of passion.

There was something almost wild about their love-making, a pagan coupling filled with raw desire and primitive heat.

Afterwards Michelle lay quietly in Nikos' arms, listening to his heart as it beat in unison with her own.

Then when she was sure he slept, she carefully eased herself free and slid from the bed.

She moved quietly into the kitchen, found a glass,

filled it with water, then drank it down in the hope it would lessen the caffeine content of the coffee.

For the life of her she couldn't return to that large bed and pretend to sleep. Without thought she crossed to the lounge and moved the drape a little so she could see the night sky and the ocean.

CHAPTER THIRTEEN

'PENNY for them?'

Michelle turned her head at the sound of that drawling voice, and her stomach did a backward flip as he linked his arms around her waist and pulled her back against him.

'It's all worked out well,' she managed evenly. 'The Bateson-Burrows have relocated, and—'

'Saska has reevaluated her options, and accepted I'm not one of them,' Nikos drawled as he rested his chin on top of her head.

So where does that leave us?

Fool, she accorded silently. Where do you think it leaves you? You'll go back to your own apartment. Nikos will remain in his—until he returns to Athens, or settles in France, or any other European city where he has a base.

Sure, he might promise to call, and maybe he will, once or twice. He'll simply take up with any one of several beautiful females, and continue with his life. While you fall into a thousand pieces.

The mere thought of him with another woman made her feel physically ill.

'I should thank you,' Michelle said quietly. 'For everything you've done to help protect me from Jeremy.'

The night sky held a sprinkle of stars, pinpricks of

light against dark velvet, and less than a kilometre distant the marina stood highlighted beneath a series of neon arcs.

If I tried really hard, she thought dully, I could count some of the stars. Perhaps I should wish on one of them. Although wishes rarely came true, and belonged to the fable of fairy tales.

'I consider myself thanked.'

Did she detect a slight edge of mockery in his voice? Dear God, of course she had thanked him. With her body, from the depths of her soul, every time they'd made love.

She was almost willing to swear that their love-making had meant something more to him than just a frequent series of wonderfully orgasmic sexual experiences.

Women faked it. But were men capable of faking that ultimate shuddering release?

Nikos possessed control…but he'd lost it on more than one occasion in her arms, just as she'd threshed helplessly in his against an erotic tide so tumultuous she was swept way out of her depth. Only to be brought back to the safety of his embrace.

'I'll pack and move into my apartment in the morning.'

Was that her voice? It sounded so low, so impossibly husky, it could have belonged to someone else.

'No.'

Michelle's heart stopped, then accelerated to a rapid beat. 'What do you mean—*no?*'

His hands moved up to her shoulders. 'Do you want to leave?'

Dear heaven, how could he ask such a question?

She was incapable of movement, and he slowly turned her to face him.

'Michelle?'

'I—how—' Oh hell, she was incapable of putting two coherent words together. 'What are you suggesting?' she managed at last.

'I want you to come with me when I fly out to New York.'

Want, not *need,* she noted dully.

Did she have any idea how transparent she was? Eyes so clear he glimpsed his reflected image in their depths. A pulse hammered at her temple, and was joined by another at the base of her throat.

Go, an inner voice urged. Enjoy the *now,* and don't worry what will happen next month, next year. Just…hop on the merry-go-round and enjoy the ride for as long as it lasts.

But what happens when the music winds down and the merry-go-round slows to a stop? Would the break be any easier then, than it is now? Worse, she knew. Much, much worse.

Yet life itself came with no guarantees. If she walked away now, she'd never know what the future might hold.

It was no contest. There could be only one answer.

'Yes,' Michelle said simply.

Nikos covered her mouth with his own in a kiss so incredibly gentle, she wanted to cry.

'There's one more thing.'

He pressed his thumb over her lower lip. 'Marry me, *agape mou.*'

Her eyes widened measurably, and for an instant her whole body stilled, then she became conscious of the loud hammering of her heart and the need to breathe.

'Yes.'

His smile almost undid her. 'No qualifications?'

Michelle shook her head, not trusting herself to speak.

'How do you feel about a Celebrant marrying us in the gardens of your parents' home two weeks from this Saturday?'

She did swift mental calculations. 'Two days before Christmas?' Dear heaven. 'My mother will freak.'

He stroked the rapidly beating pulse at the base of her throat. 'No, she won't.'

Two weeks. 'Nikos—'

'I love you,' he said gently. 'Everything about you. The way you smile, your laughter, the sound of your voice. The contented sigh you breathe when you reach for me in the night.' His mouth settled briefly on hers. 'I need you to share my life, all the days, the nights. Forever.'

Michelle closed her eyes in an attempt to still the sudden rush of tears. 'I knew you were trouble the first moment I set eyes on you,' she stated shakily.

'An arrogant Greek who took control and turned your life upside down, hmm?'

Stifled laughter choked in her throat. 'Something like that.' Her eyes gleamed with remembered amusement. 'You were always there, in my face.' Her expression sobered momentarily. 'Thank God.'

'Fate, *pedhaki mou*.' He cupped her face and smoothed away the soft trickle of tears with each thumb. 'It put us both in the same place at the same time.'

Yes, but it had been more than that, she acknowledged silently.

Much more.

'You never did intend this arrangement to be temporary, did you?'

He dropped a soft kiss onto the tip of her nose.

'No.'

'When did you decide?'

'I walked into the Bateson-Burrows' home that first evening, took one look at you, and knew I wanted to be in your life.'

'Why?'

He smiled, a self-deprecatory gesture that was endearing in a man of his calibre. 'Instinct. Then Fate dealt me a wild card.'

'Which you didn't hesitate to use,' she acknowledged musingly.

'Do you blame me?'

Michelle lifted her arms and linked her hands at his nape, then she drew his head down to hers. 'I love you,' she said with quiet sincerely. 'I always will. For as long as I live.'

'Come back to bed.'

She couldn't resist teasing him a little. 'To sleep?'

'Eventually.' He kissed her with hungry possession. 'After which we'll rise and face the first of several hectic days.'

*   *   *

Nikos had been right, Michelle mused as she kissed her mother, then hugged Etienne.

Each day had proven to be more hectic than the last. Yet superb organisation had achieved the impossible by bringing everything together to make their wedding day perfect.

There had been tears and laughter as the Celebrant pronounced them man and wife, and Nikos kissed the bride.

Photographs, the cutting of the cake, and an informal reception had completed the afternoon.

Now it was time to leave in the elegant stretch Cadillac hired to transport them to a Brisbane hotel where they'd stay prior to catching an international flight early the next morning.

'We made it,' Michelle said jubilantly as the driver eased the long vehicle away from Sovereign Islands towards the arterial road leading to the Pacific Highway. From there, it was a forty-five-minute drive to Brisbane city.

Nikos took hold of her hand and raised it to his lips. 'Did you think we wouldn't, *agape mou?*'

Her smile melted his heart. 'Not for a moment. You and my mother make a formidable team.'

He kissed the finger which held his rings, and praised his God for the good fortune in finding this woman, his wife.

When he reflected on the circumstance, the chance meeting, and how close he had come to delegating his trip to Australia... It made his blood run cold to think he might never have met her, never experienced the joy of her love or had the opportunity to share her life.

He had never seen her look as beautiful as she did today. The dress, the veil, they merely enhanced the true beauty of heart and soul that shone from within.

A man could drown in the depths of those brilliant deep green eyes, and be forgiven for thinking he'd died and gone to heaven when those soft lips met his own.

'Champagne?'

Michelle looked at the man seated close beside her, and gloried in the look of him. There was inherent strength apparent, an indomitability possessed by few men. She wanted to reach out and trace the groove that slashed each cheek, trail the outline of his firm mouth, then have those muscular arms hold her close.

'No.' She leaned against him and laid her head into the curve of his shoulder.

'Tired?'

'A little.'

'We'll order in room service, and catch an early night.'

She smiled at the delightful vision that encouraged. 'Sounds good to me.'

Nikos lifted a hand and threaded his fingers through the length of her hair, creating a soothing massage that had a soporific effect.

'Did I tell you we're spending two weeks in Paris after I've concluded meetings in New York?'

'Paris?' The Arc de Triomphe, the Eiffel Tower, the ambience that was the soul of France.

'Paris,' he reiterated. 'A delayed honeymoon.'

'Now I know why I fell in love with you.'

'My undoubted charm?' he mocked lightly, and felt her fingers curl within his.

'The essence that is Nikos Alessandros, regardless of wealth and possessions. *You,*' she emphasised.

'There is an analogy that states "'tis woman who maketh the man."'

'I think it's reciprocal,' she accorded with wicked amusement.

Michelle lapsed into reflective silence.

Everything had been neatly taken care of. She'd arranged to lease out her apartment; together, she and Emilio had interviewed several people to act as her replacement at the Gallery, and had finally settled on a competent knowledgeable young woman who would, unless Michelle was mistaken, give Emilio a run for his money.

She intended to liaise with Emilio from wherever she happened to be in the world. New York, Paris, Athens, Rome. In this modern technological age, distance was no longer an important factor.

It was almost dark when the Cadillac slid to a halt outside the main entrance to their hotel. Check-in took only minutes, then they rode the lift to their designated suite.

Flowers, champagne on ice, fresh fruit and an assortment of Belgian chocolates were displayed for their enjoyment, and Michelle performed a sedate pirouette and went straight into Nikos' waiting arms.

His kiss was both gentle and possessive, a gift and a statement which she returned twofold.

'Mmm,' she teased. 'I could get used to this.'

'The hotel suite?'

'You—me. Sharing and working at making a life together. Happiness, *love*.'

'Always,' Nikos vowed. His mouth fastened over hers, and he deepened the kiss, exulting in her response until their clothes were an unbearable restriction.

'I guess we don't get to eat for a while,' Michelle murmured as she nibbled his ear.

'Hungry?'

'Only for you.' Always, only you, she silently reiterated.

Love. The most precious gift of all, and it was theirs for a lifetime.

Born in West London, **Sharon Kendrick** now lives in the beautiful city of Winchester and can hear the bells of the Cathedral ringing out while she works. She has had zillions of jobs which include photographer, nurse, waitress and demonstrator of ironing board covers. She drove an ambulance in Australia and appeared on television in Teheran, but writing is the only job she's had which feels just right. Her passions are many and varied but include music, films, books, cooking, gazing at the sky and drifting off into daydreams while she works out passionate new love-stories!

**Don't miss Sharon Kendrick's next
sexually intense story:
The Desert Prince's Mistress.
On sale March 2004, in Modern Romance™!**

MISTRESS
MATERIAL
by
Sharon Kendrick

For my two slimmest friends –
AMANDA and MARTYN DAY –
who have put up with me for more years
than I care to remember!

CHAPTER ONE

IT COULDN'T be! Suki thought frantically. Not him! Anyone but him! And yet who else could it be? For who on earth could be mistaken for Pasquale Caliandro—the most diabolical man it had ever been her misfortune to meet?

Dear God, please no, she prayed silently, but she could do absolutely nothing to stop the slow pull of desire unfurling in the pit of her stomach as her traitorous eyes feasted themselves on the most delectable example of the male species she had ever seen in twenty-four years.

And she had seen the lot.

In the course of her career she had worked with male models, actors and rock stars—whose seductive faces and sexy bodies graced the bedroom walls of millions of women all over the world. But not one, not a single one, had come even close to the kind of impact that this man had on her. And not just her, either, she observed caustically, since every other woman present seemed hypnotised by that spectacular, long-legged frame.

Suki's heart was thumping erratically. What the hell was he doing *here*, in the South of France? And what on earth should she do? She wondered if he'd seen her—but even if he had, would he remember

5

the brazen young girl who had offered her body so eagerly to him when she was barely seventeen?

Completely forgetting that she'd loosened the thin gold straps of her bikini, Suki struggled to sit up, but she couldn't tear her eyes away from him, and then she saw that he was moving. He was walking.

Towards her!

She gave a helpless little whimper as her eyes were drawn to the powerful thrust of his thighs. Then upwards. Dear Lord! This man didn't need to flaunt himself in tight jeans—indeed, she suspected that if he ventured outside in anything other than the cool, pale, beautifully cut linen trousers he wore he would be arrested immediately for indecent exposure.

Up still further her eyes roamed. Oh, what a chest! A broad, powerful sweep of hair-darkened muscle beneath the cream silk of his shirt.

Her mouth dried as her eyes finally reached his face, lingering all too briefly on the beautifully shaped lips which somehow managed to be both sensual and cruel. And that nose—with its proud, aristocratic Roman curve. Who would have guessed that a nose could be such a turn-on? she thought, unable to stop herself from ogling it, like an art-lover confronted with a masterpiece for the first time ever. Reluctantly, her gaze drifted upwards to meet his eyes, and her heart stilled as she acknowledged the cold fire and the contempt which sparked from the dark depths and which he made no effort whatsoever to hide.

His mouth was nothing more than a derisory slash

as he reached her lounger and towered over her. 'So,' he drawled contemptuously, 'I see that the years have done little to temper your appetites, *cara*.'

Her precariously thin veneer of sophistication was vanquished in a moment by the wounding words, delivered in the deepest, sexiest voice she had ever heard, an intriguing mixture of transatlantic with a seductive European undertone.

Logical thought was impossible, and she was instantly on the defensive. 'And what's that supposed to mean?' she demanded furiously.

'Oh, come *on*...' The mouth twisted with devilish scorn. 'I refer to your leisurely scrutiny of my body, Suzanna.'

'Suki,' she corrected immediately.

Dark eyebrows were raised in a silent and aloof query. 'Ah! Of course—*Suki*.' He emphasised the word so that it sounded like some sultry profanity. 'The name you acquired along with your glittering fame as a model, and your many lovers...'

Her mouth fell open and she made a little murmur of protest at such a patent untruth, but he carried on regardless. 'But no matter,' he said softly as he surveyed her from slitted, dangerous eyes, 'what you call yourself. Your basic gutter instincts remain the same, do they not? You looked as if you would like to eat me up. Every *inch* of me,' he emphasised hatefully.

Swine!

Colour rushed up to form two heated flares over her high cheekbones as she tossed the thick waves of her hair back over her slender shoulders. Head held high, she spoke from a throat which felt as if it had been lined with the roughest, coarsest sandpaper. 'You flatter yourself, Pasquale!' she shot back. 'But then you always did!'

He gave a small smile then, allowed it to linger and play around his lips. 'Do I—*Suki*?' he returned silkily. 'Flatter myself?' And the sudden change in the timbre of his voice, the velvet caress as he spoke her name, sent her senses jangling. The flow of blood around her veins altered; became slow and heavy. She felt the pulse-points beating insistently at her temples, her wrists…and…shamefully…deep, deep within her groin as he stared down at her.

But more was to follow as his eyes roamed almost indifferently over her face, seemingly careless of her enormous eyes gazing helplessly at him or of her wide mouth throbbing in an unconsciously provocative *moue*.

The only flash of life and of interest came when his gaze came at last to alight on her breasts and then the indifference was replaced by a feral light and his eyes darkened as they took in the lush, creamy mounds. She felt them tingle, become heavy and swollen, the tips burning with tingling excitement. And as he gave a coldly triumphant smile she realised to her horror that the forgotten bikini-top had slipped right down, exposing most of her for his scathing delectation. 'Oh, no!' she cried, and clapped both palms protectively over her breasts.

He said something very softly in Italian as his eyes

narrowed. 'Please do not cover them, *cara*,' he murmured, on a husky entreaty. 'Such magnificent breasts. How I long to touch them. To take each tip into my mouth and to suckle each one until—'

Suki grabbed a towel and threw it over herself, squirming with embarrassment and an excitement which was painfully acute as she struggled to haul the flimsy gold material back into place, but faced with that look of hunger in those dark, magnificent eyes she was all fingers and thumbs.

She hadn't seen him for seven years, and yet two minutes in his company was enough to plunge her into dark and erotic waters which were threatening to completely submerge her. It was a nightmare. 'Get—away from me,' she managed, on a croak. *'Now!'*

He didn't move; he didn't need to—because he was actually standing beside her, not touching her at all, but at her words he seemed to pull himself together, because the raw heat of need was wiped from his face leaving nothing but a coldly contemptuous mask. 'Certainly,' he concurred, in a voice which was strangely harsh and a touch unsteady. 'There is little pleasure to be gained from a woman who offers herself so freely.'

Stung, Suki glared up at him from narrow amber eyes which threatened to glimmer with tears of self-disgust. But she kept them at bay.

Just.

'I wouldn't offer myself to you if you were the last man in the universe!'

'No? You have undergone a radical change of personality, then?' he mocked.

What could she say? She wasn't hypocritical enough to deny just how dreadfully she had once behaved with Pasquale Caliandro.

Still clutching the towel to her, she sat up, and the glint in his eye was unmistakable. Curiosity warred with common sense, and curiosity won hands down. 'What are you doing here?' she demanded, her heart beginning to race erratically as a schoolgirlish hope she'd thought long dead re-emerged with startling strength. 'You haven't—followed me here?'

To her fury, he actually threw his dark head back and laughed aloud, a glorious, mellifluous sound which made several people turn round to look at them. But when he'd stopped laughing the face which regarded her was cold and unsmiling. 'Followed you?' he queried, and the trace of sardonic incredulity made her blood boil. 'Now why on earth should I want to do that?'

Suki shrugged, a desire for revenge chipping away at her insistently. 'Your reputation with women is legendary,' she said coolly.

'Is it, now?' he queried softly. 'I wasn't aware that you had such *intimate* knowledge of my behaviour.'

She sought to disillusion him of the idea that she somehow spent all her spare time finding out about him and his fabled exploits with the fairer sex. 'I read the gossip columns like everyone else,' she said.

'Ah!' He nodded. 'So you do. But at least, *cara*, I do not have the reputation of breaking up other people's relationships. Unlike you,' he accused, and he nodded again when he saw her colour heighten. 'Yes,' he affirmed. 'You see, I too read the gossip columns.'

Oh, those *wretched* tabloids! According to them, she'd had more lovers than Mata Hari! 'If you're referring to that ridiculous scandal in New York— that was a pack of lies!' Suki defended hotly.

He raised a disbelieving eyebrow. 'Oh, really? So the photographer's girlfriend made the whole thing up, did she? You *weren't* sleeping with her boyfriend?'

'No, I *wasn't*!'

His mouth curved contemptuously. 'And the newly married Arabian prince who courted you so assiduously in front of his young bride last year... Tell me, was that also a pack of lies?'

Suki sighed as she remembered *that* sorry little affair. She'd met Prince Abdul at a cocktail party thrown by the Foreign Office in Paris. He had been ridiculously infatuated—mostly, Suki suspected, because she hadn't been the slightest bit interested in him. He had always had everything he'd always wanted, and he had wanted *her*!

He had actually asked her to be his second bride— but without even bothering to divorce the first one! She had intended telling Prince Abdul exactly what she thought of him, but one of the diplomats at the Foreign Office had sought her out for a quiet word. There was a big oil deal going through between Prince Abdul's country and Britain. Best not to actually turn him down outright, but to let him down gently…

In fact, afterwards the diplomat had told her that she had been a great help to her country—maybe Pasquale should hear about *that*! She held her head up proudly and looked him straight in the eye. 'There happens to be a perfectly simple explanation for that,' she said reasonably.

But it seemed that he wasn't interested in reason, or an explanation, because his dark eyes were boring into hers, an expression of scorn lifting the corner of his exquisite mouth. 'And even given *my* supposed reputation,' he gritted, 'do you somehow imagine that I am so desperate as to follow and to find you? You who are everything that I most despise in a woman?'

Stung by the biting criticism, Suki was momentarily lost for words, her cheeks flaring at the denigrating accusation he'd thrown at her. Yes, OK, she hadn't behaved too well, but surely her foolish youthful behaviour with him didn't warrant *that* kind of censure? 'I really don't think that's fair…' she faltered.

But he had crouched down so that their eyes were on a level, and she could almost see the hostility emanating from him in pure waves towards her. 'When I go searching for a woman,' he said deliberately, 'it will be for someone as unlike you as possible. Though I'm not sure that she exists—because I've certainly never come across her.

'You see, Suki, I'm waiting for the woman who

doesn't give me the green light the instant that I meet her. Most men—and certainly this man—are turned on by the thrill of the chase before the capture. Something which is gained so easily has little intrinsic value, I believe.'

Suki was shaken to the core by the depth of his dislike, but she was damned sure she wouldn't show it. Her amber eyes glinted dangerously. 'I don't have to lie here and listen to this—'

'No, indeed,' he agreed, in his deep drawl, his eyes hot and hungry with sexual mischief. 'I have a much better idea. Why don't we move away? You could lie down somewhere else. With me...'

Somehow he managed to imbue the suggestion with so much sensual promise that it took Suki every last ounce of pride she possessed to answer him back. 'Spare me your cheap innuendo!' she said, her eyes sparking amber fire. 'And make your mind up! Either you despise me so much that my very presence contaminates you or you're extending an extremely unsubtle invitation to get me into bed with you—you can't do both, Pasquale.' She shook her head sadly. 'Dear, dear—a supposedly intelligent man like you really ought to be able to see such gaping holes in your logic.'

She saw the warning light of battle in his eyes, but when he spoke his voice was very soft. 'A man does not always think with his head,' he said insultingly.

That did it! 'Get out of my way,' she said from between gritted teeth, and she swung her long, faintly tanned legs over the side of the lounger. First glancing down to check that she was halfway decent, she dropped the towel onto the lounger, then got to her feet, looking around in vain for Salvatore, the photographer who had brought her to this house-party outside Cannes.

It was *supposed* to have been the relaxing finale to two days of solid shooting for a book of photographs Salvatore was producing. Relaxing—huh! About as relaxing as being on the front line of a war-zone, with the arrival of Pasquale Caliandro. Suki began to move away.

'Oh, no. Not so fast.' In a single, snake-like movement Pasquale had captured her tiny wrist in the strong grasp of his hand and Suki was horrified how her body thrilled to that first contact of flesh on flesh. And why did he have to be so tall? So powerful? So gorgeous? Her throat constricted.

'Let me go—'

He shook his head with implacable confidence. 'No. You and I need to talk.'

'I have nothing to say to you—'

'But I,' he said, and his voice was husky with intent, 'have plenty to say to you.'

'I'm not interested.' But oh, what a lie, for despite her instinctive and purely protective need to put as much distance between them as possible she was *bursting* to know what he wanted—and she was certain that he'd guessed as much.

He gave a small, humourless smile. 'On the contrary—I think you might be.'

He still held her wrist and she was powerless to

move, and Suki realised that to an outsider it would appear that he was holding her lightly, almost affectionately—the steely determination of his grip would not be apparent to anyone else.

She tried a different approach. After all, she'd had to fend men off before. She tipped her head to one side, so that the long curls—the colour of golden syrup glinting in the sunshine, or so she'd been told—fell over her bosom. 'If you carry on like that, Pasquale,' she said reasonably, 'then you'll really leave me no choice other than to scream, and I'm sure that would do your reputation no good whatsoever.'

'My reputation is of no concern to me,' he drawled with dismissive arrogance. 'But if that is what you intend to do, then I must give you fair warning that you will really leave *me* no choice other than to silence you most satisfactorily.'

Her confusion must have shown in her eyes. 'By kissing you, of course,' he elaborated silkily. 'And as I recall you liked me kissing you, didn't you, Suki? You liked it *ve-ry* much.'

Oh! That occasional lilt to his voice was so devilishly attractive! Suki took a deep breath and met his gaze full-on. 'What do you want?'

'To talk to you.'

'And that's all?'

'For now.' The words sounded ominous.

She'd been little more than a child when she'd known him before, and then she had been so enraptured by his physical magnetism that she had seen little beyond his tantalising exterior. Now, as an adult, she recognised the quiet determination about the man which he wore like a mantle. If Pasquale wanted to talk to her, she realised, then attempting to avoid him might prove to be more trouble than it was worth.

'Very well,' she sighed. 'Talk to me. I'm listening. But I'm giving you five minutes to say whatever it is you want to say—and then I'm out of here!'

'Out—of—here,' he repeated slowly, in a voice of fascinated horror. He made a little clicking sound of disapproval. 'Such an expensive Swiss education,' he mused. 'Wasted. That all those years of tuition should culminate in such bald, inelegant little statements…'

His elegant censure hit a raw nerve as something inside her snapped. The realisation that he was playing with her, teasing her, as an angler would a fish, made Suki realise that she was putting herself into an unnecessarily weak position. She didn't *have* to stay and talk to him. She didn't *have* to do anything. She was no longer a naïve and gullible schoolgirl— she was an independent career-woman in her own right, for heaven's sake!

Without another word, she stalked off towards the house, pushing her way through the milling throng, but she knew from the buzz which accompanied her movements that Pasquale was following her.

Let him follow her! she thought with a stubborn resurgence of resolve. She would slam the wretched door in his face and then lock it! That would call his bluff. He had arrogantly stated that his reputation was of no concern to him, but she doubted whether he would want this select and privileged bunch of guests witnessing him beating her door down!

She was aware of people watching them, of the women staring at Pasquale, their eyes full of ill-concealed lust. She had been like that once. She shuddered in disgust as she glanced over her shoulder to see that he had paused to speak to one of the waitresses. Vaguely, Suki wondered where Salvatore was, but he was nowhere to be seen. But then perhaps it was better that he wasn't around. He would want to know who Pasquale was—and how could she tell him? How could she say, He's the brother of the girl who was my best friend—the man I once begged to make love to me?

And he hadn't.

That was the most galling thing.

He hadn't.

It was a story she was not proud of and to this day it had the power to make her flinch when she remembered exactly how she had behaved. Over the years she had deliberately pushed the memory to the recesses of her mind and seeing him today had brought it all flooding back with painful clarity.

She slipped through the house, her bare feet moving over the cold marble floors, her tall, dark, silent pursuer making her heart thunder with dread and excitement.

Her room was on the first floor, at the opposite end of the corridor to Salvatore's, and she hurriedly pushed the door open, aware of Pasquale's footsteps, of the soft sound of his breath, of that strange, elusive masculine scent, still so startlingly familiar, even after seven years.

She turned to face him, her chest heaving, her almond-shaped amber eyes narrowed like a lioness's. 'This is ridiculous,' she said.

His face was infuriatingly enigmatic. 'I agree,' he returned. 'You are injecting an element of farce into my simple request that we talk.'

She thought of the intimacy of the room just behind them. 'Very well,' she said. 'But not here.'

He smiled, but the smile did not reach his cold, glittering eyes. 'Oh? And why not—or can I guess? The presence of a bed bothers you, does it, Suki? Are you afraid of what might happen if you're alone in a bedroom with me?'

She swallowed. All those nights she'd spent imagining how she'd behave if she ever had the misfortune to see him again. She had planned to ignore him, look down her nose at him. In her wilder fantasies she had even been prepared to pretend not to recognise him at all, planning to stare at that dark, handsome face with bemused bewilderment, although looking at him now she knew that that would have been asking a little *too* much of her general acting ability.

It had certainly not been her intention to let him know that his presence still had the power to disturb her. Profoundly. And wasn't that exactly what she was doing now?

Taking a deep breath, she switched into superficial hostess mode. Giving him the bright smile she normally reserved for the lens of a camera, she waved her hand invitingly.

'Forgive me,' she said, sounding deliberately insincere, and saw from the cold twist of his mouth that her insincerity had been noted. 'I've been under a lot of strain recently—working too hard—you know how it is.' She glanced down at the waterproof watch on her wrist and gave him a cool, self-possessed smile. 'I can give you—ten minutes. Is that time enough?'

'Plenty,' he said abrasively, and followed her into the room.

He walked over to the window, where the balcony overlooked the poolside, and there was silence for a moment as he stared down at people tearing apart the glistening red lobsters which the waiters had now produced, at women delicately devouring the sweet pink flesh as they tried not to smear their lipstick. Suki felt a shiver of unknown origin tingle its way up her spine.

'How's Francesca?' she asked suddenly.

He tensed immediately and his face was like granite when he turned around to capture her in a cold, dark stare.

'Do you care?'

'Of course I care! She was my best friend—before you pulled her out of school and forbade me ever to see her again!'

He raised his eyebrows. 'That was a decision I

have never regretted. I did not approve of the company she was keeping.'

Suki lifted her chin. 'By that I suppose you mean me?'

He gave her a steady look. 'Yes, Suki—I mean you.'

'The bad influence,' she observed acidly.

He gave a low laugh. 'Precisely. I had no intention of letting my sister start copying the kind of behaviour you were indulging in. Young girls are notoriously affected by what their peers do. And whilst you might have considered it perfectly normal to sleep around I had no intention of letting Francesca do the same.'

Sick at heart, Suki turned away from those dark, intent, judgemental eyes. He still thought of her as nothing more than a tramp—so why bother defending herself? Indeed, how could she possibly defend herself when he spoke nothing more than the truth?

'Is that what you've come here for?' she asked bitterly. 'To go over the past? You've made it clear what you think of me—not that I care what you think any more—'

'Did you ever?' he interrupted softly. 'Or was I just one more virile male for you to wrap those beautiful legs around?'

Suki hesitated painfully, the cruel censure behind his words making the erotic image they created disintegrate immediately. Her amber eyes glittered as she found herself speaking without bothering to analyse her words. 'Of course I cared! You were the older brother of my dearest friend—I was a guest in your house, and you threw me out! Hustled me away like some criminal—flown away at high speed, my holiday cut short. Having to explain to my mother…'

A look almost of pain crossed his face. 'What,' he said, very softly, 'did you tell your mother?'

Her eyes were amber ice. 'Oh, don't worry,' she told him scornfully. 'Your telephone call to her managed to allay any worries she might have had. I don't know how you managed it, but you certainly sweet-talked her into thinking that everything was just fine and dandy. I certainly wasn't going to enlighten her with the truth—that you kicked me out of your bed and out of your house within a few hours!'

'Dio!' he swore raggedly. 'Must you put it quite so—crudely?'

'I'm sorry if it's *crude*,' she said deliberately. 'But it's the truth. It's horrible, it's something I'd rather forget—and I will tell you for the last time that I'm simply not interested in rehashing the past—if that's why you've come.'

He stared at her for a long moment of consideration before shaking his head. 'That isn't why I've come,' he told her.

'What, then?' she asked him in bewilderment.

'I've come to ask you to do something for me,' he said simply, but as she was caught up in his direct stare the substance of his words drifted away like gossamer on a breeze because the soft, dark blaze of his eyes had the power to confuse her, to merge the years and send her mind racing back to a time almost eight years ago—the first time she had ever set eyes on Pasquale Caliandro…

CHAPTER TWO

'ARE you sure they won't mind?' asked Suzanna hesitantly as, with a flick of charcoal, she completed the small portrait she'd been doing of her friend, just as the plane began to make its final descent towards Rome airport.

'Who?' Francesca was too busy batting her eyelashes outrageously at the uniformed male flight attendant to pay much attention to her schoolfriend.

'Your family, of course.' Suzanna flicked her pale auburn plait back over her shoulder. 'It's very kind of them to invite me to stay with them.'

Francesca shrugged. 'They don't care who I invite—they're never around. Papà's always working and is away a lot on business, and my stepmother's away in Paris, apparently. She'll probably be trawling the streets looking for gigolos—'

'*Francesca!*' exclaimed Suzanna in shocked horror. 'You're not serious?'

'Aren't I?' queried Francesca with unfamiliar bitterness. 'She's twenty years younger than my father. She spends his money like water, and she flirts with anything in a pair of trousers,' she finished, in disgust.

'So why does he stay with her, then?' asked Suzanna softly.

'Because she's beautiful. Why else...?' Francesca's voice tailed off momentarily, and when she spoke again it was with her customary, rather sardonic verve. 'Which only leaves big brother—and he's worse than any jailer. But at least with you there you can be my alibi.'

'Alibi?' echoed Suzanna uncertainly.

'Sure.' Francesca's dark eyes flashed. 'He tries to stop me going out with boys, so I don't tell him any more. And if he asks *you* anything, then you tell him you last saw me praying in church!'

'Francesca!' said Suzanna uneasily because she didn't know sometimes whether to take her effervescent friend seriously, and her fingers began to pleat the hem of her white dress nervously. 'You know you don't mean that!'

'I know that going home for the holidays is going to cramp my style,' muttered Francesca. 'The discos I go to during term-time are *fantastic*—I wish you'd come along too.'

Suzanna shook her head. 'Discos aren't really my thing.' In discos she felt gangly, awkward. And when you stood at almost six feet in your stockinged feet that was inevitable.

'That's because you've never given them a chance!' Francesca's attention was caught by the thumbnail sketch in Suzanna's hand. 'Hey! That's good—it's me, isn't it?'

'Do you like it?' smiled Suzanna.

'Yeah. May I keep it?'

'Sure.'

The plane was coming in to land, and there was little time for talking again until they were seated in the back of the shiny, chaffeur-driven limousine and heading towards the Caliandro mansion. Francesca spent the entire journey chattering as she freed Suzanna's hair from her plaits and teased it into a blazing and magnificent furnace of waves, and Suzanna was so enraptured at the spectacular landscape passing them by that the subject of alibis was all but forgotten.

Suzanna and Francesca were both at finishing school in Switzerland. 'It's bound to finish me off sooner or later!' Francesca always joked. It was the expensive kind of school which was intended to produce young ladies. Daughters of the rich and the noble attended, most of them from privileged but broken homes.

Suzanna's own father had died, leaving a wife, a son and a daughter, and a car-manufacturing plant which her brother had over-ambitious plans for. Money was tight, but a savings plan taken out at her birth had ensured that at least Suzanna's expensive education would be paid for. But she worried about her mother's well-being, and she worried about her feckless brother, Piers, being in charge of the family business…

Francesca's own mother had died a few years back, and her father had quickly remarried. A mistake, according to Francesca, and it seemed that there was little love lost between her and her stepmother.

'And my brother really *hates* her!' she'd added. 'He can hardly bear to be in the same room as her.'

It didn't sound like a very *happy* house, thought Suzanna suddenly.

Francesca's voice broke into her thoughts. 'We're here!' she exclaimed as the car swept down a gravelled drive and came to a halt in front of an imposing white building, and then her voice dropped to a dramatic whisper. 'And here comes Pasquale, my brother—so don't forget—if he asks whether I date men you just tell him that I've shown bags of disinterest!'

Through the window of the limousine, Suzanna could see the most handsome man she had ever set eyes on, and her heart lurched painfully in her chest. She blinked several times, as if afraid that she'd simply dreamt him up.

Quite unbelievably, she hadn't.

He was tall—quite spectacularly tall for a man of Italian origin. His shoulders were strong and wide and his hips were narrow. His nose was a proud Roman curve and his eyes were dark and glittering. For Suzanna, naïve and unused to men, the experience of staring up into the face of Francesca's brother was like something out of the romantic novels she'd read since her early teens; she looked, and was, completely smitten.

Afterwards, she was to tell herself that she had been ripe to fall for someone—*any*one. It was just unfortunate that it had happened to be Pasquale…

He greeted his sister with a kiss on both cheeks and then held his hand out formally to Suzanna.

The sun was behind her and seemed to create a halo of golden-red around her hair—or so Francesca whispered to her later that night when Suzanna's heart was still pounding in that strange, unfamiliar way which hadn't left her since she'd first set eyes on Pasquale.

The short white cheesecloth dress she wore merely hinted at the outline of the smooth young flesh which lay beneath, but when he looked at her a stillness and a watchfulness came over Pasquale Caliandro. He caught her small hand in his firm, warm and masculine grip and as she gave him a look of helpless fascination his eyes narrowed, his mouth hardening as he stared down at her.

'I think my brother fancies you,' Francesca said that night as they got ready for bed. 'He gave you a real mean, hungry look!'

'Rubbish!' said Suzanna, blushing furiously.

Of course it was rubbish, she convinced herself as she dived into the pool one morning, a few days after she'd arrived. Men who fancied you didn't virtually ignore you in a way which she thought bordered on downright rudeness. And they certainly didn't speak to you in that awful, brusque way he had of addressing her. One day he'd actually had the *nerve* to tell her to stop hanging her head and to be proud of her height!

Sometimes, she thought as she ploughed up and down the swimming pool in an effort to get rid of

the heat in her veins which just wouldn't go away—
sometimes she thought that Pasquale almost *disliked*
her—his manner towards her was so abrupt.

And yet at others...

She shivered. Other times she would turn around
to find him watching her. Just watching her with a
dark and brooding intensity which frightened the life
out of her, yet thrilled her at the same time.

Just about the only nice thing he'd said to her had
been when he'd found her sketching quietly in the
garden one day.

He had stood silently looking over her shoulder
for at least a minute, and had given a little nod as
he'd watched her long fingers cleverly re-creating the
glass summer house, which was overhung with vines.

'That's good,' he observed. 'Good enough to make
it your career, I think.' And Suzanna had blushed
furiously at the unexpected praise.

She turned on her back and lazily kicked her legs
around in the cool water. It was indeed a strange
household she was staying with, she reflected. Francesca seemed to spend her whole time concocting
schemes to get to one of the discotheques in the city,
but so far she hadn't succeeded, since Pasquale vehemently blocked every suggestion. 'You're far too
young,' he'd told her emphatically, and then his eyes
had narrowed and he had given Suzanna one of his
rare looks. 'Do you girls go to many discos?' he'd
queried, his dark eyes suspicious.

'Never!' Suzanna and Francesca had replied in
unison, but Suzanna hadn't been able to stop herself

from blushing at Francesca's easy lie, and she was certain that Pasquale's sharp eyes had noticed, for he'd frowned severely.

Francesca and Pasquale's father she hardly saw at all. A still handsome man of sixty, with streaks of silver in his dark hair, he seemed to spend most of the time working—as Francesca had prophesied— making it home only in time for the evening meal. Usually at dinner it was just the three of them, as Pasquale always seemed to be out on a date with one of the many glamorous-sounding women who telephoned him, and their stepmother was still in Paris.

But today Suzanna was alone in the house. Pasquale was working and Signor Caliandro had flown to Naples for the day. Francesca had gone to visit her godmother on the other side of the city. She'd invited Suzanna to go along, but Suzanna knew that the elderly lady spoke little English and had decided that it would be fairer to let Francesca go alone. Besides, she rather liked having this luxurious house to herself.

The swimming pool was vast and deliciously cool and Suzanna dived to the depths of the turquoise water and swam around. She'd almost used up all her air, when the devastatingly sharp pain of cramp stabbed ruthlessly at her calf.

Perhaps if she'd had a lungful of air and hadn't been near the bottom of the pool she wouldn't have panicked, but panic she did, doing the worst thing she could possibly have done—she gulped water down, her arms and legs flailing wildly in all directions.

Her head and chest felt as though they might actually burst, but suddenly she felt a pair of hands tightly grasping her waist. She tried instinctively to wriggle free, but whoever was holding her had an indomitable strength and would not let her go.

She found herself being propelled to the surface, where her mouth broke open and greedily sucked in air, and she fell back against the chest of her rescuer, a solid, hard wall of muscle, but she knew without turning to look at him that it was Pasquale.

His arms were still around her waist, and his head dropped briefly to rest on hers.

'*Dio!*' he exclaimed savagely, and kicked off and swam towards the pool steps. He climbed out first, then picked her up easily and carried her to lay her down on the soft, sun-warmed grass.

She realised that he had dived in fully dressed—that he had not even bothered to kick off his beautiful, soft, handmade shoes, which were now sodden. His silk shirt clung to him like a second skin and his sopping trousers now etched every hard sinew of the strong shafts of his powerful thighs.

His eyes were blazing. 'You fool! You crazy little *idiot*!' he cried out, and he ran his hands thoroughly but dispassionately over her body, like a doctor examining for broken bones.

'I—I'm sorry.' She trembled as her body felt his warm, sure touch.

'And so you should be!' he told her furiously.

'Don't you realise that you could have drowned?'
His eyes narrowed as he took in her white, frightened
face. 'Do you hurt anywhere?' he demanded.

Humiliatingly, her teeth stared to chatter so that
she couldn't speak.

'Do you?' he demanded again, still in that same
grim tone. 'Hurt anywhere? Tell me!'

She couldn't cope with his harshness, not when
she was feeling so vulnerable, and she did what she
hadn't done since her father had died the previous
year—she burst into tears.

Instantly, his attitude altered. He looked appalled
with himself as he gathered her into his arms and
laid his strong hand protectively against the back of
her head.

'Don't cry, *bella mia*,' he whispered. 'There is no
need for tears. You are safe now.'

But the shock of realising what might have happened if he had not been there made her sob all the
harder, and he made a little sound, a small, rough
assertion beneath his breath, as he picked her up and
carried her towards the house. She was too weak to
do anything other than rest her head against his chest,
and gradually the sobs receded. It was just like visiting heaven, being in his arms like this, she realised,
her body all wet and clingy and close. She could
have stayed like that all day.

'Wh-where are you taking me?' she wondered
aloud as he mounted the stairs.

'To get you dry,' he answered. His gentleness had
vanished, and he spoke again in that grim, terse tone

which left her wondering why he still seemed so angry with her.

He carried her to her own room and set her down on the thick carpet, glancing quickly around, his eyes narrowing as they alighted on a tiny pair of knickers which were lying in an open drawer, together with a matching bra.

Suzanna blushed.

'Do you have a towelling robe?' he asked.

She shook her head. A towelling robe wasn't the kind of thing you brought to Italy in the middle of summer. She only had a silk wrap.

'You'd better wait here!' he told her, and left the bedroom.

He returned minutes later with what was obviously his own robe—a luxurious, almost velvety towelling garment in a deep, midnight-blue colour—and threw it down on the bed. 'Now strip off,' he told her. 'Completely. Put the robe on and I will run you a bath.'

If any other man had issued such a curt and intimate order, Suzanna would have screamed for the police, but because it was Pasquale she simply nodded obediently. He set off for the *en suite* without a backward glance, his shoulders curiously stiff and set, and Suzanna began to do as he had told her.

Easier said than done. She'd never thought that it would be so difficult to remove two tiny scraps of bikini, but the wet material was clinging to her cold, damp skin and her fingers were stiff and trembling with the cold.

So when, minutes later, the bathroom door opened and Pasquale came back in, accompanied by clouds of delicious-looking, scented steam, it was to find her almost sobbing with frustration as she attempted to slide her hands round to her back to unclip the clasp of her bikini-top.

There was a moment when he froze, as though he'd never seen a woman almost naked before—but that was nonsense. Francesca had already regaled her with stories of Pasquale smuggling girls out of his room when he was still at boarding-school. And you only had to look at that brooding, almost dangerous physique to know that Pasquale would have tasted most of the pleasures of lovemaking...

A strange look crossed those tight features. A look of anger, but of something else too—something which even the totally innocent Suzanna recognised as desire—and then he said something very softly and very eloquently in Italian, before moving quickly to her side.

'I...I'm sorry,' she mumbled. 'I can't... My fingers are all...'

He shook his head, said not a word but deftly undid the clasp with a single fluid movement that sent a brief spear of jealousy through her as she found herself imagining those strong, bronzed hands undressing other women too. Her unfettered breasts bounced free and she heard him catch his breath on a muffled, almost savage note.

He almost flung the robe over her and swiftly knotted the belt around her narrow waist, and then he knelt at her feet, his hands moving inside the robe until they were on her bare hips. Suzanna held her breath with dazed and exultant shock as she felt the heat of his fingers on her cool flesh, but he kept his eyes averted as he peeled the damp bottoms off all the way down the slender length of her thighs, and her cold and discomfort vanished completely as she felt the brief slide of his hand against her inner thigh.

Something hot and potent and powerful bubbled its way into life in her veins as rapidly as bush-fire, and Suzanna was racked with an uncontrollable shudder as she became sexually aware of her body for the first time in her life.

Had he seen her automatic response to his touch? Was that why his mouth had twisted into that harsh, almost frightening line? Why the hard glittering of his dark eyes now transformed him into some unfor-gettable but slightly forbidding stranger?

'Now get in the bath,' he said roughly, and he tossed the bikini away from him as though it had been contaminated. He rose to his feet and moved towards the door, but without his customary elegance and fluidity of motion. 'And be out of there in twenty minutes—no longer,' he ordered, but then a wry note which bordered on amusement entered his voice and, thankfully, removed some of the awful tension from the air. 'No falling asleep is permitted! Understand?' he finished softly.

'Yes, Pasquale,' she answered meekly.

'Good. I'll be downstairs making you some coffee.'

She wandered into the bathroom in a heady daze, wrapped in the thickness of his robe, reluctant to remove it because the scent of it—of *him*—was just too heavenly for words. She hugged her arms against her breasts, then wiped away some of the steam from the mirror and stared into it, mesmerised by the heightened colour of her cheeks and the strange, almost feverish glitter in her eyes.

But what was she imagining? That he had been as affected by that brief encounter as she had? Pasquale Caliandro, the toast of Rome, bothered by a schoolgirl?

No way! she thought with honest reluctance as she pulled off the robe and stepped into the fragrant, steamy water.

The bath made her feel almost normal again. She washed her hair and left it hanging loose, dressing in a pair of white jeans and a loose white cotton sweater before going downstairs to find Pasquale, and the coffee.

She stood in the doorway watching him, enjoying the sight of such a very masculine man looking so thoroughly at ease in the domestic domain of the kitchen.

His dark eyes flicked over her impassively. 'Feeling better?' he enquired.

Physically, yes, certainly. But there was still that tingling awareness fizzing around her veins which his touch had brought to life. 'Much better,' she answered politely, and then her gratitude came out in a rush. 'I wanted to thank you, Pasquale—for...' it sounded a bit over the top to say it, but say it she must '...saving my life,' she gulped.

He shook his head and smiled gently. 'Let's forget it.'

But she would never forget it, she knew that, and the burgeoning, almost schoolgirlish attraction she had felt towards Pasquale suddenly flowered and blossomed into mature life.

I'm in love with him, she thought, with a calm certainty.

'Sit down,' he offered, and she drew up one of the tall stools he'd indicated and sat, leaning her elbows on the counter as she struggled to say something which didn't involve the fact that he'd seen her half-naked just minutes ago. Sitting there, with her still damp hair and her face completely bare of make-up, she suddenly felt very young and very boring.

'You look very efficient in the kitchen!' she remarked brightly. 'I'm surprised!'

He raised his dark eyebrows fractionally, but didn't comment on the sexism inherent in her remark; instead he began to pour the fragrant brew into a large porcelain cup. 'The Italian male is renowned for many things, but not, I think, for his prowess in the kitchen,' he said as he pushed the cup towards her.

She knew that. She knew, too, exactly what they *were* renowned for... For being wonderful...lovers... She gulped, and took a deep breath. 'So you decided to break with tradition?' she joked.

A sudden bleakness dulled the magnificent eyes as

he added sugar to his own cup. 'Unhappily, yes. One cannot have servants on hand every minute of the day, and when my mother died...' He hesitated. 'Well, Papà was in a state of shock for such a long time, and Francesca was too young...'

Suzanna could have kicked herself for her blundering insensitivity. 'Oh, Lord,' she groaned softly. 'I didn't mean to put my foot in it.'

He gave a small smile. 'Time gives a certain immunity against pain, Suzanna.' And his accent deepened. 'Didn't your own father die very suddenly?'

Suzanna went very quiet. 'Francesca told you?'

'Yes.' He paused, and the dark eyes were very direct. 'It was a car crash, I believe?'

If it had been anyone else but him, she suspected that she would have found the question a gross intrusion, but Pasquale asking it seemed like the most natural thing in the world. 'Yes,' she said, and swallowed.

'You were thinking of him by the pool—when you began to cry?'

His perception quite took her breath away. 'How on earth could you know that?'

'I know quite well the difference between shock and grief. And bottling it up won't help, you know.' He gave her a gentle smile. 'Now drink your coffee and I will take you out for lunch. Will that cheer you up?'

'*Lunch?*' She felt like Cinderella. 'Are you sure?'

His mouth moved in an enigmatic smile. 'Quite sure,' he said drily. 'You see, another characteristic of Italian men is their enjoyment of being seen with an exceptionally beautiful young lady.'

She knew that he had deliberately emphasised the young bit, but she didn't care. Pasquale was taking her for lunch and that was all that mattered.

In the event, that lunch ruined her for every future meal of her life. He took her to a lovely restaurant, and he was charm personified. The food was delicious and the half-glass of wine he allowed her incomparable. He seemed so at home in the discreetly elegant surroundings, and she tried to emulate his cool confidence. The down side was that at least three women came over to greet him—women with stacks more experience and poise than Suzanna—and she found herself wishing that they might totter and trip on the ridiculously high heels they all seemed to be wearing!

It was past three when they drove back, and she felt warm and contented and wondered what he would suggest doing that afternoon. But he did not get out of the car.

'I will leave you to amuse yourself,' he told her, and he gave her a stern look. 'But please—no more swimming—not today!'

She found it hard to hide the disappointment. 'But where are you going?'

'To work. Be so kind as to tell Papà and Francesca that I shall be late—and that I shall not be in for supper.'

Suzanna felt as flat as a pancake as she walked

slowly back into the flower-covered villa. She spent the rest of the afternoon trying to write a letter, but it was difficult, because outside a wind was insidiously whipping up, while in the distance she heard the ominous rumble of thunder.

She began to long for the return of the others, but no one came back. No Francesca or Signor Caliandro. The villa suddenly seemed awfully big and awfully empty with just her and the cook, who was busy in the kitchen.

Francesca rang at six to say that she would be staying at her godmother's. 'The storm is very bad here,' she explained. 'And it's moving down towards your part of the city. Will you be all right? Is Pasquale or Papà back yet?'

Suzanna didn't want to worry her friend, so she didn't bother telling her that Pasquale was not in for supper and that there was no sign of her father.

She decided to keep herself busy, and there were enough adult toys in that house to amuse anyone— rows of film classics in the room where the video and large viewing screen were kept and a whole library of books, with an English section which would have kept an avid reader going for years.

So Suzanna passed the rest of the day amusing herself as best she could. She gave herself a manicure and a pedicure. She borrowed Francesca's tongs and made her curls hang in brightly coloured corkscrews.

The cook was clearly worried about the weather, and so Suzanna told her to go home early.

But later, as she perched upon the stool in the

kitchen, eating the chicken and salad which had been prepared for supper, Suzanna could hear the distant rumbling of the storm growing in intensity.

At the best of times she wasn't fond of storms, but when she was marooned and isolated in a large villa in a strange country—well…

She went around securing the windows as the wind began to howl like a hungry animal outside, and the rain spattered and thundered in huge, unforgiving drops against the glass.

She was sitting up in bed reading a book, when the room was plunged into darkness and she screamed aloud at the unexpected blackness which enveloped her like a suffocating blanket.

She tried to reason with herself that it was just a power-cut, not unusual in a storm of this ferocity, but it was no good—she began to scream anew as a branch hurled itself against the window-pane, like an intruder banging to come inside.

She didn't know how long she lay there, cowering with fear, but suddenly she felt the cover being whipped back and there stood Pasquale, his clothes spattered with rain, his dark, luxuriant hair plastered to his beautifully shaped head.

He took hold of her shoulders and levered her up towards him to stare down intently into her face.

'You're OK?' he asked succinctly for the second time that day, and she nodded tremulously.

'Sure?'

'Yes.'

'Where are the others?'

'Francesca says the storm's too bad to travel back. I don't know about your father.'

'They've closed the airport,' he said briefly, and then his eyes softened. 'Were you very frightened here, on your own?'

Bravado made her lie. 'Not—really,' she said in a small voice, but as she stared up at him all in her world suddenly felt very, very safe.

'Wait here,' he told her. 'Don't move. I'm going to try to do something about the lights.'

She had no intention of going *anywhere*! So she sank back obediently against the pillows until she heard him calling her, then leapt out of bed to find him outside the door, holding a candelabra in his hand, with three flickering candles casting strange, enticing shadows onto his face. He looked like someone who had stepped out of a painting; someone from another age, she thought fleetingly.

'Come downstairs and get warm,' he said, and she followed him downstairs, watching while he built a fire and fetched two brandies, which he placed on a small table in front of the roaring blaze.

He'd changed, she noticed. Gone was the sodden suit, replaced by a black cashmere sweater and black jeans. On his feet he wore nothing, and she couldn't help noticing how beautifully shaped his toes were. Imagine even finding someone's feet attractive! She really *was* in a bad way! Her mouth dried and her heart thundered as he looked up from the logs and answered her shy smile almost reluctantly.

'Brandy?' he asked coolly.

She remembered him policing her at lunchtime and allowing her only half a glass of wine, and perhaps he remembered it too, because he laughed.

'It's purely for medicinal purposes. You look white and shocked to me. This has been quite a day for you, Suzanna.'

It would sound extremely naïve to say she'd never tried brandy before, wouldn't it? she thought. Besides which, his words were accurate enough, and she *felt* shocked. 'I'd love some,' she agreed, and sat on the rug, holding her hands out towards the blaze.

The brandy was hot and bitter-sweet in her throat, but she felt its effect stealing over her immediately, and she wriggled her toes as the warmth invaded her.

'Feeling better now?' he asked.

'*Mmm!* Much!' She briefly closed her eyes and gave a blissful smile and when she opened them again it was to find him staring at her intently, something unfathomable written on his face, and, quite suddenly, he got to his feet.

'Bedtime,' he said abruptly, in a firm voice. 'It's late. I'll tidy up down here—you go on up. Here, take this candle, but don't leave it lit.'

But Suzanna couldn't sleep. Outside the storm raged, but inside her own storm was raging. She recalled the feel of his arms as he'd carried her upstairs from the pool. The feel of those firm hands freeing her breasts, removing the bikini.

Restlessly, she tossed and turned, until she gave up the whole idea of trying to sleep. She decided to go in search of some matches to light the candle and read her book.

She pulled on her silken wrap and silently made her way downstairs to the kitchen, and after a bit of hunting around she found the matches she was after.

She was just creeping back along the corridor towards her bedroom when a dark figure loomed up in front of her and she almost collided with Pasquale.

He wore black silk pyjama trousers and nothing else. She found her eyes drawn to the beautiful breadth of his hair-roughened chest. His dark hair was ruffled and his chin shadowed in the strange yellow light of the storm.

'What are you doing creeping around the house?' he demanded in a voice which managed to sound both dangerous and soft, his eyes briefly flicking to the rise and fall of her breasts beneath their thin layer of silk. 'Why aren't you in bed?'

He made it sound as if she'd been committing some sort of crime. 'Because I couldn't sleep,' she told him defensively.

There was a moment's silence, broken only by the harsh sound of his breathing. 'Neither could I,' he said eventually, and then his voice softened. 'Does the sound of the storm frighten you?'

She nodded. 'A little.'

'There is nothing to be frightened of,' he said, and with his hand in the small of her back he propelled her along to her bedroom door. 'Don't you know that it's simply the gods clapping their hands? Didn't they tell you that when you were a little girl?'

But at that moment an enormous clap of thunder seemed to rock the very foundations of the house, and Suzanna jumped in fright.

'Get into bed,' he told her brusquely.

She did as he asked, but her eyes were huge in her face as she stared up at him in mute appeal.

He shook his head. 'No, Suzanna. No. You don't know what it is you're asking,' he told her obliquely.

She hadn't really been aware that she was asking anything, but now it dawned on her that she wanted him to stay. She wanted him to shield her from the elements which raged outside.

And those within? she wondered briefly.

She heard his reluctant sigh.

'Very well—I'll sit here until you fall asleep,' he said in an oddly resigned kind of voice.

Suzanna slithered down beneath the duvet, hearing the slow, steady thump of her heart beating loudly in her ears.

Pasquale sat on the edge of the bed, as far away from her as possible. 'Now sleep,' he urged softly. 'Nothing can hurt you while I am here.'

She awoke to find herself wrapped tightly in his arms beneath the duvet, her head resting on his shoulder while he slept. She heard the comforting steadiness of his breathing, and, acting purely on the instincts of one who was only half-awake, she nestled even closer into his embrace. He tightened his arms around her, and she had never felt so cosseted or so safe in her whole life. She let her head drift down so that her cheek lay on his bare chest and she could hear his heart beating loud and steady as a drum.

She couldn't resist it; she simply couldn't help herself. Lifting her mouth, she kissed his neck, and he sighed and stirred, his hand moving lazily from her waist to cup her breast over the thin silk of her nightdress, finding its tip and inciting it into immediate tingling life, stroke by glorious stroke.

He began to kiss her neck as he unbuttoned the nightdress and slowly bared her breasts, murmuring all the while in his native tongue.

She didn't understand what he was saying to her, but she could hear the pleasure in his voice, the soft lilt of the seductive Italian language sounding almost like poetry. And then he began to kiss the tip of one breast, and she shuddered as his hand moved down to begin to slide the silky material of her nightdress up over her knees.

He started to kiss her mouth, long and hard and deeply, and Suzanna opened her lips to him as though she had been born knowing how he wanted her to kiss him back.

She heard him give a low, husky laugh, a cross between appraisal and stark hunger, as his hand began to tantalisingly stroke the sensitive skin of her inner thigh, and a moan of delight was dragged from her lips as he sent her desire soaring out of control, and she moved restlessly against him.

He gave another low laugh then moved her hand down over his chest to the waistband of those black silk pyjama trousers which did absolutely nothing to conceal his arousal, uttering something low and fervent against her ear as he did so.

Her Italian was sketchy, but she knew what he meant—his hands showed her what he meant and the urgent appeal in his voice made his meaning as clear as if he had spoken it in English. *Undress me.*

She had been born for this. She gave a whimper of pleasure as she slid her hand inside the waistband, knowing instinctively and without shyness exactly what he wanted her to do. Her slender hand captured the swollen silky shaft, her fingers moving delicately up and down, and she revelled in the small sound he made in the back of his throat.

Suddenly urgent, he peeled the nightdress off her body, and she suddenly realised where all this was leading. He was going to make love to her.

Right now.

His eyes were slitted as his hand slid under her head and he bent his own to dazzle her with a storm of kisses which had her almost sobbing with pleasure. She loved him—yes, she did. She would die for him.

'Oh, Pasquale,' she whispered ecstati-cally. '*Pasquale.*'

He stilled at her words. She realised that they were the first she had spoken, and it was as if they had been in the midst of some erotic spell which had been shattered into smithereens by that helpless little plea.

His eyes snapped wide open, and he stared down at her face with a look of growing horror.

She saw the struggle echoed in his features as his

mind obviously sought for supremacy over his body, and there was one moment when she thought that his mind had lost—when his furious gaze strayed to her swollen breasts, and she felt him move, was certain that he was going to just impale her, take her there and then, regardless.

But the moment passed.

He pushed himself away from her as though she were something unspeakably distasteful, and the look of undisguised disgust on his face shook her to the core.

He waited until he had roughly pulled his pyjama trousers back on with unsteady hands before he turned round, and his face was as cold as marble.

'You manipulative little…!' His words tailed off then he whispered, also in English—just to make sure that she understood every damning word he spoke—'You scheming little temptress—with your come-to-bed eyes and your bright hair and your per-fumed body! Do you know that men talk of women like you? Yes, and sometimes they even dream of them. You're every man's fantasy—ripe and willing and eager.

'But do you know something, Suzanna? It leaves a bitter taste in my mouth to have almost lain with someone who has such little regard for her body.' His mouth twisted. 'Dear *God*!' he said in disgust as he shook his dark head in disbelief. 'You're barely seventeen! When the hell did you start?'

She had to lie there and take it for what choice did she have? She could just imagine his scornful disbelief if she tried to tell him she was a virgin, particularly after the way she'd just behaved. What defence for her wayward behaviour could she possibly have? And to tell him that she believed herself to be in love with him would be to heap even more scorn down about her.

He paced the room and came back to stare down at her, and by now every last trace of passion had vanished. To judge by his expression, he had about as much regard for her as he would for a squashed insect.

'And this is the kind of woman I have allowed my sister to associate with!' he thundered. 'To bring into my home! No wonder her end-of-term report was of such an appallingly low standard. No wonder she is seemingly obsessed with discos and with boys.' His dark eyes looked almost black with condemnation as he studied her with icy distaste.

And Suzanna, who had opened her mouth to protest at being condemned out of hand as the bad influence on Francesca, shut it quickly, knowing that she could now say nothing. She certainly couldn't drop her friend in it by suggesting that Francesca was her own woman, and that Suzanna was the *last* person to influence her in wild ways.

And, loyalty apart, he wouldn't believe her. Why should he? She had behaved in a way which was already beginning to make her cringe, as she remembered just what she had been doing with him, and what she had been prepared to do with him...

'No defence?' he quizzed softly.

Suzanna bit her lip and turned her head away, but he moved forward with the lissomeness and stealth of some threatening jungle cat to capture her chin in his olive-skinned hand and turn it to face him, so that she was trapped in the blazing hostility of his stare. 'Listen to me, and listen to me carefully,' he said, in a voice as dangerously soft as it was possible to imagine, and Suzanna felt herself shivering as she registered that touch, that searing look. 'I want you packed and ready to leave this house by six tomorrow morning—'

'But I—'

'Shut *up*,' he told her callously. 'You will do as I say. I want you ready to leave by six. I will have a car take you to the airport, and you will be put on the first available flight to England, where I will arrange to have a car meet you and take you to your home. I'm assuming that your mother is at home?'

'Yes,' she said miserably. 'But what on earth am I going to tell her?'

For a moment he hesitated, but it was just a moment, before the contempt hardened his features once more. 'Leave that to me,' he said harshly. 'I will ring her and tell her that Francesca and I have to go away unexpectedly. Which is true,' he added grimly, 'since I intend spending some time alone with my sister to teach her just what is and what is not acceptable behaviour in a young woman.' And with a final withering look he strode towards the door, where he paused briefly.

'Oh, and there's one other thing,' he said softly.

She wondered just what else he could throw at her. 'Don't *ever* attempt to contact my sister again. You are to have nothing to do with the Caliandro family ever again. Is that understood?'

Suzanna lifted her chin in a show of pride she was far from feeling. 'Perfectly,' she said, in a voice that was so steady that she marvelled at it. But now that he was no longer in such close proximity normal reasoning began to assert itself, and she seized with delight on the fundamental flaw in his stern lecture to her about morals.

Her eyes sparked with their own danger. 'But surely you don't imagine that you can heap all the blame for what just happened at *my* feet, Pasquale,' she told him quietly, and she saw the sudden tension in his body. 'It does, as they say, take two,' she added coolly. 'And you were, after all, the one who instigated it.'

'Oh, was I?' he mocked.

She blushed, but she didn't flinch from the accusation in his stare. 'If the idea of making love to me so appalled you, then you could have stopped a lot sooner than you did.'

'When a man is aroused like that from sleep, he doesn't generally go in for analysis.' His face was like stone, his eyes scornful as he turned to twist the doorhandle. 'Let's just say that I mistook you for somebody else,' he added insultingly.

And as Suzanna looked at that dark, furious figure retreating from her bedroom she thought that she had never, ever hated anyone so much in her whole life.

CHAPTER THREE

THE mists of memory cleared and Suki found herself standing in the room staring at Pasquale, trying to remind herself that seven years had passed, and that this man had hurt her as badly as she could ever have imagined being hurt.

Though in a way she had Pasquale to thank for her startling transformation from chrysalis to butterfly. After the humiliation of her experience with him, she'd felt that nothing could ever possibly hurt her that much again. Her shyness had become a thing of the past. From gawky Suzanna, the new Suki had emerged, with a brand-new, slightly brittle exterior which would guarantee that she would never get hurt like that again.

Remember that, she thought as she stared at the man in front of her.

She had known him when he was twenty-four and he had been utterly devastating. Seven years on and that charm and charisma was even more potent, and Pasquale at thirty-one had acquired a lazy arrogance which she was quickly discovering she was not immune to...

Protectively, she pulled a silk wrap on over her bikini, and saw his mouth harden.

'I cannot believe that the years have made you so

shy,' he mocked, 'when once you flaunted your body so proudly for me to see!'

She decided to ignore that; getting into a fight with him would give him the opportunity to defeat her, and that was something she would never allow to happen. Not again. 'So what do you want to talk to me about, Pasquale?' she asked coolly as she picked up a hairbrush from the mantelpiece and began to drag it through her heavy silken waves of pale auburn hair.

His dark eyes penetrated her. 'How long have you known Salvatore Bruni?'

Suki's mouth opened in amazement as he said the name of the photographer who had brought her here. 'You know him too?'

He arrogantly ignored her question. 'I said—how long have you known him for?' he repeated ominously.

She lifted her chin defiantly, outraged at the heavy-handed tone he was using. 'I really don't think that's any of your business.'

'Let me be the judge of that!' His eyes narrowed. 'Tell me,' he said, very softly, 'are you congenitally programmed to only have affairs with men who belong to other women?'

Suki stared at him, genuine bewilderment in her eyes. 'I don't know what you're talking about.'

He stared at her in silence for a few moments, as if weighing up whether or not her perplexity was genuine.

'Salvatore Bruni, the man you are currently having

an affair with, just happens to be engaged to my secretary. I had a phone call from her late last night—she was sobbing her heart out because he had gone away for the weekend with one of the world's most beautiful women without bothering to tell her. A woman, moreover, whose reputation with men goes before her.' His eyes glittered ominously. 'Even if I did not have firsthand experience of it myself,' he concluded softly.

Suki's world spun. 'I don't happen to be *having* an affair with Salvatore, actually,' she told him frostily. 'He's taking photos of me for a book he's doing. We happen to be here *working*.'

He gave her a cold stare. 'Oh, really?' he drawled disbelievingly, and his eyes roved around the room, coming to rest pointedly on an old pair of faded jeans—and very obviously a man's pair of jeans—which were lying in a heap on the chair beside the bed.

Suki flushed in horror, realising how incriminating those wretched jeans looked. Beneath her exquisite exterior she was a born *hausfrau* and she happened to be very nifty with a needle. So when Salvatore had torn his jeans she had automatically offered to sew them for him. 'Oh, those,' she said, stung into defending herself, aware that Pasquale was eyeing her stained cheeks critically. 'Yes, they belong to Salvatore. I promised to mend them for him. They got ripped.'

'I can imagine.' He laughed cynically. 'In your eagerness to tear them from his body, no doubt?'

Suki swallowed down the lump of distaste in her throat. 'He ripped them on a rock while we were shooting at the beach this morning, if you *must* know!'

'And so you're going to sew them for him, are you?' he asked in a voice of deadly saccharin. 'How sweetly domestic.' And then his voice hardened into a threat. 'But, as I told you before, he's engaged to someone else. So just keep those beautiful little hands off him, will you, Suki?'

Oh, the sins of her past. Was her one youthful misdemeanour going to damn her for ever in his eyes? 'Are you suggesting that I'd go on holiday with a man if I knew that he was engaged to someone else?' she snapped.

He shrugged. 'Why not? We established a long time ago that you have very little in the way of morals. Nothing would surprise me about you in the sexual stakes, *bella mia*.'

Why had she permitted him to enter her room in the first place? she wondered wildly. She was no longer a naïve young girl staying in *his* house, subject to *his* whims and orders. 'I did not invite you here to insult me,' she said with fierce determination. 'So if that's all you intend to do you can get out. Right now.'

But he didn't move an inch; there wasn't even a flicker of expression on that hard, implacable face in response. 'I am staying here until I have your word that you will leave Salvatore alone.'

Little did he know that she wouldn't touch

Salvatore or any other man—engaged or not—with a bargepole! Men were far more trouble than they were worth! And she might have told him if he'd been anyone other than the man who had trampled all over her tender, youthful emotions. One sight of that coolly confident face telling her to lay off was enough to set her blood boiling.

'I see that you still like to play the puppet-master, Pasquale,' she scorned. 'First you try to run your sister's friendships for her, and now you're meddling in your secretary's love-life. Tell me, do you get some kind of kick out of trying to control people?'

'Sometimes a little intervention is essential,' he stated arrogantly, untouched by her criticism.

'You think so?' She gave him an acid smile. 'Your secretary—what's her name?' she enquired.

He frowned, the dark eyes narrowing dangerously. 'Cristina. Why?'

Suki stared at him. 'Poor Cristina,' she said, shaking her head from side to side.

He continued to frown. 'Poor Cristina?' he repeated.

'Mmm. I mean, it's *terribly* protective of you, but do you really think it's a good thing that she's engaged to a man she patently doesn't trust? A man who takes another woman away to the South of France?'

A muscle ticked ominously in the dark, olive cheek. 'If it was any woman other than you, Suki, then yes, I would certainly be concerned for her future happiness.'

A red flame of fury swam before her eyes. 'And what's that supposed to mean?'

He laughed—a chilly replica of sardonic humour which had the tiny hairs on the back of her head standing up like soldiers. 'Simply that while I do not condone Salvatore's behaviour I find it understandable to some degree. After all, I have been victim to your charms myself.' His voice dropped to a silky caress. 'You see, you are a born Circe. You tempt beyond reason. That beautiful body of yours is born for love, those cat's eyes promise pleasures too manifold to believe. What man could resist such promise? I myself almost succumbed.

'Salvatore is a red-blooded man and Cristina a respectable young woman, both members of the Italian community in New York. Proprieties have naturally been observed. It is not our custom for sex to take place before marriage, and a woman who indulges in such behaviour is not to be respected. Do you get my drift, *cara*?'

Yes, she got his meaning all right, and, though it shouldn't have done—oh, how it hurt! 'Loud and clear,' she murmured, somehow masking her feelings from him. 'You're saying that it's OK for a man to play around before marriage—as long as it's with someone else? And that for the woman there is nothing but the long wait until the matrimonial night?'

'I was right!' he stormed, and in his rage he sounded so very Italian, the American twang in his accent, picked up during his Ivy League college days, light years away. 'Still the alley-cat! What woman would admit to such thoughts?'

'Any woman who's sick of the double standard, I should imagine!' she shouted, aware that she was in danger of ascribing false standards to herself, but she didn't care what he thought of her—she simply *didn't care*! 'How dare you say that a woman must remain as pure as the driven snow, whilst giving a man carte blanche to do exactly as he pleases? That's like saying that men have uncontrollable urges, whilst women can sublimate theirs!'

He was suddenly alert. 'And you don't think that's true, *cara*?' he murmured.

She knew what she *thought*—she just didn't have any experience to back up her words; but Pasquale didn't know that. More importantly, he wouldn't believe it in a hundred years—so what did she have to lose? She raised her chin up and stared at him defiantly, not caring now what she said, only determined that she should rile him. 'No, I don't! I believe in equality! You can't have one rule for men and another one for women. Either they both live by the same rules or you abandon those rules altogether!'

The dark eyes were hooded as they surveyed her. 'And you?' he said softly. 'You have had many lovers, Suki?'

She saw the flash in his eyes, and instinctively, incredulously, she knew what had provoked it. Pasquale was *jealous*! *Jealous!* He had wanted her all those years ago, yes, but he had not made love to her because he had not respected her. Was he now regretting that decision? And suddenly Suki knew a way to hit back. 'And what if I have?' she asked softly, deliberately letting a small, secret smile hover around the edges of her lips.

He stilled as though he'd been struck, the brief flare of fury in his dark eyes making him seem like some modern-day incarnation of the devil. Then he nodded. 'I was a fool,' he ground out, 'not to have had you when you were mine for the taking! Not to have taken you over and over again, so that you would never forget me. To imprint myself on your body and on your mind—so that whenever you lay with another man it would be *me* you thought of, *me* you tasted, *me* you longed to have in your arms, *me* filling your body, making you sob with pleasure.'

The savage sexual boast had precisely the wrong effect on her. It started that awful aching; it unleashed that nebulous emotion which only he had ever inspired, the one she had once mistakenly thought was love, but now, with hindsight, realised had been nothing more than an overpoweringly primitive need to be possessed by him which at the time she had not been able to control.

And now?

Was it possible that she was still prey to the same appalling needs, an identical hunger which he could somehow provoke with just one hot, dark look?

Her lids fluttered to shade the confused and feverish glittering in her amber eyes. 'Please go,' she told him from between parched lips, afraid even to look at him, for fear that he should be able to read her longing and her confusion with the uncanny perception he had once had in such abundance where she was concerned.

'Go?' he echoed softly, and Suki jumped, startled, to find that he had moved soundlessly across the carpet and was now beside her, was staring down at her, so close that she could feel his breath fanning her cheek.

'Yes, go,' she whispered, wondering what dark magic he could weave just by being there.

She could hear the smile in his voice as he spoke. 'But you don't want me to go, do you, *cara*?'

'Yes.' But she lied. She wanted only one thing and that was to taste his lips on hers again, and she closed her eyes and unconsciously swayed towards him.

No!

Her eyes snapped open in horror at what she had almost let happen, but she was frozen by the astounded look of disbelief she saw on Pasquale's face—as though he too was gripped in the power of something far stronger than reason.

He pulled her unprotesting into his arms then and stared down at her face. 'Exquisite,' he murmured softly as his gaze slowly and deliberately raked over her dazed face to where her eyes glittered like amber jewels. 'Utterly exquisite. And just begging to be kissed.'

'No,' she whimpered even as she looked with longing at the lips poised just inches away.

'Oh, yes, Suki,' he contradicted. *'Yes.'*

But the kiss was not the brutal and punishing on-

slaught she was expecting. It was tender and evocative—and it hinted at something she had been searching for all her life. She heard him make some small,
indistinct sound as her lips opened beneath his, and
as if from a long way off came the sound of her own
voice, echoing his sigh as his tongue moved inside
her mouth to deepen the kiss.

Suki was lost, his sweet, sweet kiss sucking her
into the irresistible vortex of desire. She felt it flooding her veins with wild power, to centralise into a
flickering flame which slowly began to unfurl in the
pit of her stomach. She tried to stop him, just once,
but it was a pathetic little effort, and the two hands
which had started to push ineffectually at his shoulders somehow instead became entwined at the back
of his strong neck, her fingers fluttering helplessly
into the luxuriant black hair which grew there.

His hands moved to her hips, and he ran them
deliberately down over the slender curves before
sliding them beneath her buttocks and lifting her
quite effortlessly to carry her over to the bed and
tumble them both down on top of it.

And even after that bold declaration of intent she
did nothing to stop him. Her breathing was erratic,
her thought processes gone haywire as she stared at
him with hungry, confused eyes. 'Pasquale...' she
managed. 'Don't do this. Please.'

There was no softening of the implacable line of
his mouth as he traced a finger from neck to breast
and she shivered in helpless response. 'But you want

me, *cara*. Quite as much as I want you. Don't you? *Don't you?*'

Wordlessly, she shook her head.

'Yes. You do. So why stop when we both know how very good it will be?'

He moved his arm up the pillow to smooth her hair back from her face, but Suki could have sworn that his gaze flickered to the wristwatch which gleamed gold against his olive skin. That odd movement jarred, and was enough to make her begin to pull free from the tempting circle of his arms, when suddenly there was a light rap on the door.

'Hi, Suki,' called a cheerful voice. 'Are you decent? I got your message!' And the door opened to reveal Salvatore standing there, his face rigid with shock as he took in the sight of Suki lying tangled in Pasquale's arms on the bed.

'Dear God!' he exclaimed, and his face went white. 'Pasquale!'

Pasquale gave a lazy smile. 'Yes?'

Salvatore swallowed. 'What the hell are you doing here?'

'I'm making love to a woman—what does it look like? And you happen to be disturbing us.'

'But I—'

Pasquale's eyes were like steel traps. 'Get out, Salvatore—before I'm tempted to punch you. In this instance, I'm happy to take your place to keep the lady happy—but I'm warning you that if you ever think of straying again, then wherever you are I'll come and find you and tear every limb from your body. Is that understood?'

Salvatore swallowed with fear, and Suki couldn't blame him. She struggled free, an acrid taste in her mouth, feeling as though she was in the middle of some bizarre dream as she stumbled off the bed. 'What the hell is going on?' she demanded.

'Salvatore is just leaving,' came the grim voice. 'Aren't you?'

Salvatore nodded, swallowing convulsively, before backing towards the door.

Fragments of conversation came fluttering back to Suki as she moved as far away from the bed as possible, while he continued to lie there, a mocking look of amusement on his face as he watched her.

'Message?' she said aloud, frowning as she spoke. 'Salvatore said that he'd received a message—but I sent him no message.'

He gave a low laugh. 'No, indeed, but he spoke the truth—I left a message with one of the waitresses that he should come to your room in half an hour. That was the amount of time I estimated it would take for me to have you in my arms.' He glanced briefly at his watch with a sardonic smile. 'But it seems that my estimation was conservative, since I managed to accomplish it in just twenty minutes.' He sighed. 'Always so responsive, *bella mia*.'

The knowledge that he was right did little to soothe Suki's temper, and a red mist of fury swam before her eyes. She lifted the heavy silver-backed hairbrush from the dressing table and hurled it at him without thinking of the consequences, but he caught it in mid-air with the confidence of a county-class cricket player.

'Naughty!' he murmured, and casually got up from the bed as though she hadn't been scrabbling around like a madwoman for further missiles to launch at him.

A shoe, a coat-hanger, a full handbag... Humiliatingly he caught them all and tossed them onto the bed, still with that contemptuous half-smile on his mouth.

Out of breath now, hurt and bewildered, Suki stared at him. 'Why?' she asked him. 'Just tell me why.'

'Why what?' he queried softly.

'Why you tricked him into coming here, and let him see us...us...'

'On the verge of making love?' he prompted helpfully.

Colour rushed in to stain her cheeks. 'No, we weren't,' she mumbled.

'Liar!' he taunted softly.

Did he have a better nature for her to appeal to? She turned to him. 'Why couldn't you have just settled for telling me to lay off? That he was engaged to Cristina? Surely you know that I would never have anything to do with a man who was engaged to someone else?'

He shrugged. 'That's just the problem; I know very little about you, Suki—other than the fact that you have an extraordinary physical appeal, which actually has me in its thrall too.' A note of puzzlement came into his voice and his eyes hardened into slivers of jet. 'Which is extraordinary in itself, since I am not usually attracted to women I dislike.

'And, since you ask, the reason I did not simply ask either you or Salvatore to "lay off", as you so inelegantly expressed it, and leave it at that is because I am a man who leaves nothing to chance. I could not guarantee that you would heed my request, and, yes, I could have threatened Salvatore into leaving you alone, but I preferred him to witness with his own eyes just what kind of woman he had chosen to have his affair with: the kind of woman who would deceive him with another man at the first opportunity which arose. Why should I expect him to take *my* word for it, when firsthand experience would doubtless be so much more effective?

'Take my word for it, *cara*—Salvatore shall not stray again. And the very qualities which make you such ideal mistress material will reinforce Cristina's suitability as a wife.'

For a moment, Suki was stunned into speechlessness as she stared back into those cold, mocking eyes. But not for long. 'My God,' she breathed in disbelief. 'You cold-hearted, manipulative *bastard*! Get out! Get out of here before I scream the house down.'

He nodded, looking as though this time he was about to accede to her demand. 'Certainly. Doubtless you wish to change.' His eyes briefly flicked over her body, and Suki remembered that she was wearing nothing but her bikini covered by a wholly inadequate silk wrap. 'But before I do I have a proposition to put to you which you may find interesting.'

Suki's mouth tightened. '*Nothing* you could say would ever be remotely interesting to me!'

'Don't be melodramatic, Suki. Never turn an offer down before you've even heard it. I'm giving you the opportunity of a lifetime—'

'The promise that I'll never have the misfortune to set eyes on your conniving face again?' she hazarded acidly.

'On the contrary,' he said, in a voice as smooth as honey. 'I want you to become my mistress.'

There was a stunned silence as Suki stared across the room at Pasquale with growing horror. 'I don't believe you just said that,' she said eventually, her voice rising with incredulity. 'You must be completely mad!'

His dark eyes glittered as he acknowledged her remark. 'Perhaps just a little,' he murmured. 'But that is the effect you seem to have on me.'

'Either that or you've got a very warped sense of humour.'

'No. I never, ever joke about business,' he said as coolly as if he had this kind of bizarre conversation every day.

'*Business?* You define your ludicrous and insulting proposition as *business*?'

'But of course. That is what being a mistress is about, is it not? An exchange of commodities. You would have all the many advantages of being my lover. As well as the obvious pleasure, there would be all the baubles and the luxury trips, and in return I would possess that exquisitely beautiful body.'

He frowned at her expression. 'Oh, come, come, Suki; please don't insult me by fixing me with that shocked look, as though you've just left the convent. You must have been propositioned many times before. Very recently, too. Or are you telling me that you would have gone off for a weekend with Salvatore if the destination had been a grimy, industrial town somewhere instead of a luxury villa in the Mediterranean? Admit it, why don't you—that like most women you are dazzled by the accoutrements of wealth?'

What a cynic! she thought in disbelief. Suki's voice was very soft as she looked at him with real loathing, her amber eyes sparking as if they were lit from behind with fire, and said, 'I don't intend to justify my behaviour to you—quite frankly, your mind is so warped I doubt that whatever I said would make any difference.

'But I will tell you one thing, Pasquale—that if you were the last man on earth I still wouldn't consent to be your mistress—and that's no idle promise! You see, for one thing I earn enough money to buy my *own* baubles, and finance my *own* trips. I'm an independent woman and I never have and I never *will* be bought off by some man!'

She glowered at him, quite out of breath after her passionate response. 'But even more importantly,' she continued, once she'd got her breath back, 'mistresses, like all women, require more than baubles and luxury trips—even the most hard-hearted of them require some modicum of affection and respect. But those don't seem to be words which figure in your vocabulary—perhaps they never did. You seem to be incapable of either. Anyway—' she glared at him '—I don't wish to discuss it any further. So go.'

'And I gather I am to take that as a refusal?' he mocked, then gave ΅ sexy, sardonic smile. 'Such fighting words, Suki, and I respond to nothing better than a challenge!'

If only his voice didn't sound so rich and velvety and downright irresistible, Suki thought resentfully. 'Take it as a permanent refusal, Pasquale—I would so *hate* you to get your hopes up,' she finished with a sarcasm which he seemed to find amusing. 'Now are you going?'

'Yes, I'm going.' He spoke with quiet emphasis as his hand curved over the shiny brass of the door-handle. 'But we shall see,' he threatened, on a silky note. 'We shall see just how ''permanent'' a refusal it is. I am a determined man. Believe me when I tell you, Suki, that I want you more than I've ever wanted *any* woman, and, what is more, I intend to have you. Seven years ago we started something that I want to see finished,' he concluded on a husky note, and the door closed softly behind him before a shocked Suki could even begin to formulate an answer.

Ten minutes after he had left her room there was another tap on the door, which a dazed Suki scarcely heard. She was sitting on the edge of the bed, deciding that Pasquale's bizarre invitation to become his mistress, and his talk of responding to a challenge, had merely been made in a mad moment of sexual frustration. And that there was absolutely no reason why she ever need see him again.

The tapping resumed.

'Go away!' she yelled automatically.

'Suki! I must talk to you! Please! It's important!'

It was Salvatore's voice, and Suki stormed over to the door and flung it open.

'Why the hell didn't you tell me you were engaged to Pasquale Caliandro's secretary?' she demanded. 'In fact, why the hell didn't you tell me you were engaged—full stop?'

'But it was all perfectly legit—a working weekend,' said Salvatore plaintively. 'We weren't *doing* anything to be ashamed of!'

'Too right we weren't, but that isn't how it must look to Pasquale, the interfering tyrant.'

Salvatore looked anxiously up and down the corridor, as if he was expecting the man himself to suddenly materialise. 'Someone might hear you—can't I come in?'

'No, you can't come in! Are you out of your mind? If you value your health I'd recommend staying away from me, and any other woman as well—apart from Cristina. Pasquale isn't the kind of man to give you more than one chance. So if you really *do* want to marry Cristina I'd strongly recommend that you adopt the masculine equivalent of purdah!'

He held the palms of his hands up in appeal. 'Suki, please let me come inside and I can explain every-thing—but what I *don't* want is for Pasquale to see me here.'

'Why not?'

'Because he terrifies the life out of me,' Salvatore admitted ruefully.

'Then you probably have more sense than I gave you credit for,' said Suki grimly, and opened the door wider. 'OK, you can come in. And I'm giving you five minutes to explain. *Everything!*'

Salvatore sighed. 'It's difficult.'

Suki looked at him questioningly. 'Just what did you tell your fiancée about this trip? Why was she crying down the phone to Pasquale?'

He licked his lips nervously. 'Er—that's just it— I didn't. Tell her anything, that is. Or rather I told her that I was doing a shoot. I just didn't tell her that it was with you.'

'And why not?'

He shrugged apologetically. 'She gets—er—you know—very jealous.'

Suki's eyes narrowed disbelievingly. 'Oh, come on, Salvatore! You're surely not expecting me to be-lieve *that*? As a photographer, you work with models all the time! If she was jealous then the relationship wouldn't last a minute.'

'It isn't other models,' he told her, with an em-barrassed look. 'Just you.'

Suki's eyes glittered dangerously. 'I think you'd better explain what you mean, don't you?'

He shrugged again helplessly. Suddenly, for all his photographic genius, he looked terribly, terribly young. 'Just that she knows that I've always been desperate to take your photo. And when I first met her I had a bit of a thing about you. I even—er—had a poster of you on my bedroom wall.' He blushed.

Suki closed her eyes briefly and then gave a slightly hysterical laugh. 'If only you knew how old that makes me feel,' she said wearily. 'Didn't it occur to you that she'd find out some time and that she would react in precisely this way?'

He shook his head. 'I didn't really think at all,' he admitted. 'I was so keen to photograph you, and I couldn't believe it when you said yes. I'm sorry, Suki.'

Suki sighed. How had she managed to do it again? Now there was a fiancée on the war-path, for absolutely no reason. Was she just too trusting? Or simply a fool? 'You'd better go back to New York and make your peace with her,' she told him. 'No doubt your friends can vouch that we've been given separate rooms, but for goodness' sake you'd better leave now.'

'And what will you do?' he asked her anxiously.

'Me? I'm on the first plane out of here,' said Suki grimly. And with a bit of luck I can put this whole ghastly incident out of my mind, she added silently.

And when the door had closed behind Salvatore Suki strode over to the wardrobe and, without bothering to fold anything, swept all her clothes out and began piling them into her suitcase.

CHAPTER FOUR

SUKI unlocked the front door of her London flat and slammed it shut behind her, dropping her suitcase in the hall and hurrying along the corridor to turn the central heating on.

Brr! Her fingers fumbled with the dial.

How great to be home, she thought appreciatively as she kicked off her shoes and padded through into the sitting room whose bright crimson walls were almost completely covered with her own paintings.

She had flown into Heathrow from Nice to be greeted with absolutely *foul* weather—just the kind of thing you expected in England in the middle of summer! It was grey, windy and rainy.

And it matched her mood exactly!

She had upgraded her air ticket to first-class for the flight home, and consequently had had enough leg room to sleep for the short flight home, but, typically, had been unable to catch even a wink. And now she was exhausted. Absolutely exhausted. Which wasn't that surprising when she thought about it. Apart from the emotional stress of seeing Pasquale again, she was suffering from the effects of jet lag.

Still, at least she had managed to sneak away from the villa without bumping into Pasquale. She must be grateful for small mercies.

The red light on her Ansaphone was flashing. Just two messages—but then she *did* guard her telephone number as though it were Fort Knox!

Suki punched the button. The first call was from her brother. His voice sounded strained, but then these days it always seemed to sound strained.

'Hello, Suki; I need to talk to you urgently. Can you ring me at the office—*not* at home? I don't want Kirstie worrying.'

Suki sighed. It couldn't be *another* request for money to bail him out, surely? She'd only just injected some funds into the ailing family business. At least when their mother had been alive she had managed to exercise a little restraint over Piers's expensive tastes. But lately the requests for money had been getting more and more frequent. Piers had taken several foolish risks on the stock market which hadn't come off, and although his wife, Kirstie, was a dear, Suki privately thought that she let Piers get away with murder.

If *I* were married to him, I wouldn't let him fritter it all away, she thought grimly. But their son, Toby, was almost two years old, and Suki doted on her adorable little nephew. And it was concern for *his* welfare more than anything else which made it impossible for her to refuse any of Piers's requests for funds.

She immediately picked up the receiver and dialled Piers's office, to be told that he wasn't back from lunch yet.

Suki glanced at her watch. At *four o'clock*? 'Will

you please tell him that his sister called?' she said to his secretary. 'And I'll be at home.' No wonder the business was doing badly if its managing director spent the whole afternoon closeted in a restaurant, she thought crossly as she replaced the receiver.

The second message was from Carly, her agent, and the confident American accent rang out.

'Hi, honey. I know you're in France, but ring me just as *soon* as you get back. Something's come up and, believe me, it's a once-in-a-lifetime! So *ring* me!'

Suki was contemplating doing just that when the phone rang.

It was Carly again.

'You're back! Thank heavens!' she exclaimed.

'I just got in.'

'Good time?'

Pasquale's face loomed darkly in her mind, despite all her vows not to give him another thought. 'In a word—no.'

'What happened?'

Pasquale Caliandro, that's what happened, she thought grimly. 'Salvatore Bruni, the photographer,' said Suki grimly, 'neglected to tell me that he has a pathologically jealous fiancée, who sent a knight in shining armour—' now *why* had she automatically given Pasquale such a romantic association? '—to warn me off,' she finished lamely.

'Oh, dear!' laughed Carly. 'Never mind—I have just the thing to cheer you up.'

'What? A one-way ticket to the moon?'

Carly laughed again. 'Come on, Suki—it's not like you to be negative; after all, this isn't the first time this kind of thing has happened.'

'Exactly. I'm thinking of having my head shaved and going into a monastery—'

'Nunnery.'

'Whatever,' quipped Suki, thinking that a male-free zone seemed like a more attractive prospect by the minute.

'Well, before you do you'd better hear what it is I've got to say. Can I come round?'

'When?'

'Now! It's rather important.'

Half an hour later Carly was in Suki's sitting room, dunking a rosehip and wild cherry teabag into a mug of boiling water.

'Yuk!' shuddered Suki as she sipped her hot chocolate. 'I don't know how you can touch that stuff!'

'It helps me stay thin.' Carly eyed Suki's mug reprovingly. 'Did I ever tell you that your metabolism is grossly unfair?'

'Constantly.' Suki smiled. 'Now what did you want to see me about?'

Carly beamed. 'How would earning five million bucks in the next five years grab you?'

Suki pulled a face. 'Yes, I know—and the moon is made out of green cheese! Come on, Carly, I'm too tired for jokes.'

Carly shook her head, her shrewd blue eyes sparking with excitement. 'It's your lucky day, honey—I know that much.' She took a deep breath. 'Formidable. Heard of them?'

'Of course I've heard of them. They're one of the biggest make-up and perfumery companies in the world, aren't they?'

'Second biggest—but they're aiming for the top. And they're offering you a contract over the next five years. They want you to become the new Formidable girl. The offer only came in over the weekend; I still can't believe it!'

Suki just stared at her agent as her mind tried to take in this astonishing news. 'Work for Formidable?' she asked slowly.

'You've got it in one, honey!'

'On an exclusive contract?'

Carly shrugged. 'Sure. That's the way these things go—the company won't want you advertising for anyone else. When the public see your face, they think Formidable. But the money's *fantastic*—and I've had my lawyer take a look at the contract.' She paused. 'He was impressed. *Very* impressed.'

Which really *was* saying something. Carly's lawyer should have had 'CYNIC' emblazoned across his forehead!

Suki shook her head in bemusement. Exclusive contracts were few and far between. 'But why me?' she wanted to know.

Carly sipped at her tea. 'They've just been taken over by some hot-shot who apparently saw you in last year's suncream commercial. So either he likes redheads or he's a sucker for tall women!'

It took Suki about five seconds to think it over. She thought of the lecherous photographer in New York. She thought of Piers and the constant drain he was on her resources. She thought about getting older, of having to compete on the catwalk with models of sixteen. Of desperately searching in the mirror for the lines on her face which would signify the beginning of the end.

She drained the last of her hot chocolate and put the cup down. 'When do I sign?' she asked.

Carly gave a satisfied smile. 'How about Monday?'

'If you could just sign both copies of the contract, Miss Franklin. That is, if you're satisfied with the contents, of course.'

Suki took the pen from the Formidable lawyer, who had spent the last half-hour gazing at her like a moonstruck schoolboy. They were sitting round the glossy round table in the vast boardroom of Formidable's impressive London headquarters. 'On the dotted line, I presume?' she queried, hoping that she sounded efficient, and not like someone to whom legal jargon was about as understandable as hieroglyphics!

'The very same!' he said admiringly.

Suki couldn't help feeling a little fizz of excitement as she signed her name with a flourish.

'I do hope you realise that you've just signed your life away!' said the Formidable lawyer jovially.

'Rubbish!' laughed Suki as she put the top back

on her fountain pen. 'My lawyer has been through it with a fine-tooth comb.'

'I've never known a deal go through so *quickly*,' said Carly admiringly, an irrepressible smile hovering around her lips. Probably thinking of her ten per cent, thought Suki wryly.

The lawyer ran his hand back through his elegant silver hair. 'That's our new owner for you,' he murmured, directing his attention entirely towards Suki. 'A man not noted for letting the grass grow beneath his feet.'

'Anyone I know?' asked Carly immediately, her antennae out, her curiosity roused.

The lawyer gave a discreet shake of his head. 'I'm not at liberty to discuss that. He's a man who prefers to make his own introductions.' He glanced down at his watch. 'But he'll be here at any minute to do just that. Ah!' And he stood up as the door of the boardroom opened.

The frightening thing was that Suki *knew*. Whether or not it was just some sixth sense she had in connection with the man, she couldn't have said, but Suki actually knew in the few moments before she turned round and stared into those dark, mocking eyes just who it was who was now the new owner of Formidable.

Outraged, she sprang to her feet as she stared across the room in horror at Pasquale's infuriatingly handsome face. '*You!*' she accused. 'You cheating, underhand, manipulative—!'

'Suki!' mouthed Carly in horror.

'Miss Franklin, *please*,' begged the silver-haired lawyer, who couldn't have looked more shocked at her outburst if he'd just seen an apparition.

Suki ignored both of them. 'You think that you can go through life getting your own way all the time, don't you? Well, you're wrong! *Wrong!* Completely and utterly wrong! Just because I didn't fall down at your feet and agree to become your... your...*mistress*, you actually have the blatant nerve to think that you can *buy* me! Well, you can't, Pasquale—and what's more I'll prove it to you!'

And, so saying, Suki picked up the contract nearest to her and deliberately ripped it into tiny shreds which fluttered down like snowflakes onto the thick cream carpet.

Like two people hypnotised, Carly and the lawyer just sat in stunned silence and watched, while, to Suki's outrage, Pasquale's reaction was the last in the world she would have anticipated. She had expected him to be absolutely furious that she had announced his nefarious designs to all and sundry, but to her astonishment he was laughing. Actually *laughing*! With the corners of that too delectable mouth quirking upwards in a smile which was quite devastating in its impact.

'Bravo, *bella*!' he applauded softly. 'Bravo! Truly an inspiring performance!'

The silver-haired lawyer had hastily grabbed the remaining contract and was holding it protectively against his chest like a shield. 'Miss Franklin!' he admonished sternly. 'I have to tell you that you are in breach of contract. And that I am afraid you give me no option other than to—'

'Leave us,' Pasquale interjected smoothly.

The lawyer fixed him with an astonished stare. 'But Signor Caliandro...' he began.

But Pasquale was shaking his head. 'I said leave us,' he said emphatically.

Suki was still so angry that she was literally shaking. 'Good!' she stormed wildly. 'I'm glad if I've broken the contract! It's no longer worth the paper it's written on!'

Carly shuddered as she stared in horror at the scraps of contract which littered the thick carpet. 'Suki, honey,' she hissed, 'I don't know what all this is about, but please, *please*—just don't say any more. I beg you.'

Pasquale indicated the door with an impatient shake of his head. 'If you would leave us now.'

Carly and the lawyer reluctantly trooped out of the boardroom like children ordered outside into the garden to play and Suki sent a hot, angry glare at Pasquale.

'So how's the great controller?' she asked sarcastically. 'Have you managed to sort out your secretary's love-life?'

'I have advised Salvatore to bring the wedding forward,' he said blandly as he held out the nearest chair for her. 'Please sit down.'

He had done this, and he had the *nerve* to ask her to sit down? 'I won't be here long enough to sit

down.' Just long enough to give the arrogant manip-
ulator a piece of her mind!

'As you wish.' He sat down on the edge of the
Camelot-sized table, spreading his long legs out in
front of him and regarding her with interest from
beneath the dark, hooded eyes as if waiting to see
what she would do next, and Suki met his cool gaze
with a steady stare, her mind and her eyes working
separately as one tried to deny what the other reluctantly admitted.

That he looked an absolute knockout.

He was dressed for work. The suit he wore was
everything she liked on a man but so rarely saw. No
man had the right to look that good in a suit. In
beautifully cut grey linen, it merely hinted at the
muscular strength which lay beneath, and yet in a
peculiar way that emphasised his fabulous physique
far more than if he'd been wearing something clinging. He wore with it a wonderful pale blue silk shirt
and a dark blue silk tie knotted at his throat. The
outfit was wildly expensive, yet beautifully understated. Pasquale had, she acknowledged, a style all
his own.

She could see that he was subjecting her to his
own cool appraisal and she was glad that the circumstances which had led to her being here meant that
she'd dressed in her most businesslike outfit. Not that
she *felt* in the least bit businesslike at the moment—
especially not with those dark eyes glittering at her—
but she certainly looked the part.

Her slub-silk suit, with its short skirt and boxy

jacket, was in a vivid shade of purple, contrasting flatteringly with the pale auburn of her hair which today she wore knotted back into a sophisticated chignon. Beneath the suit she wore a cream body. Her long legs were encased in pale stockings and her purple, high-heeled suede shoes matched the suit exactly. In these shoes she towered over most men, but not, infuriatingly, over *this* man.

This man towered over *her*.

He gave a slow smile. 'Yes,' he said finally. 'I like the way you look. I like it very much…' His voice tailed off on a suggestive murmur, and Suki was shocked to feel her body respond to that murmur in spite of her anger, her nipples hardening beneath the silky rub of the body. What had he done to her all those years ago? Imprinted and dominated and stamped himself on her psyche to such a degree that he, and only he, could make her melt beneath that dark gaze?

'I'm not looking for your approval,' she told him, shaken by her physical response to him. 'And I can tell you now that I won't work for you.'

'But you wouldn't be working for me, not directly.' He gave her a cool look and his voice sounded almost reasonable.

Snake!

'After all, it isn't as though I'm asking you to sit in the typing pool, now is it?' he added smoothly.

Suki almost spluttered with indignation. 'Directly or indirectly, the answer's the same. I won't do it! And you can't make me!'

'Oh, can't I?' he queried silkily, surveying her from beneath the hooded flare of his eyes until she could bear it no longer.

'Why me?' she demanded. 'Are there no lengths you won't go to to get your own way? I simply can't believe that you would actually hire me—at vast expense—to be your in-house model, just to…to…'

'To?' he interrogated coolly, but there was a spark of amusement in the dark eyes.

'To make me your mistress!' she declared.

He gave a faint smile. 'You do me a dishonour, *cara*,' he murmured. 'I am first and foremost a businessman.'

Business. There was that wretched word again. The one he'd used about mistresses, too. 'Oh, really?' she mocked.

'Yes. *Really*.' He looked at the stubborn set of her jaw. 'What would you say if I told you that you had been selected to be the Formidable woman because you have the looks, the charisma and the image we're looking for to portray our products perfectly?'

'I'd say you were lying out of the back of your teeth! There are *thousands* of models you could have chosen.'

'But unfortunately, *bella mia*, none that look quite like you,' he said, very softly, his eyes narrowing as they appraised her, and she had to steel herself not to tremble at the seductive undertones in his voice and that frankly gorgeous stare. Suki drew in a deep breath preparatory to flouncing out, but he stayed her with his next words.

'My lawyer is perfectly correct, you know,' he observed quietly. 'If I choose to sue you, you don't have a leg to stand on. Metaphorically speaking, I could take you to the cleaners, Suki.'

'And I don't care!' she answered defiantly. 'Sue me! Take every penny I've got! Poverty would be an attractive alternative to working for you!'

To her fury, he laughed again, showing teeth which looked brilliantly white against the olive of his skin. 'I see that over the years you have developed a magnificent fighting spirit. And a proud, stubborn streak. That is good—I like a woman with backbone.'

'What did you expect? That I'd be the same young and naïve, docile little girl who—?' She broke off, her cheeks flushing scarlet as she realised what she had been about to say.

'Begged me to make love to her?' he interjected in a silky voice. 'For one so young and so naïve— as you claim—you certainly knew how to give voice to your desires.'

She stared at him, her cheeks hot, her heart racing. 'Will you never let me forget that?' she whispered.

He shook his head. 'How can I, *cara*, when I cannot forget it myself?' he declared simply.

Something in his voice sounded softer than mere desire, and Suki found herself reacting to it as a starving dog would leap on a scrap of meat. She became aware that her nipples were peaking painfully, hidden by the looseness of her jacket. It was as if her body was no longer hers, no longer governed by the self-control she was determined to fix on it. And Pasquale was responsible for this frightening loss of control.

He was dangerous. He always had been dangerous. At seventeen she had found him irresistible. Seven years on it was disturbing to discover that his appeal had only become magnified. She could not fight him, not effectively—which left her with only one alternative.

To run.

She swallowed the lump in her throat. 'I think I've made myself clear,' she told him. 'So there's really nothing more to say.'

'Suki,' he told her softly, 'I don't think you quite realise your position.'

She looked him straight in the eye, the stubborn pride he'd spoken of blazing from her face. 'Oh, I think I do, Pasquale. I'm no fool. Sue me, and I'll take the consequences. I mean it.'

'So I see.' He frowned, then spoke his next words almost reluctantly. 'Do you realise that your brother is on the verge of bankruptcy?'

Something in the tone of his voice sent a frisson of fear skating down her spine. Piers? 'Of course he isn't,' she said calmly, though her heart was hammering in her chest like a piston.

'I'm afraid he is.'

There was a confidence about the way he spoke, a certainty, which chilled her. 'How on earth can you know about Piers's financial situation?' she said.

'You haven't gone and bought *his* company, have you?' she finished sarcastically.

He acknowledged the jibe with a nod of his dark head. 'I don't take on losing ventures.'

'Everyone has been hit by the recession,' said Suki defensively. 'But the end is in sight; everyone says so.'

'And that,' he answered sardonically, 'is certainly true in your brother's case.'

Suki somehow knew that he wasn't lying to her, and yet still she sought to deny it. She shook her head and a strand of auburn hair came loose. 'He can't be. He can't. I gave—' She clamped her mouth tightly shut, aware of what she had been about to say.

'Yes, *cara*?'

'Nothing.'

'You gave him—money?'

Suki held onto her purple clutch-bag as though it were a lifeline. 'That's between my brother and me—'

'*No!*' And he stood up from the table, his face dark and suddenly furious. 'It isn't just between you and your brother. There are other people involved, Suki. There are the shareholders, for one thing—people who have a right to know that their investment is safe, not being squandered away by some spoilt boy who cannot or will not accept that his endeavours simply won't support the kind of lifestyle he has become used to!'

His quick glance took in her white face, but he

carried on regardless. 'He also has a wife and a very young child, does he not? What right does your brother have to jeopardise their very livelihood?'

Suki sat down suddenly, her legs buckling beneath her, and Pasquale immediately reached over to the centre of the table and poured her a glass of mineral water.

'Here,' he said abruptly.

She took the glass and drank from it, her long eyelashes fluttering to shield her eyes as she shakily replaced the glass on the table. When she raised her eyes to him again her voice sounded miraculously calm. 'What do you want?'

He nodded, satisfied now that he had her capitulation. 'I want you to stop dishing out money to your brother, for a start. Though that in itself is now becoming academic, since your funds wouldn't even make a small dent in the kind of debts he is in the process of building up. But even if you carry on supporting him in the smallest way, then you're simply helping him to deny that there's a problem. And unless he admits that there *is* a problem, then there is little hope for him in the future. With your assistance, he'll never be prepared to change.'

Suki tried and failed to imagine Piers ever changing. 'And what if he refuses to change?'

Pasquale's mouth was a thin line. 'He doesn't have any alternative. In a few days the banks will foreclose on the loans he's taken out.'

'Then it's too late anyway!' said Suki wildly.

He shook his head. 'Not if I buy into the company—make sure that the loans are paid.'

Suki frowned. 'But you said—'

'I said *what*, *bella mia*?' he asked, in a voice of velvet and silk.

'That you—you never take on losing ventures.'

'Bravo!' he applauded softly. 'So she listens, too. A woman who listens is a rare prize!'

She really wasn't in any kind of position to point out his chauvinism, and, what was more, her heart was thudding as the realisation of just how trapped she was slowly began to dawn on her.

'But I am prepared to make an exception in this case,' he told her, with a flash of his dark eyes. 'Besides, under my guidance Franklin Motors will undergo a dramatic change of fortunes; it will assume greatness once again.'

'And then what?' she asked him shakily. 'You sack Piers?'

'Sack him? You think I am such a hard man?'

'Yes, I do.'

He laughed. 'I do not intend to sack him, *cara*, no. As I told you, under my guidance we will get the company up and running.'

'Oh? Have you suddenly become an expert on car manufacturing?' she asked sarcastically.

He smiled. 'I am an expert on manufacturing in general,' he said. 'The specifics can easily be adapted to the theory—that supply should never outstrip demand. I am also an expert in predicting trends, and currently there is a demand for the small, specialist sports car for which the Franklin firm rightly became so famous. Your brother's error was in overexpanding and trying to compete in the mass market, but that is easily remedied.'

Suki digested this. Unfortunately, he was right—damn him! He was doing nothing more than succinctly voicing the vague fears she'd had for ages. How very galling! She met the speculative look in his eyes. 'And I suppose you're an expert on women, too, are you?' she heard herself saying.

A sardonic dark eyebrow was raised. 'Let's just say that any expertise I may lay claim to in that *particular* field has never been questioned.' He gave her a mocking glance. 'But maybe that's all about to change, Suki.'

Her heart pounded. What did he mean by that? 'So you're going to buy into Piers's company? That's very—kind—of you, Pasquale.'

He gave her a strange look. 'Kind? I do not do it out of kindness, *cara*; but I think you know that. Call it a favour, if you like.'

'And in return for this—favour?'

'That too I think you know.'

His eyes told her what he wanted in return—*her*! But she wasn't going to let him wriggle out of saying it, admitting it. Let him acknowledge aloud the depths to which he was prepared to sink to to get her into his bed—the barbaric swine! 'No,' she said flatly. 'I'm not sure that I do. Why don't you tell me, Pasquale?'

He smiled, but it was a cold smile, totally lacking in humour. 'It's simple. Be the Formidable girl.'

That completely took the wind out of her sails. 'You mean just that?' she queried incredulously. 'You mean you don't want—' she blurted out, before pulling herself up short.

'Mmm?' he prompted softly.

She held her chin up. 'That's all?' she asked proudly.

He shook his head, and his eyes glittered with terrifying promise. 'No, it is not all, but it will do for now. I have stated my claim and my desire for you to become my mistress. And I can wait, Suki, but not for long. Believe me when I tell you that I am not a patient man.'

She gave him a long, steady look as she acknowledged his outrageous audacity in talking about it so coolly. Clearly not a man who was governed by the normal social niceties! 'And how far do you propose to go to get what you want—namely me?'

He seemed momentarily surprised by *her* frankness, for his dark eyes glittered briefly as he met her stare full-on. 'I'm not sure I understand exactly what you mean, *cara*,' he said softly.

'I want to know whether force is one of your less charming characteristics,' she said brutally, pleased when she saw his mouth harden with displeasure.

'Force?' he echoed. 'I think you know in your heart that it is not, Suki. I never take anything from a woman that she is not prepared to give.'

And his eyes issued her a mocking challenge which she did not dare to answer.

CHAPTER FIVE

PASQUALE indubitably had the upper hand, Suki realised as she stared up into the steely glint of his eyes, and there wasn't a damned thing she could do about it. 'And if I accept this bizarre offer to work for your company—'

'You really have no choice,' he interrupted smoothly, shaking his dark head. 'Do you?'

No. That was just it. She didn't.

He was right. Again. That was the most infuriating thing. She really *couldn't* keep on pouring cash into Piers's company while he carried on squandering it. Quite apart from the fact—as Pasquale himself had infuriatingly pointed out—that Piers's debts were far outstripping her capital.

And if she refused to become the Formidable girl, then not only would Franklin Motors be ruined but Pasquale could still rightly sue her for breach of contract. He could ruin her financially. He could label her as unreliable. He could see that she never worked again. She had to face it, she thought wearily— whichever way she turned, he had her—she was trapped.

'Let me get something straight,' she said slowly.

'I'm listening.'

'The deal is that I work for you—nothing more than that?'

He lifted both elegant shoulders in a very Continental shrug. 'As I said before—nothing more than you wish to give.'

'And what are the terms of employment?'

'The terms will remain the same as those in the contract you signed,' he said, his mouth twisting into a deprecating half-smile as he surveyed the fragments of contract which still littered the carpet. 'And you had no problems with that until you knew that I was behind it, did you?'

'No,' she replied reluctantly. 'And when do I start?' she asked, realising that the question had effectively sealed her fate, a fact which did not escape him either, for he gave a bland smile.

'There will be a party at the Granchester Hotel tomorrow evening to introduce you to the international press. A car will be sent for you at eight.'

Smoothing her short skirt down, Suki rose to her feet. 'And just what image am I to project as the Formidable girl?' she queried.

He smiled. An exciting smile this time. A predatory smile. It made her shiver. It made her thrill. It made her want to rake her nails down the side of that delectable face. It made her want to kiss him.

'Well, certainly not one of innocence,' he said cruelly. 'You will be the embodiment of glamour, *bella mia*. And sex appeal,' he added, his eyes straying from her face to her body in a lazy stare.

Suki suppressed another small shudder. Surely she

should feel affronted when he looked at her like that? Surely she shouldn't experience that aching little frisson of excitement?

'A stylist from the advertising agency will be around at seven with a complete outfit for you to wear. We use Lomas & Lomas,' he finished. And then, quite without warning, he reached down and caught her hand, moving it slowly to his lips, his eyes never leaving her face, capturing her reluctantly, enthralling her. 'I am very happy, *cara*, that you have seen sense enough to acquiesce to my wishes...'

His breath was soft on her skin, his lips warm as they touched the palm, and Suki knew a frightened feeling of being dragged into a sensual trap from which there could be no painless escape.

Hastily, she pulled her hand away and gave him a very frosty look. 'You've made it perfectly clear what it is that you want from me, Pasquale, but I'm warning you that you won't get it.'

'Oh, really?' he mocked.

'You'd better believe it!' And, her head held as proudly as the figurehead of a ship, she swept past him and out of the office, past Carly and the silver-haired lawyer, who still looked in a total state of shock.

Carly leapt forward. 'Suki!' she exclaimed. 'For God's sake...'

But Suki didn't look back as she heard Pasquale's deep voice saying smoothly, 'I apologise for having kept you both waiting. If you'd like to return to the office, we can discuss the contract at length, since

Miss Franklin has rescinded her earlier decision and has now happily agreed to honour the agreement.'

Happily! If only they knew! Suki kept her face stiff and set until she was outside the Formidable building and had hailed a taxi.

And it wasn't until she had collapsed onto the back seat that she was able to give in to the feelings of impotence and anger which had built to a peak inside her, and she drummed violently at her purple suede clutch-bag as if it were Pasquale's chest she was beating.

It was ten to eight. The stylist had just left and Suki studied herself in her bedroom mirror while she waited for the car which would take her to the Press launch. But even she was unprepared for the impact of the gown she had been given to wear for her debut as the Formidable girl.

Like most models, she was riddled with self-doubts about her appearance, waiting for the day when someone told her that it had all been a big joke, that she wasn't beautiful at all. When she looked in the mirror she usually saw only the flaws in her looks—much, much too tall, with too long legs and the rather narrow hips overemphasising the surprising lushness of her breasts. But tonight even she found it difficult to fault her appearance.

Her hair spilled down her back in a fiery blur of auburn waves, and the heavy lids of her amber eyes had been cleverly frosted with silver. And the gown itself was exquisite, though where it clung it really

did cling, emphasising almost indecently the swell of
her breasts and snaking silkily down over her hips.
It was the kind of dress that if you had gained even
a kilogram of excess weight would define the fact
with cruel clarity, she thought, never so glad of the
taut flatness of her stomach as she was now.

The sharp ring of the doorbell disturbed her rev-
erie, and she peered through the peephole to see a
uniformed chauffeur standing outside.

She opened the door, and the man flashed an identification card. 'Miss Franklin?' he asked.

'That's me!' She gave him a bright smile—after
all, it wasn't the poor driver's fault that she was attending this wretched Press launch under such duress!

'The car is waiting downstairs to take you to the
hotel,' he told her.

'Thanks. I'll be right down.' Feeling a sudden kin-
ship with the Christians who had been fed to the
lions, Suki pulled the matching silver-threaded shawl
around her bare shoulders, and followed the chauffeur downstairs and outside into the dark golden
summer evening, where a Daimler sat gleaming at
the kerbside.

The driver opened the back door and Suki stepped
inside the car, but the door had closed behind her
before she realised that there was another occupant,
and even though the shaded windows meant that the
light was comparatively dim she knew immediately
just who was reclining against the soft leather seat,
watching her from between lazy, narrowed eyes.

Her heart started thumping as her eyes became accustomed to the light and she saw just what his physique could do for a formal dinner-jacket and snowy-white shirt. It really was unfair—a man as unscrupulous as this man simply didn't deserve to look *that* good. She slid into the corner, as far away from him as possible, and gave him a frosty look.

'Good evening, Suki,' he said softly as the car purred into life and pulled away from the kerb.

'Well, what a surprise!' she said coolly, though her pulse continued to race. 'And a singularly unwelcome one, too. Tell me, Pasquale, do you intend to accompany me on *all* my official engagements?'

'Perhaps,' he answered, unperturbed, a faint smile playing about the corners of his mouth. 'And almost certainly if you are going to look as breathtaking as you do in that dress.'

The murmured compliment, and the slow, appraising look which accompanied it, made her senses fizzle like static electricity. It didn't seem to matter a jot that Pasquale was her enemy, that she disliked him intensely, and that he had nefarious designs on her, because her body, if nothing else, jolted into life when she saw him, welcomed the sight of him with a delight which was causing a feeling of delectable tension to invade her blood.

She tried hard to behave as she would towards any other business acquaintance. Friendly, but *distant*. 'It *is* a beautiful dress,' she conceded. 'You have a very talented stylist.'

He smiled at the polite and stilted tone of her

voice. 'Yes. She brought a number of gowns, but the moment I saw that one…'

There was something darkly proprietorial about the way he said it, and Suki's heart thumped painfully. 'You mean that you—*you* chose it?' she queried in disbelief.

'Of course.'

The thought of him selecting the dress which now lay next to her naked skin and very little else made her cheeks flame with an excitement she was bitterly ashamed of, and she was grateful for the dim light of the car. She waited until the heat had left her face before demanding, 'And is that normal practice for you? To choose what your models wear?'

'What do you think?' he answered obliquely.

She was finding it very difficult even to breathe normally right then, let alone *think*. 'I really have no idea,' she answered frostily. 'That's why I'm asking.'

She saw his mouth soften from its cynical hardness, saw his eyes grow impossibly dark, and she knew that at that moment he was aching for her, just as much as she ached for him.

'No, of course I don't normally choose. But the moment I saw this…I wanted to see what you looked like in it. I imagined the contrast of the silver with the gold glitter of those eyes which promise a man so much. I wanted to see the silk caressing the softness of your skin. Because I knew that you would be sensational wearing it; utterly sensational,' he murmured. 'And I was right, wasn't I, Suki? So right…'

Suki had been flattered and complimented by many men in the course of her modelling career, and yet nothing had ever made her heart beat as quickly as it was now, at Pasquale's candidly sexual tribute. And it brought it slamming home that that was all she was to him. Nothing more than a body he wanted to conquer.

She felt her heart clenching as she recognised dully how much it *hurt* that Pasquale should think of her in that way, and that way only. Her breathing was shallow as she attempted to cut him down to size.

'I feel I ought to warn you that making me lose my temper, which I am extremely close to doing, is hardly going to be conducive to getting good photographs of the Formidable woman. So if it is your intention to make me feel like some object you've bought, every time we have the misfortune to meet, then I'd strongly advise against it.'

He shook his head. 'Not at all. It is my intention to have you admit that you want me to kiss you,' he parried softly, and his remark drew her eyes inexorably towards his mouth. 'How about right now, Suki?'

His head was near enough that if he bent forward just a little then their mouths would collide in a soft, sensual encounter. Suki saw the glitter in his dark eyes, and felt her lips part as if some unseen finger had prised them open. Instinctively, she shrank even further away from him, sinking back into the soft leather of the seat, daring him, just *daring* him to try...and she clenched her small fist on top of her silk-covered thigh in preparation.

He smiled as he observed the movement. 'But we wouldn't want to smudge your lipstick, now would we? So we'll postpone that very enjoyable diversion until later. It will be something to look forward to.'

'Like hell!' she spat, like a cat confronted by water.

'More like heaven, I suspect,' he countered on a note of sexy promise.

She searched around desperately for a suitable put-down, but didn't get the chance to use one, because Pasquale changed the tone of the conversation completely, his dark eyebrows meeting in an impatient frown as he clipped out, 'I had a meeting with your brother this afternoon.'

This sounds ominous, thought Suki gloomily. 'Oh?' she said lightly. 'And how was he?'

He continued to frown. 'He was stinking of booze. In the middle of the day,' he added repressively.

'I am not my brother's keeper,' she said. And then, in an effort to distract him, she asked, 'How did you get on with him?'

He shook his head like a disillusioned schoolteacher. 'Frankly, I'm surprised that he's managed to stay in business a *day*, let alone eight years. The man's an absolute liability!'

'There's no need to be quite so offensive!' defended Suki, unable to stop the guilt rushing through her because secretly she tended to agree with Pasquale's every word. 'He tries very hard.'

'He's certainly very trying,' said Pasquale, dead-pan.

'And *you're* just showing off your English!' observed Suki acidly as the bright lights of Harrods illuminated the faint smile that her last remark had provoked.

'The most disturbing thing,' continued Pasquale, 'is that he simply doesn't seem to have any grasp of the most fundamental concepts of business. He just looked at me blankly when I mentioned supply and demand and a sympathetic cash flow.'

'That's because *he* didn't have the benefit of doing a business management course at Harvard! Piers inherited the company when my father died, when he was only twenty, just in case you didn't know.'

'Yes, of course I knew,' he said softly. 'And he told me that your mother died last year. I was sorry to hear that, Suki—very sorry indeed.'

She turned to face him. She could bear anything, she thought, but not that soft, almost gentle voice which mimicked the finer human feelings and not just the desire which he felt for her. She swiftly turned her head to stare fixedly out of the window, so that he would not see the sudden moistness in her eyes, and she had time to recover her composure before she heard him tapping on the smoked-glass partition in front of which the driver sat. The electrically controlled panel moved aside immediately.

'Just draw up here, would you?' asked Pasquale. 'I intend taking Miss Franklin round by a side-entrance.' He looked down at her. 'Are you OK now?'

She nodded, surprised at the concern underlying his question. 'Don't you want to make the big entrance, then?' she asked curiously, and he shook his head.

'There's usually a scrum of photographers. Sometimes it can get out of hand, as I'm sure you know, and there's absolutely no need for you to have to fight your way through them all.'

She felt ridiculously touched by his solicitude, even though he spoilt it rather by murmuring, 'Besides, the element of surprise is always an advantage, don't you think, Suki?' However, she didn't get a chance to object, for suddenly she found herself being handed out of the car and he caught her hand in his and led her through a discreet side-door. For a few moments their palms were in contact, his fingers firmly gripping hers, and it took everything she had to stop her own fingers from curling possessively around his hand.

And it wasn't until they were speeding upwards in one of the service lifts he'd managed to locate that she noticed that he was smiling.

It was quite something, that smile.

'You're *enjoying* this!' she accused. 'Aren't you?'

There was a pause. His face was quite serious for a moment. 'More than I would have imagined, little one. I thought, perhaps foolishly, that your capitulation would be instant,' he murmured. 'The signs in France were so promising.'

Suki was scarcely able to believe her ears. 'The signs in France were so promising'. Oh, *were* they? So he thought that her 'capitulation would be instant', *did* he? 'Of all the most arrogant, conceited things I've ever heard—'

'I had no idea, *cara*,' he interrupted shamelessly, his eyes never leaving the curve of her lips, 'that you were going to fight me all the way, or indeed how much I would enjoy the fight, the anticipation of victory.'

She *could* protest. She *could* start twittering on about honour and decency and the shameful expectations of brutish men like him.

She *could*.

And he, no doubt—arrogant beast that he was—would indulgently smile and nod as he listened to all her protestations.

Before kissing her to death.

Suki shuddered. What did they say about actions speaking louder than words? If he attempted to take her into his arms again she would be as responsive as a block of ice. She clamped her lips together in a tight line, which was exactly what she was intending to do if he tried to kiss her.

The dark eyes mocked her as the lift doors slid open. Along the corridor Suki could see a scrum of photographers waiting.

Pasquale put a hand at the small of her back and looked down at her. 'Ready?' he asked.

'For *anything*,' she replied, and as their eyes

clashed with the light of battle her heart began to
pound painfully because she heard the sultry throb
of a woman's voice calling his name.

CHAPTER SIX

'PASQUALE, *darling*! So there you are!' And an imperious-looking woman in her late twenties, with sleek blue-black hair, came bearing down on them. She was wearing a military-style scarlet dress which positively *exuded* class, and she made Suki, in the slinky silver silk, feel half-naked in comparison.

She rarely met women other than models who equalled her in height, but this woman certainly did. She also seemed to know Pasquale very well indeed, since she was proffering him alternate cool, pale cheeks, and Suki watched, fascinated, while he gave her three kisses.

'Where the hell did you spring from?' the woman asked, adding something in Italian in a low, sexy undertone, but Pasquale shook his head.

'We took the service lift. And Suki doesn't speak any Italian, so we'd better not,' he said smoothly.

The woman held two beautifully manicured hands in the air. 'Of course she doesn't—how silly of me!'

Suki glared but said nothing.

Pasquale smiled. 'Have you two actually met before?'

'No-o,' said the woman, and gave Suki a cold scrutiny from head to toe. 'I don't *think* so.'

'Suki,' said Pasquale, 'this is Stacey Lomas. She

heads Lomas & Lomas, the advertising agency I happen to use—'

'For more years than I care to remember!' trilled Stacey, batting her eyelids like crazy.

OK, so you know him pretty well—I get the message, thought Suki, masking her strange feeling of disappointment behind a bright smile.

'And Stacey,' continued Pasquale, 'may I present the new Formidable girl? Of course, you'll recognise Suki from her portfolio.'

'Of course,' echoed Stacey, her elegant eyebrows ever so slightly raised in a gesture of surprise, as though Suki in the flesh bore little resemblance to the Suki of her portfolio photographs.

'Hello,' smiled Suki, thinking that you wouldn't need to hold a doctorate in human behaviour to realise that the elegant Ms Lomas was very keen on Signor Caliandro. Very keen indeed. That much was obvious from the amused glances she kept throwing him, and the secret little smile which played around her rather sultry, scarlet-painted lips.

'Hello, Suki,' responded Stacey at last, very coolly. 'Well, now you're here, we can get started. I guess we'd better introduce you to the gentlemen from the press corps.'

'Gentlemen?' joked Suki. 'From the *press corps*? Now this I have to see!'

She saw Pasquale smile, but she moved away, eager to begin, glad to be able to do what she had been employed for: sell the product. It meant that she could slip into automatic pilot, doing her job with the utmost professionalism which had always been her trademark, instead of thinking and wondering just how far the relationship between Pasquale and Stacey Lomas went. And if he was unscrupulous enough to want more than one mistress at the same time...

A large function room had been set aside at the Granchester Hotel and had been completely decorated in gold and blue, which were the colours which adorned the Formidable packaging.

And they'd certainly gone to town, thought Suki admiringly as she looked around, if perhaps a little over the top...

There were gold and blue ribbons and streamers, and gold and blue metallic balloons with the legend 'C'est Formidable' printed on every one. There was every kind of blue flower imaginable—delphiniums, cornflowers, irises, hyacinths—all standing clustered in flamboyant golden bowls which were dotted strategically around the room.

And on a table next to the stand which displayed bottles of Formidable perfume, as well as all their make-up and toiletry ranges, were blue-stemmed glasses filled with champagne, which the press corps were quaffing back like men who had been denied hard liquor for years.

'Would you like some champagne?' asked Pasquale.

She shook her head. 'Not when I'm working—thanks.'

'Then could I ask you to come and stand over

here?' interjected Stacey hurriedly. 'And we'll put you to work.'

Like a beast of burden, thought Suki crossly, though her bright smile never faltered as she moved fluidly across the room behind the advertising boss. She resented Stacey Lomas's implication that she was nothing more than an airhead, which was unusual. All the normal preconceptions which people had about professional models didn't normally bother her. After all, she wasn't trying to impress anyone. She earned a generous amount of money and she paid her taxes. People liked her or they didn't, and she could take or leave their opinion.

So what was it about Stacey Lomas?

Her apparently close relationship with Pasquale?

The hell it was! Suki tossed her auburn hair in abandon and fifty flash bulbs exploded into incandescent blue-white light.

She was aware that Pasquale was there in the room with her and it affected her performance intensely. She played it like she'd never played it before. He'd wanted her to sell the product, so sell it she damned well would!

He'd wanted glamour and he'd wanted sex appeal—well, look out, Pasquale, she thought wickedly—here it comes!

She pouted. She smiled seductively. She playfully hid behind her long curtain of auburn hair. She slitted her amber eyes so that they gleamed with promise. And the press corps went mad, whistling their appreciation and snapping away like mad.

When she had given them every photo they could possibly want—plus a few more besides—the session was called to a halt. Suki stepped off the small platform, close to where Pasquale stood, and she was taken aback by the thunderous look of anger on his face as his dark eyes clashed with hers.

Now what was the matter with him, the moody brute?

And who cares? she thought defiantly as she slung the silver wrap over her shoulders.

Stacey was smiling like a woman who had just won the lottery. 'Pasquale, *cara*,' she was saying. 'I'm starving. Have you eaten yet?'

'No,' he answered tersely, his face tense as he continued to cast daggers in Suki's direction.

'Then let's try that new Thai restaurant in Soho, shall we? I've heard it's excellent.'

'So have I, but I'm afraid it will have to be another time,' he answered smoothly, but there was still an abrasive glitter in his eyes.

'Oh?' Stacey pouted, the pout looking more petulant than seductive, thought Suki with sudden, triumphant glee.

'Sorry.' He shrugged broad, elegantly clad shoulders. 'I'm catching a flight to New York first thing, and I need to catch up on sleep.'

Suki couldn't help wondering just *why* he needed to catch up on sleep, but blocked the thought in an instant. His nocturnal habits were nothing to do with her. 'Is the car still outside?' she asked him neutrally. 'Because I'd like to go home now.'

'I'll see you downstairs,' he said.

Suki shook her head. 'There's really no need,' she replied, just *daring* him to challenge her.

He did.

'Oh, but I insist,' he said softly, and there was an edge of unmistakable menace in his voice.

Short of having a ding-dong with him which would no doubt enthral the remaining photographers who were finishing off the last of the champagne, there seemed little alternative but to go with him. And Suki did derive some small amount of satisfaction from the look of fury which Stacey Lomas sent flashing in her direction.

This time they used the main lift, and as there were two other people in it they said nothing, but Suki could sense the anger in Pasquale; his normally relaxed body was held rigid and his face was tight with tension.

In the lobby she turned to him. 'If you'll just point me in the direction of the car—'

But he did no such thing. He firmly took hold of her hand and led her towards the revolving glass doors.

'What—the hell do you think you're doing?' she spluttered.

'Taking you home.'

'I don't want to go home with you!'

'Tough!' came his uncompromising reply. Gosh, but he could sound like an American gangster sometimes!

Even worse was to come.

The gleaming Daimler she had arrived in was nowhere to be seen. One of the hotel's doormen was just getting out of a long, gun-metal-grey sports car, and was handing a set of keys to Pasquale.

'Your car, sir,' he said, then grinned. 'She handles like a dream!'

For a moment, Pasquale was charm personified. 'Doesn't she? Thanks very much.' He smiled lazily, and discreetly handed the doorman a whopping great tip.

Pasquale opened the passenger door. 'Get in,' he said shortly.

Suki opened her mouth to refuse, then hastily shut it when she saw the grim line of determination on his face which was masquerading as a mouth. Besides which, she was quite enjoying seeing him in such a temper. She didn't know what had caused it, but it seemed strangely out of character for the formidably controlled and controlling Pasquale!

The car roared off sounding like a schoolboy's dream, and Suki stole a glance at that stark, uncompromising profile.

'Would you mind explaining—?'

'Shut up,' he told her.

'But—'

'Not *now*, Suki! I'm trying to keep my eyes on the damned road!'

'Do you realise you're crunching the gears?' she asked sweetly, and saw his knuckles whiten in response.

'Don't say another word,' he grated in a scarcely audible voice.

'Or what?'

'Or I may just lose my temper,' he warned her.

'And is that supposed to frighten me?' she taunted.

'Yes,' he gritted as he skidded up outside her block with a screech. 'If you happen to be a sensible girl.'

Suki unclipped her seat belt. 'Well, thanks very much for the pleasant chat,' she mocked. '*Now* what do you think you're doing?'

He swung himself out of the car and came round to open her door. 'I should think it's very obvious what I'm doing,' he said. 'I'm coming inside with you.'

His face was dark and determined. Her heart thumped. 'Oh, no, you're not!'

'Just try stopping me,' he said silkily.

The most bizarre thing was that she wasn't frightened. Far from it. And she was honest enough to admit to herself what the source of her thundering heart was.

Excitement.

She gazed into the glittering blackness of his eyes. 'You think I wouldn't dare?' she challenged.

'I have no idea. I should be delighted to see you try,' he answered, with a quiet determination which renewed the racing of her heart.

And he didn't even wait until her front door was closed before pulling her ruthlessly into his arms, kicking the door shut behind them with a deafening slam.

'Been watching too many cowboy movies?' she 'taunted breathlessly, refusing to be intimidated by his cavalier behaviour, or lulled by that strong hand which clasped her waist so firmly.

His eyes were blazing down at her. 'How the hell could you do it?' he demanded harshly.

Now she really *was* confused. 'Do what?'

'Behave like that!'

'Like what?'

'Don't play the innocent with me!' he exploded dramatically and his accent deepened. 'You know damned well what I'm talking about!'

'*What?*'

'My God,' he breathed. 'The way you were tonight; the way you looked. Those lips, those eyes, that body in that dress—'

'Which *you* chose!' she retorted in disbelief.

'Yes, I chose, and, Mother of God, what a fool I was,' he said, half to himself, before renewing his onslaught. 'You looked like you were making love to every man in the room! Was that your intention?'

'Oh, for goodness' *sake*!' Suki tore herself out of his arms. 'Just what did you expect? You employed me to help sell your product, didn't you? You wanted me to be glamorous and to use sex appeal—those were *your* words, if you remember! *Yes*, I flirted! And *yes*, I looked provocative—because that is specifically what you asked for, Pasquale. And models do that kind of work all the time, and don't pretend you're so naïve and so stupid as not to know that! It's totally harmless—'

'Is it?' he asked dangerously.

'Of course it is!'

'And if I hadn't been there, don't you think that some of those photographers—some of them the worse for drink—would have been hanging around, waiting to take you home? Would you have gone with any of them, Suki?'

She was so angry that she lifted her hand and slapped his face hard, but he didn't flinch; he didn't react at all, save for a brief flash of fire in his dark eyes and the harsh tightening of his mouth.

'How *dare* you?' she said, in a voice so shaky that her words sounded almost indistinct. 'Apart from the fact that I'm perfectly capable of saying no, most of those guys are happily married with children—and those who aren't know that it's just a job. I doubt whether anyone there would have resorted to the kind of primitive behaviour which *you* seem to indulge in—namely dragging me off in your car like something out of the Stone Age!'

'And do you think that I normally behave like this?' he demanded, in a strained kind of voice.

Suki angrily pushed a strand of hair off her forehead. 'How should I know how you *normally* behave, when what's normal for you seems pretty eccentric to me? Normal for you seems to be getting a foothold into my brother's business and using that to bribe me into working for you. That is, of course, when you aren't threatening me with breach of contract…'

He shook his dark head. 'No. Forget that.'

She narrowed her eyes suspiciously. 'Forget what?'

He sighed. 'I won't sue you for breach of contract. I made you take the job under duress. You don't want to work for me, and you will no longer have to. I'm dropping you as the Formidable girl.'

Suki blinked in astonishment. 'But financially that could be disastrous for you—you've just introduced me to the *Press*, for heaven's sake!'

He shrugged his broad shoulders philosophically. 'My bank balance can withstand the occasional mistake.'

Suki frowned. This was a complete turnaround. 'And what about Piers, and Franklin Motors?'

'Don't worry—I won't go back on my word to invest in your brother's business. I shall follow that through.'

His words sank in, and she realised that here she had the opportunity to be free of him. And her reaction to that was not at all what she would have predicted.

'You are not,' she said coolly, 'doing any such thing.'

'What?' he said softly, his eyes flaring, as if he couldn't believe what she had just said.

'You are not dropping me as the Formidable girl, because I've decided that I happen to quite like it.

And if you do, then I shall sue *you* for breach of contract. Do you understand *that*, Pasquale?'

There was a stunned silence and then he did something totally unexpected.

He laughed.

And Suki almost melted under the impact of that laugh.

'Ah, Suki,' he murmured appreciatively. 'I see that I have found myself a truly worthy adversary.' He paused, and gave her a discerning look. 'Is it intentional, I wonder?' he quizzed softly. 'Do you know what you're doing?'

'About what?' she asked, momentarily perplexed. 'You're speaking in riddles.'

He smiled. 'Do you realise that the more you fight and resist me, the more I want you—?'

'Yes, I know,' she cut in acidly. 'The more you want me to be your mistress! A loathsome word!'

To her surprise, he nodded, and his face became serious. 'I agree, *bella*. And I was wrong. Very wrong.'

'Wrong?' Suki found it very difficult to take in the fact that Pasquale was admitting fault!

'Mmm,' he murmured. 'A mistress is someone who can be bought, owned—an inappropriate word for someone as fiery as you, Suki. For, even if he held you in chains, I can imagine no man ever owning you. No, I can think of a far better description for you than mistress.'

Somehow she managed to keep her face neutral,

even though her heart was racing like crazy. 'Oh, really? I can't wait to hear it.'

'*Lover*,' he whispered, in a voice of dark velvet. 'Will you? Be my lover, Suki?' He caressed the word with his mouth as he reached out and pulled her back into his arms, his fingers beginning to delicately caress the narrow span of her waist.

Disappointment stole over her as she banished for ever the romantic fantasy of what she had foolishly been imagining that he was about to say. Not something which sounded as expendable as 'lover', anyway. She lifted her chin proudly. 'No, I won't!' she said quietly, and with the most monumental effort she pulled away from him and went to stand next to the window.

'I don't believe you,' he said simply. 'Why are you denying what we both feel? Fighting it so hard, when I know and you know that you want more than anything else to give in to it?'

Suki turned abruptly away, hating what his words did to her equilibrium, unwilling to face him for fear that he would read the vulnerability in her eyes. He was right. She *did* want him—wanted him in a way she had never wanted a man before. But what he was offering wasn't enough—could never be enough: the temporary lover, to be replaced when he had tired of her.

'No, Pasquale,' she answered in a low voice.

'And yet you will continue to be the Formidable girl, knowing that our paths will constantly cross. Have you asked yourself why? Don't you imagine that our continued proximity will wear down your already weak defences?'

She gave him a cool look. 'Is that a challenge?'

'I'm not entirely sure,' he murmured. 'Will you accept it, if it is?'

She shook her head. 'I'm too tired for all this game-playing.' And then she saw the faint red mark on one olive cheek and her own face paled. 'Your cheek is marked,' she said, biting her bottom lip in horror. 'I'm sorry, Pasquale—I should never have hit you.'

He shrugged. 'I deserved it—my criticisms were unjust. You were only doing your job.' His dark eyes blazed. 'I was jealous, you see.'

And that means *nothing*, Suki assured herself.

'But you can make it up to me if you like,' he said softly.

'I can imagine how,' she responded acidly.

He raised his dark brows speculatively. 'By making me some coffee,' he said. 'I could kill for a cup.'

And to her consternation he allowed his long-limbed frame to settle itself languidly on one of her sofas and smiled beguilingly up at her.

She stared at him, taking in that easy assurance he wore like a second skin, and she couldn't help laughing, despite her misgivings. 'All that—and you ask me for coffee! You're impossible—do you know that?'

'It has been said,' he conceded, and the look he gave her was loaded with amusement, and *that*, Suki discovered, was a far more powerful weapon in his armoury than his potent sexual charisma. Because shared humour could somehow be incredibly intimate, too...

'How do you take your coffee?' she heard herself saying.

'As it comes,' he smiled. 'Thank you.'

'And if you're about to launch into the charm offensive,' she told him archly, 'then please don't bother.' But she swung out of the room to the sound of his low, mocking laughter.

Suki clattered around in her kitchen, getting down a couple of the bright pottery cups she collected, and which she had brought back from her various travels, wondering what kind of woman would be making coffee for the man she loved to hate. A madwoman, that was who, she told herself with some of her customary humour as she began to grind the coffee-beans. And if she was trying to play games, then she was playing way out of her league with Pasquale.

Still, she tried to reason with herself, perhaps if they did something as civilised as drinking coffee together, then he wouldn't go into caveman mode every time she was around. Perhaps he would stop asking her to become his...

Lover.

The word thrilled her yet chilled her. And if it had been anyone else but Pasquale she *might* have felt tempted. But if you took on Pasquale you could guarantee yourself a broken heart, and a broken heart she could do without.

Which left her with the still unanswered question

of just *why* she hadn't accepted his offer to terminate her Formidable contract. Was it stubborn pride— wanting to prove to herself, and to him, that she could resist him? Or was it simply because she wanted to thwart his wishes?

She shook her head in confusion as she added a plateful of home-made biscuits to the tray, and carried it through into the living room, where Pasquale had moved from the sofa and was standing studying one of her paintings as intently as if he were about to undergo an examination on it.

Remember, she reminded herself as he turned towards her. Be civilised. Drink some coffee with him, European style. Do that and it may arouse the chivalry in him, rather than the passion.

It seemed that it did. He took the tray from her protesting hands and put it down on a small table which was next to one of the two ice-blue sofas which stood facing each other.

She warily watched him sit on one sofa and she chose the one opposite.

She was not used to men indolently lounging in her flat, and yet Pasquale looked so *right* sitting there, she thought as she poured their coffee. So dark and so powerful, and yet at the same time so graciously at ease. He took the cup from her. 'Thanks,' he said, and observed her from beneath dark, thick lashes as he sipped the fragrant brew. 'Excellent coffee,' he said, on a note of unconscious wonder.

'You mean for an English woman?'

'I'm sorry—that was extremely pompous of me,' he said.

'Your English is excellent,' she remarked mischievously.

His eyes gleamed. *'Touché!'*

She realised with an unwelcome shock that she found him as stimulating intellectually as physically. Which didn't help. I don't want to find him any *more* attractive than I already do, she thought plaintively. 'Would you like a biscuit?' she enquired hurriedly, proffering the plate.

'Thank you.' He took one, bit into it and raised one dark eyebrow. 'Also very good,' he observed. 'You didn't bake them yourself by any chance?'

'Didn't I? What suppositions you make, Pasquale,' she reprimanded mockingly. 'Actually I did, and there's no need to sound surprised.'

'Oh, but I am.'

'Why?'

A broad olive hand indicated the room with a broad sweep. 'Your whole flat is a surprise.' His gesture took in the deep red walls which provided such a dramatic backdrop for her paintings, the clutter of bright, beautiful vases which adorned the mantelpiece, the brightly embroidered cushions she'd brought back from India which should have clashed violently with the cerise sofa but somehow set it off magnificently.

'In what way?'

He shrugged his broad shoulders. 'This room,' he

said, 'is exactly the opposite of what I would have expected of you.'

'And just what did you expect?'

'Something minimalist, elegant, streamlined. Certainly not this.'

'This being...?'

He shrugged again. 'It is wild and it is beautiful, but it is not safe. It is a room into which the guiding hand of an interior designer would never be admitted. And it is not the room of an independent career-woman,' he stated finally.

She suspected that he had more experience than most of analysing the decor of women's homes. 'And that's how you see me, is it, Pasquale—as an independent career-woman?'

'Of course. Isn't that what you are?'

She supposed that she was. But it didn't sound like her at all—it somehow had a very cold-sounding ring to it. She made a restless little movement. 'Sure it is.'

'And yet—' his dark eyes were appreciative '—you grind coffee-beans and you bake biscuits.'

She certainly couldn't let *that* go unremarked upon! 'Well, I *am* a woman,' she purred demurely.

He smiled as he acknowledged the jibe. 'Mmm. You most certainly are,' he murmured. He finished the last of his coffee and leaned back, his dark head resting against the palms of his hands as he studied the walls. 'And you still paint—quite beautifully, in fact.'

She liked his praise of her work, she realised. She

liked it very much. 'But why should that surprise you?' she asked. 'I always did paint. Remember?'

The light died in his eyes. 'Yes. I remember. I thought that you should take it up as a career; do you remember *that*? But you chose to capitalise on your looks instead.'

She bristled indignantly at the implied criticism. 'That's because modelling pays and painting doesn't!' she retorted. 'And, unlike you, I had to go out and earn a living!'

'Is that how you see *me*?' he questioned coolly. 'The poor little rich boy? Perhaps you think that I was handed everything on a plate? If you do, Suki, then you are quite wrong.

'My father put me into the business at the bottom end of the ladder; he wanted to make sure that I knew every part of how it should be run. And being the boss's son isn't all roses, you know. A lot of people resent you for what you will one day inherit. Inevitably, your position isolates you. I worked damned hard to build the business to the level it's at today. I still do,' he finished, on an odd note.

'You sound bitter,' she said quietly.

'A little. It galls me that so much money has been eaten up by the greed of my stepmother over the years, but that, fortunately, will soon be remedied.'

'Oh?'

He gave her a cruel kind of smile. 'My father is in the throes of divorcing her. It has taken him some time, but he has seen the light at last.' The smile vanished without a trace.

'So in effect you're condemning her just because she got a bit carried away with the credit cards, are you?'

He met her gaze with a steady look. 'Greed is forgivable,' he told her harshly, 'but infidelity is not.'

She was imprisoned in that bright, hard stare. Pasquale would never need fear infidelity, she thought. No woman of his would ever look at another man. 'And your sister?' she asked suddenly. 'How is she these days?'

'Francesca is well—like you, the independent career-woman. She practises law in Rome.'

Francesca? Crazy, impetuous Francesca—a *lawyer*? 'Good grief,' said Suki faintly.

'Now *you* sound surprised,' he observed.

'I am. She must have changed a lot.'

'Yes, she has. Changing schools so that she was closer to home was the best thing that could have happened to her.'

She waited for him to rake up her old, supposed sins, but his next words took her completely by surprise.

'Don't you ever long for a real home, Suki?' he probed suddenly. 'With the clutter of a husband and children?'

Something wrenched at her heart as she pictured what he was describing, but the image which stubbornly refused to budge had a male lead who bore an uncanny resemblance to Pasquale, with several dark-eyed children playing around his feet. 'Not really,' she replied, her voice threatening to tremble.

'As you said yourself, I'm an independent career-woman—husband and children don't fit in very well with my kind of work.'

'And is that why you've never married?' he persisted.

No, it wasn't. The reason she'd never married was sitting right opposite her. She'd never married because she'd never met another man to equal him. And the frightening and very real prospect which lay ahead of her was that she probably never would.

'I'm still too busy playing the field,' she lied, and was stunned by the look of anger which began to smoulder in the depths of his eyes.

'Yes, I'll bet you are!' he affirmed harshly.

Civility had just vanished, she realised, and conflict—dear, familiar conflict—had returned with a vengeance to replace it. She hurriedly stood. 'I really must ask you to leave now, Pasquale,' she said with deliberate politeness. 'I'm very tired.'

This time he made no demur. He rose to his feet. 'Thank you for the coffee,' he said with equal courtesy, and moved forward to replace his cup on the tray at exactly the same time as Suki bent to deposit her own, and their fingers unwittingly brushed together.

Suki took a step back, but her legs were suddenly shaky and she might have slipped had not one strong hand whipped out in a lightning-sharp reflex and caught her by the wrist.

Just that brief contact was enough to remind Suki of how devastating his touch could be and her skin seemed to throb with heated blood where he'd touched her.

Could he feel the acceleration of her pulse beneath his fingertips? Was that why he was looking down at her with that odd expression in his eyes, that disturbing softening of the normally hard line of his mouth?

'Thank you,' she said breathlessly, but she made no move to pull away, and he made no move to let her go.

'My pleasure,' he said softly.

Pleasure. It was a word he was comfortable with, familiar with. Pasquale could give her pleasure...untold pleasure. It was hers for the taking; she only had to ask. Involuntarily, the tip of her tongue edged out to slick around her arid lips, and his eyes darkened with desire.

'You must not do such things, *bella mia*,' he reprimanded her softly, his eyes never leaving her mouth, now glossy and trembling from the dark hunger she read on his face. 'Make such gestures...such provocative gestures.' His finger reached up to lightly touch the moist fullness of her bottom lip. 'Unless you are prepared to face the consequences.'

She stared up into his face, dazed and dazzled and entranced by him. He was still, she realised dully, holding her wrist. Oh, for heaven's sake, Suki, she thought despairingly.

She tried to pull away but failed, knowing that it was not his strength to blame, but her own inertia. And suddenly it was too late to move, because his hand had dropped from her mouth and moved to the slender band of her waist, and the rhythmical expertise of his fingers sensuously rubbing against the hopelessly inadequate silver silk was simply too much for her; it felt as though he was touching her bare flesh. God help her, she thought fleetingly as she began to sink helplessly into the sensation.

'Pasquale,' she whispered weakly, all the fight and the lies and the good intentions gone out of her.

'What?' The desire in his voice made it sound like honey trickling slowly over rough gravel.

'Let me—go.'

'In a minute I shall have to, though I am most reluctant to do so. Such a pity that I have to fly to New York tomorrow, *cara*,' he said regretfully. 'However…' and his voice dropped to an irresistible murmur '…I shall leave you something to remember me by. A taste of things to come.' And his eyes glittered as he lowered his mouth to possess hers.

She tried doing what she'd vowed to do much earlier that evening—an age ago—becoming a block of ice in his arms—but the thaw happened within seconds of his soft, sweet touch.

The other thing she had vowed to do was to keep her lips tightly clamped together, but that too proved fruitless, because when he pulled her decisively against the hard, aroused length of his body her lips fluttered open on a sigh, and his tongue penetrated her mouth with an erotic promise of unimaginable delights to come.

She swayed, but he held her firm, and she decided

that since she really *was* powerless to resist his kiss, then she might as well do what she really wanted to do.

She kissed him back.

She let her hands slide luxuriously over his broad back, fingering the thick silk of his black dinner-jacket, plucking at it restlessly as if anxious to feel the muscles beneath, and she delighted in the small moan he gave as he deepened the kiss.

She didn't know how long he kissed her for, only that at one point she feared that she might actually faint. 'Pasquale,' she whispered helplessly.

He raised his mouth from hers and looked down into her face. His breathing was almost as unsteady as her own as he took in the hectic flush which stained her high cheekbones, the febrile glitter of her eyes, and the parted, swollen lips which were dark with the pressure of his kiss.

The half-smile he gave then was neither soft nor gentle nor humourless. It was nakedly, unashamedly predatory.

'Yes,' he affirmed, almost harshly, 'I should take you now and quench this heat in my loins which threatens to overwhelm me.' He ceased holding her, and it took all she had not to crumple in a heap at his feet.

And perhaps he guessed that, for he moved a hand again as if to steady her, but mutely she pushed it feebly away, righting herself against the arm of the sofa.

'But I have an early flight,' he continued remorsely. 'And I can promise you one thing…that when I finally gain access to your bed I don't intend to creep out at dawn. I intend to stay there making love to you for just as long as it takes, *cara mia*.'

And the mocking words rang in her ears as he left and quietly closed the door behind him.

CHAPTER SEVEN

IN THEORY, with Pasquale in New York, Suki's life should have been less stressful.

But that was in theory, and the reality was startlingly, frighteningly different.

She found that she missed him. In fact, if she was being painfully and brutally honest with herself—she missed him quite badly.

She did two shoots for Formidable but found herself constantly glancing around the studio, as if hoping to catch a glimpse of that dark, proud head.

She lost her appetite, her sense of humour and she couldn't paint. Staring aimlessly out of the window one sunny morning, four days after he had gone, she decided to ring her sister-in-law to ask if she could take her young nephew out for the day. It would give Kirstie a break, and Toby was such fun to be with, he'd be bound to take her mind off Pasquale.

There was no reply at home, so Suki decided to ring Piers at the office to ask if he knew where they were.

She dialled his direct line, and almost dropped the receiver when she heard a familiar deep voice say, 'Yes?'

He's back from New York, she thought, with a dull ache where her heart should have been. He's back, and he hasn't been in touch, was her *stupid* reaction to hearing him speak.

'Hello?' he said, a touch impatiently.

'Hello,' echoed Suki eventually, when she had convinced herself that it would be childish to simply replace the receiver.

'Suki?' he said instantly. 'Is that you?'

'Yes, it's me. Is Piers there, please?'

'He is.'

There was a pause. 'May I speak to him?'

'In a moment. How are you?'

He sounded as though he was genuinely interested. He sounded as though he'd missed *her*, too. Oh, Suki, she thought, he probably had plenty of female diversions in New York. 'I'm fine,' she said, rather stiltedly. 'How are you?'

He laughed, as if he found her formal tone amusing. 'Tired. Very tired. It was a busy trip.' His voice deepened. 'Did you miss me?' he asked softly, putting words to her errant thoughts with shocking perception.

'Sure, Pasquale. Like the proverbial hole in the head!'

But he simply gave a low, mocking laugh. 'I hear from Lomas that your two shoots for Formidable went very well.'

'So they tell me.'

'Will you have dinner with me tonight?' he asked suddenly.

I—I'd love to, she was about to say as common sense momentarily flew swiftly out of the window, but she brought herself up sharply and pushed the temptation away as firmly as if it had been a cream cake and she'd needed to lose a kilo. Besides, it was easy to refuse him when she didn't have to look into those devilish black eyes of his. 'I can't,' she said coolly.

She heard the frown in his voice. 'A date?' he queried abruptly.

'I'm busy,' she said evasively.

'Too busy to cancel, I suppose?' he drawled, the familiar arrogance back again.

'Has a woman ever said no to you before?' she queried in disbelief.

'You wouldn't really want me to answer that, would you, Suki?'

'Why should it bother *me* what you answer?' she returned frostily. 'Your private life is of no interest to me whatsoever.'

He laughed softly. 'No?'

'No. And in answer to your question—I wouldn't dream of cancelling,' she said witheringly. 'That would be so rude, don't you think?'

'You're absolutely right, of course,' he agreed. 'I didn't expect you to—and I'd have been disappointed if you'd done so. It doesn't matter. I can wait.'

'But you told me you weren't a patient man,' she reminded him, wondering how he managed to make what was essentially a threat sound like the most enticing promise. 'Have you forgotten?'

'No, I haven't forgotten, but maybe I was wrong.

I seem to be discovering all kind of things about myself, Suki. Like how stimulating I find it to do battle with you.'

'Oh, do you?' she said repressively. 'Well, I'd like to speak to my brother now, if you don't mind!'

Again she heard the smile in his voice; she could even imagine it creasing his arrogant, kissable mouth. 'Sure. I'll put him on. I'll see you at the launch tomorrow.' He hesitated. 'Enjoy your date,' he said softly, and then he was gone.

'Suki?'

It was Piers's voice. 'Hello, Piers,' she said. 'How are things?'

His voice sounded strained. 'Fine!' he answered, in a tone which belied his words. Then his voice lowered. 'I'm bloody exhausted, to be honest. Don't worry—he's gone out of the room. This Caliandro chap thinks that starting work before eight in the morning is quite normal.'

'But it is, for a lot of people,' Suki pointed out.

'But I'm an *executive*, honey-child! I'm the flaming managing director, for heaven's sake!'

'But the title will mean nothing if you don't have a viable company!' said Suki impatiently.

'I know! I know,' he sighed. 'Don't nag me, Sukes. It just takes a bit of getting used to, that's all. Now, what can I do for you?'

'I was wondering if you knew where Kirstie is? I tried calling her at home but there was no reply.'

'She's taken Toby down to the health centre first thing—'

'He's not ill, is he?'

'No, he's fine. Just a routine assessment. She should be back by ten. What did you want to speak to her about?' he asked suspiciously.

'Well, certainly not about you! I was hoping to take Toby to the zoo.'

'Gosh, he'd love that, Suki,' said Piers appreciatively. 'And so would Kirstie.'

'And so would I!' laughed Suki. 'I love zoos, but I rarely get a chance to indulge myself—you really need a child in tow!'

'Well, if you take him there on a real, live London double-decker bus he'll be your friend for life! We keep promising him a ride on one, but we've never quite got round to it.' And then he said something which Suki couldn't quite catch.

'What was that?' she said.

'Oh, nothing. Pasquale just walked back into the office and was intrigued by my conversation.'

'Oh,' said Suki flatly, and felt the briefest pang of jealousy. Just because her brother had easy access to the man she claimed to hate?

Please!

'Mmm,' carried on Piers, as though she hadn't spoken. 'It seems that *he's* never been on a double-decker bus either.'

'Really?' said Suki in a sarcastic voice that she hoped was loud enough for the man in question to hear!

She waited until ten then rang her sister-in-law, who was delighted to take her up on her offer, so

Suki slung on a pair of old jeans and a white ruffled shirt, and set off to collect Toby from the pretty tree-lined road in Primrose Hill where they lived.

'Arnie Sooty!' shrieked Toby with excitement as she walked into the playroom, and hurled himself into her arms with all the speed and enthusiasm of a young dynamo. Suki picked her nephew up and cuddled him.

'Want to come to the zoo with me?' she asked.

'Big lions?'

'Lions and tigers and elephants and polar bears, too!'

'And snakes?' he said hopefully.

Suki shuddered. 'Unfortunately, yes, Toby—there will be snakes.'

Suki watched while Toby wriggled out of her arms and banged on a drum excitedly.

'He gets more like Piers every day!' she told Kirstie.

'Piers says he's got your mother's nose, though,' said Kirstie softly.

'Mmm.' For a moment Suki was pensive, a fleeting sadness showing briefly on her lovely face. 'It's strange, isn't it, how familial likeness gallops through the generations? Though perhaps it's not so strange,' she added thoughtfully. 'That's our little bit of immortality, isn't it?'

Kirstie sent her a curious look. 'You sounded quite wistful there, Suki. You're not getting broody, are you?'

Suki forced a laugh as again that disturbing image

of Pasquale as father to her child leapt to the fore-
front of her mind. 'No, I'm not! Toby is my bit of
motherhood by proxy, and that suits me down to the
ground!'

'There are four nappies, his book and his baby
beaker in here,' said Kirstie as she handed over the
bag she'd packed. 'Do you want to take the pushchair?'

'I'd better, hadn't I?'

But a hundred yards down the road her nephew
firmly decided that he wanted to walk, so Suki folded
up the pushchair and carried it underneath one arm,
while Toby clung onto her hand and toddled along-
side her. And then Suki's steps faltered as her eyes
focused on the tall figure at the end of the street who
was standing watching them.

He began walking towards her, his dark eyes never
leaving her face, and her heart gave an unsteady
lurch as each step brought him closer to her.

He was wearing a white T-shirt which was tucked
into black jeans which moulded the narrow line of
his hips, and the casual clothes made him look un-
familiarly carefree and young. The T-shirt was clinging indecently to his chest, outrageously defining the
solid sinew and muscle which lay beneath, and Suki
felt the first, inevitable shimmerings of desire beginning to stir.

She swallowed, momentarily rendered motionless
by the sheer force of his physical impact, feasting
her eyes on him as though it were the first time she

had ever seen him. Four days, she realised, could be one hell of a long time.

'Hello,' he said softly.

Her heart seemed to slow before picking up speed again, and she felt her cheeks flame as they stared at each other.

'Do you know,' he said, 'I don't think I've ever met a woman who blushes quite as easily as you do?'

'Deceptive things, appearances, aren't they?' she mocked.

'Are they?' His eyes gleamed. 'So *did* you miss me?'

'What do *you* think?' she returned sweetly.

'I suspect that you have. Very much. I think that you've probably lain awake at nights unable to get me out of your mind. Am I right?' he enquired silkily. 'Because I know that I have, Suki.'

Suki felt tiny, cold beads of sweat break out on her forehead. She opened her mouth to speak, to deny the truth of what he'd said, but she was saved from the lie by Toby, who had obviously had enough of not being the centre of attention. He stared up at Pasquale pugnaciously. 'That Daddy's man!' he announced.

Suki tried very hard to imagine Pasquale as *anyone's* man, wondering if Toby's words might have offended his monumental ego, but she saw that he was laughing as he crouched down to Toby-height and smiled at the child.

'You're quite right,' he said gravely. 'How's your big wooden train set these days?'

'He go "choo"!' said Toby, delighted when Pasquale echoed 'choo-choo', in an astonishingly realistic impression of a steam-train. Surely there must be *something* he didn't excel at? thought Suki. Yes, of course there was—tact and diplomacy!

'Where you going?' asked Toby.

'I heard your daddy say that you were going to the zoo, and I was kind of hoping that you might let me come with you. May I?'

'Yes!' grinned Toby.

Pasquale rose to his feet and Suki gave him a remonstrative look.

'That wasn't fair!' she protested.

He shrugged, then grinned, and the formidably handsome face became suddenly boyish. 'Who said anything about being fair? You know I'm dying to ride on a double-decker bus.' He gave her an outrageous little-boy look which nonetheless was devastatingly effective. 'You don't mind, do you, Suki?'

'And would it make any difference if I did?'

He shook his head as he took the folded pushchair from her and tucked it underneath his arm. 'Not a bit,' he replied cheerfully.

At the zoo, he took Toby on donkey rides and the old-fashioned carousel which was enjoying a revival. After each eating a burger for lunch they helped the keeper throw fish to the sea-lions and watched the big cats prowl around their reserve. And Pasquale teased Suki relentlessly when she refused to go into the reptile house with them. It came as a sudden

shock to Suki to realise that she couldn't ever remember having quite so much fun.

She had never seen Pasquale look quite so relaxed
and she found herself staring at him curiously as
Toby selected a particularly disgusting-looking ice-
cream and Pasquale paid for it. 'I suppose you'll be
telling me in a minute that you're prepared to change
his nappy?' she asked frankly.

He gave her a half-smile, not the expected shudder
which she had anticipated. 'I will if you want me to.'

'No,' she said hastily. 'It's OK.' And she began
to study the wing colour of one of the parrots in the
bird house as if her life depended on it.

But it wasn't so much his attitude towards *her*
which was affecting her so much—it was his behaviour with Toby which was surreptitiously seeping
into her defences and threatening them with immi-
nent destruction. It was very difficult not to warm to
a man who was so gentle with children.

She couldn't contain her curiosity any longer.
'You're very good with children,' she observed as
she turned away from the parrot to face him, and then
she blanched as a new and very disturbing thought
tripped into her mind. 'You haven't got any of your
own?' she asked before she had time to think about
the question carefully.

He frowned. 'I'm not married,' he said immediately.

'So?'

The frown increased. 'So I'm an old-fashioned
man at heart, Suki, and I would not contemplate hav-

ing children out of wedlock.' He shook his head with a smile as he refused Toby's offer of a lick of ice-cream. 'Any knowledge I have, I have picked up from my niece. Francesca's daughter Claudia—she's a little older than Toby.'

'Francesca has a *daughter*?' exclaimed Suki.

He slanted her a look. 'What's so extraordinary about that?'

'Just that the other day you told me that she was a high-powered career-woman—'

'And the two are incompatible, is that it?' he cut in sardonically. 'As a matter of fact, in Francesca's case, they are. She has continued to work full-time, and Claudia has been brought up by a series of nannies, several of them entirely unsuitable, in my opinion.'

God, but he was autocratic! 'You sound as though you disapprove of working mothers,' she said, with deliberate understatement.

He nodded. 'I'm afraid that I do.'

'Afraid?' It seemed a curious choice of word.

The dark eyes glittered like chips of jet behind the dark, luxuriant lashes. 'I know it isn't the modern way of thinking, but I happen to believe that a child is best brought up predominantly by its parents—'

'But mainly the mother, of course?'

'That's right.'

If she was perfectly honest, she secretly agreed with him, but that was just her own emotional response, and intellectually Suki found herself leaping to the absent Francesca's defence. 'So a woman who may have spent many years establishing herself in a chosen career must then let it all go because of the way that nature distributed the hormones?'

He elevated his eyebrows into two dark, sardonic curves. 'I think that's oversimplifying matters, don't you? A career can always be put on hold—'

'Not one like mine,' put in Suki quickly, 'which is age-dictated.'

His mouth twisted. 'No. Not one like yours. But others can—'

'It's never quite the same,' said Suki stubbornly, 'as for a man.'

He stared at her very intently. 'No, of course it isn't the same,' he agreed. 'But the hormonal thing is a fact, and there's absolutely nothing we can do to change that. Women have the babies; men don't,' he finished.

'So in effect you're saying that equality between the sexes can't exist?' she challenged.

He wiped a blob of ice-cream which had fallen from Toby's cone from one lean thigh and absently licked his finger. 'I prefer the concept of compromise between the sexes, of acknowledging the differences between them and working around those differences.'

Suki plucked a tissue from her shoulder-bag and bent down to wipe Toby's chin, before straightening up. 'Is that why you've never married?' she asked suddenly, wanting to know, *needing* to know, and yet dreading to hear what his answer would be. 'Because you've never found anyone willing to agree to compromise with what some people would say are your—er—rather outdated ideas about men and women?'

He stared fixedly into the distance, at a cluster of flamingoes which glowed golden and pink in the afternoon sunshine. 'You mean the conflict between career and maternal duty?' he asked. 'It's true that I tend to be attracted to the type of woman who *does* have a career, and, perversely, the type that would be least likely to give it up.

'But no, Suki.' And he turned to look at her, some indefinable spark lingering around the depths of his dark eyes. 'Quite apart from the fact that my own career is incompatible with family life, the reason that I have never married is that I've never met anyone I wanted to spend the rest of my life with.'

Suki bent down to unnecessarily wipe Toby's chin again, not wanting to look at Pasquale, painfully aware of the fact that she had been very subtly issued with a warning. Pasquale's analysis had, in effect, served to define the boundaries of any relationship which might occur between them. It was probably kinder that way, and sensible too. But his words hurt, and they only renewed her resolve not to get involved with him.

'It's getting late,' she said. 'We'd better be getting back.'

Unfortunately, not only did he treat Toby to piping-hot fish and chips on the way home, but he then insisted on accompanying her all the way back to

Piers and Kirstie's house, and Kirstie smiled with delight when she saw him on the doorstep.

'I gatecrashed,' Pasquale explained, with a smile.

'Piers rang and said you were intending to. Do come in,' she urged, and to Suki's annoyance he agreed immediately.

He seemed to dominate the room with his dark, masculine presence, and Suki was left feeling like a small animal who had strayed unwittingly into a trap.

She spotted Toby tiredly rubbing his fists into his eyes and saw her escape route. 'Can I bath Toby for you?' she asked.

Kirstie's eyes crinkled at the corners. 'I'll give you three guesses!' she joked, and headed across the room towards the drinks cabinet.

Suki took far longer than was necessary. She and Toby splashed around with his rubber duck, before she washed his hair and brushed his teeth. She read him three Thomas the Tank Engine stories but once he was sound asleep there really was no excuse not to go back into the sitting room, so she reluctantly put the book back on his shelf. Surely Pasquale would have gone by now?

He hadn't.

He was sitting in one of the chintz armchairs sipping a glass of sherry and looking almost like part of the family.

Kirstie, who had been showing him some photos of Toby's christening, including an appalling one of Suki in a hat she had been persuaded to wear against her better judgement, looked up and smiled as she walked in the room.

'Is he OK?'

'Sound asleep. I washed his hair.'

'Did you?' asked Kirstie in admiration. 'How on earth did you manage that? He screams the place down when *I* do it! Sit down and have a sherry— you deserve one!'

Suki reluctantly refused to look into a pair of dark eyes which mocked her. 'I won't, thank you—'

'Nonsense!' said Kirstie. 'You certainly look as though you could do with one!'

They drank sherry and chatted about nothing in particular—or rather Kirstie and Pasquale did most of the talking, while Suki listened in moody silence as he turned on that careless charm, thinking that he really could have coaxed blood from a stone if he'd put his mind to it.

Even in the ordered calm of Kirstie's sitting room, drinking dry sherry in the early evening, she found it impossible not to be aware of his physical appeal— his almost overwhelming masculinity which lay coiled and tense beneath his outwardly cool and urbane appearance. Again and again, she had to resist the urge to let her eyes hungrily stray over towards him.

Eventually, she couldn't stand it any longer, and was just about to leave when Pasquale again surprised her, as he seemed to have been surprising her all day, by placing his empty glass down on a small table and getting to his feet. 'It's time I was going,

Kirstie.' His eyes glittered as he looked down at Suki. 'May I offer you a lift anywhere?'

She shook her head. 'No, thank you. I'd planned to stay for a while.'

'Had you?' His tone was faintly mocking, but he didn't push it. 'Then don't linger too long, or you may be late for your date.'

Her *date*?

He gave her a sardonic smile as he read the genuine puzzlement in her eyes, and it took several seconds before the mists which had temporarily clouded her memory cleared. Of course! She'd lied about having a date this evening when he'd asked her to have dinner with him.

'You know, your date,' he reminded her coolly. 'Don't tell me you'd forgotten all about it, Suki?'

'N-no,' she stumbled. 'Of course not.'

Kirstie saw him to the door and when she came back into the sitting room she was still smiling. 'Oh, I *do* like that man!' she said. 'I've only met him once before,' she confided, 'but I thought he was absolutely *charming*.' She sighed. 'He took us for lunch to a beautiful restaurant overlooking Hyde Park—the three of us—Toby too. He made *such* a fuss of him, but then they say Italian men are very good with children. I know that he *is* Italian, but with that accent you can't really be sure, can you...?'

'No,' said Suki flatly, hoping that this was the end of the eulogy.

A questioning look grew in Kirstie's eyes, and Suki didn't think that she could face an interrogation—or rather she knew that wouldn't be able to lie to her sister-in-law.

'How are things?' she put in quickly, in her cheeriest manner. 'Generally.'

Kirstie shot her a look which spoke volumes. 'Generally? Fine. And specifically they're absolutely wonderful too. I could kiss that man Pasquale Caliandro. Since he took over the company, Piers is like a new man. Oh, he has the occasional moan—that's inevitable—but he works hard and he seems to have won his self-respect back. What's more, when he finishes work, he comes home—to *me*—not to some yuppy wine-bar!'

She blushed to the roots of her flaxen hair, and suddenly looked wildly young and pretty. 'We've been getting on better than we've done in a long, long time. And now that you've managed to change the subject,' she said perceptively, 'tell me one thing—*have* you got a date tonight?'

Suki shook her head. 'No.'

'Then why the hell didn't you let Pasquale give you a lift home?'

'Because I didn't want to.'

'Oh? And what's the matter with Signor Caliandro?'

'He's not my type.'

'Rubbish!' said Kirstie briskly. 'He's everybody's type! And it's quite obvious he's absolutely bananas about you!'

'No, he isn't,' said Suki gloomily. 'He just wants to go to bed with me.'

Kirstie giggled. 'Well, what's so wrong with that? That's what men generally *do* want to do, eventually, and I imagine that most women would be delighted to oblige.'

'That's just the trouble,' Suki said on a long sigh. 'I don't want to be ''most women''.'

Kirstie nodded and a look of comprehension slowly dawned in her bright blue eyes. 'Oh, I see,' she said slowly. 'We're talking exclusive here, are we, Suki? One-man one-woman stuff?'

That was exactly it. In one sentence, Kirstie had managed to hit on what Suki had been trying to deny that she wanted from Pasquale Caliandro since the moment she'd first met him. One-man one-woman stuff indeed. There was even a word for it.

Marriage.

Dumbly, she nodded.

'And how do you know that isn't what *he* wants?' persisted Kirstie.

Suki remembered his words at the zoo. About the kind of women he usually fell for. About never having met a woman he wanted to spend the rest of his life with. You couldn't get much clearer than that! 'He told me,' she said baldly.

Somehow she made her escape without breaking down and blubbing in front of Kirstie, but when she arrived back home she decided to indulge herself, and spent the remainder of the evening alternately calling him every name under the sun and trying not to burst into miserable tears. Because she had a make-up launch at the Granchester tomorrow, and woe betide that her eyes should be swollen.

And, not for the first time lately, she finally fell asleep thinking how crazy it was to have a career which relied on something as unimportant as beauty.

CHAPTER EIGHT

THE following morning, wearing blue shorts and a blue T-shirt with 'C'est Formidable!' emblazoned in gold across her bosom, Suki walked into the vast mirrored ballroom of the Granchester Hotel where the launch was taking place.

And Pasquale was the first person she saw—indeed the only person she saw.

Oh, there were loads of people milling around the place, but one darkly proud head registered itself in her field of vision as though she was destined to see only him.

Their eyes met; his were questioning and hers were—what? Oh, heavens, what were they? How much of herself did she give away with her eyes? Did he know that seeing him again had stirred her senses and her heart into life? Did he realise that when she saw Stacey Lomas bearing down on him she felt a primitive kind of jealousy overwhelming her like a tidal wave so that she felt like screaming out loud?

He nodded and smiled at something Stacey said to him, and then he walked over towards her. 'Hello, *bella*,' he said softly.

'Pasquale.' She inclined her head courteously.

'Did you sleep?' he enquired out of the blue.

147

'Of course I slept,' she lied. 'What on earth makes you think I didn't?'

'These.' And with his finger he touched the delicate skin beneath her eyes. 'There are faint blue smudges which even your make-up cannot disguise—'

'Oh, God!' Now even her looks were going to pieces. It was all very well moaning about her job, but if this continued she soon might not *have* a job! 'What about the photos?'

He shook his head. 'Don't worry. They'll be bleached out by the lights. I doubt whether anyone has noticed them. Except me,' he finished softly, and he sent her a lazy smile which was redolent of sheer, sensual promise.

Suki's skin prickled in helpless response. She felt dizzy just being *near* him, and knew that she had to get away from him quickly before she did something irrevocably stupid, like telling the man that she wanted him to marry her. 'Excuse me, Pasquale—I think they're ready to start shooting.'

'Wait.' He forestalled her with one hand placed on her arm. 'Have lunch with me afterwards.'

'No,' she said instantly.

'Why not?' he taunted softly. 'Afraid to?'

Not afraid—absolutely terrified. She opened her mouth to speak but he prevented her with a gentle shake of his head. 'Don't let's play these games any more, Suki,' he told her softly. 'I have a great deal that I need to say to you.' The dark eyes compelled her to look at him and it would have taken a stronger woman than Suki to resist that gaze.

The expression in his eyes was so mesmerising that she found it impossible to look away. 'What is it?' she whispered.

He shook his head. 'Not now. They're waiting for you. Let's have lunch. That's all.'

'Give me one good reason why, Pasquale,' she told him quietly.

'Because we both want to,' he said simply, and smiled. 'And, as I said, I need to talk to you. And what if I promised you that throughout the meal I would play the gentleman most assiduously?'

'Well, that I would *have* to see!' she mocked.

'Then so you shall. Come—Stacey's on her way over. Let's get these photographs done.'

It was past midday when they called a halt to the session, and Suki was beginning to regret ever having agreed to have lunch with him, but he swept aside all her protestations as he led her out of the ballroom and towards the lift.

'Where are we eating?' she enquired as he pressed the button.

'In my suite.'

For sheer effrontery, he was gold-medal class. She started to shake her head. 'If you think I'm going anywhere near your—'

But he stopped her with an emphatic, 'Suki?'

'What?'

'Didn't I give you my word? And if you stop to allow yourself to think about it instead of jumping to conclusions you'll agree that it's the ideal venue. Quite apart from the fact that it has one of the best views in London, I want privacy when I speak to you.' His eyes flicked over her outfit briefly. 'And I really don't imagine that you particularly want to go into a restaurant dressed like that.'

She had completely forgotten what she happened to be wearing, and looked down to see the gold Formidable logo which was emblazoned all the way across her chest. Subtle it was *not*!

He sighed. 'But if you really cannot bring yourself to trust me, then we could go into the hotel boutique and get you kitted out in something more suitable before going down to the restaurant. Alternatively, we could take my car to your flat and I could wait while you get changed.' His eyes flicked to the gold watch which gleamed on his wrist. 'But if we do that you will miss your lunch, and you look as though you could do with some, because if I'm not mistaken you have lost weight in the last week.'

'Is it any wonder?' she retorted.

'No, not in the least,' he agreed quietly. 'You see, I too have had little appetite.' He saw the cynical look on her face. 'You don't believe me? Look—' And he laid one olive hand against the flat planes of his stomach, and Suki swallowed. Just about the last thing in the world she needed was an anatomy lesson, with Pasquale offering himself as a demonstrator!

'I'll take your word for it,' she said quickly.

It seemed that there was a separate lift just for Pasquale's suite, and when they had arrived at the eighteenth floor Suki could understand why. They stepped straight out of it into a vast, white-carpeted area.

He saw her look of surprise as he gestured her towards one of the rooms off the main vestibule. 'It *is* rather spectacular, isn't it?' he said without boast as she followed him into the room he'd indicated, where a table was lavishly set. 'Do you see what I mean about the view?'

She did. It was breathtaking. 'It's—stunning,' she said faintly as she realised that she could actually read the numbers on Big Ben.

'Come through and I'll get you a drink,' he said.

She looked across at where the damask-covered table was laid with silver and cut glass. Tall candles stood waiting to be lit amidst a fragrant centrepiece of dark pink roses.

She stared at him, her amber eyes narrowing. 'This meal must have taken some foresight.'

He nodded. 'A little.'

'And were you really so certain that I would agree to have lunch with you?'

He didn't seem in the least perturbed by the accusation in her voice. 'I am not a betting man, Suki,' he smiled. 'I could not be certain—let's just say that I was pretty confident.'

'You are *so* arrogant,' she said quietly, and he laughed.

'I know,' he replied, unabashed. 'What are we going to do about it?'

'Absolutely nothing,' she said furiously. 'Because I've just changed my mind about lunch—'

'Suki,' he interrupted softly, 'I'm sorry if I've been flippant. Please stay.'

She willed her legs to move, but they stubbornly refused to obey her. Instead, with all the gullibility of a lamb being led to the slaughter, she allowed him to pull back a chair, and she sank down gratefully.

'Would you like some wine?' he asked her as he took his place opposite her.

She was half tempted to say no—lunchtime drinking always made her sleepy—but never in her life had she needed a drink so much and so she broke the habit of a lifetime. 'Yes, thank you,' she said.

He filled their glasses with the Chablis which was chilling in the ice-bucket beside him and Suki sipped at the fruity wine, appreciating the immediate feeling of relaxation which crept over her.

She put her glass down on the table and gave him a cool, quizzical look. 'So, Pasquale—what did you bring me here to talk about?' she asked, but he shook his head firmly.

'Not yet. First, eat,' he commanded.

She *hadn't* had much appetite recently, and she didn't think she could eat anything, but when she saw the giant peeled prawns, the delicate slivers of smoked salmon, and the delicious salads, she felt genuinely hungry for the first time in days.

All the time they ate, Pasquale talked to her about Franklin Motors, about the deal he'd just pulled off in New York, and even though she was fairly dense when it came to understanding finance he explained it so patiently, and in such simple terms, that she felt as though she could have walked out of the room and started dabbling successfully in the stock market!

She had just eaten her way through half a plateful of strawberries drenched in a raspberry coulis when she glanced up to find him silently watching her. The strawberries suddenly lost all their appeal, and she quickly put her spoon down.

'Let's take our coffee through to the drawing room,' he said. 'We can be more comfortable in there.'

Lulled by the good food and wine, Suki rose to her feet, and soon she was settled on one of the big, squashy white sofas, a demitasse of steaming coffee on the table in front of her, watching him pace the floor with the stealth and the grace of a tiger sizing up its prey.

Quite without warning, he suddenly said, 'I owe you an apology.'

It was the last thing in the world she had expected him to say. 'Oh?' she said, completely taken aback. 'For what?'

'For the way I have behaved towards you. Insulting you. Threatening you. And for not believing you when you spoke the truth.'

She wondered what particular truth he had in mind as she gazed at him in amazement. 'And what has brought about this sudden change of heart?'

'I spoke to Salvatore when I was in New York.'

'And?'

His mouth gave a wry twist. 'He convinced me that your relationship with him was purely professional. That you *were* simply mending his jeans.'

Suki held her breath for a moment. 'But *I* told you that!' she declared. 'And you didn't believe me!'

His mouth thinned into a hard line. 'I know. And I was wrong.'

'And that's it?' she queried incredulously. 'That's what the lunch and the view were in aid of—just to say that?'

'No, not just to say that,' he said, and shook his dark head. 'I have scarcely begun, *cara*.'

She leaned back against the sofa and gave him a steady stare. 'Oh?'

'How would you say that we got on yesterday?' he asked suddenly.

She blinked. 'Yesterday?'

'At the zoo,' he supplied, his dark eyes watching her very intently. 'Would you say that we got on well together, you and I?'

Suki looked at him in confusion.

'Be truthful,' he urged.

'Er, well…' She couldn't really *deny* it, could she? Not if she *was* being truthful. 'Yes,' she said eventually. 'Yes, I suppose we did.'

He grinned, and as always it made the hard lines of his face soften. 'Yes, we did. I thought so too. I enjoyed myself—more than I have enjoyed myself for a long time.'

'I'm not sure that I understand,' said Suki slowly, but the trouble was that she suspected that she understood what he meant only too well, and the disdain must have shown in her face. 'What point are you trying to make?'

'I just want you to ask yourself, Suki, who is benefiting from your refusing to acknowledge the attraction between us. Why do you continue to fight it? Fight me? Fight *us*?' he concluded huskily.

Her lips stayed open in genuine surprise. 'But there is no "us", Pasquale.'

'Isn't there? Tell me that you don't think of me every minute and I'll call you a liar,' he said, holding his hand up to silence her as she began to protest. 'There is no shame in admitting that,' he said. '*I* am admitting it, and for me it is something I am not used to—this obsession I have with you. Do you believe me when I tell you that?'

'Oh, yes—I *believe* you,' she answered coolly. 'It's because I haven't given in to you. You're a man who is used to getting everything he wants in life, whenever he wants it. Now you've found something that isn't just yours for the taking, and so you yearn for it all the more. If I went to bed with you this afternoon, you would have forgotten me by tomorrow.'

'*No!*' He shook his dark head in vehement denial. 'That is not so!' he contradicted softly. 'How can it be so when I have not forgotten you all these seven long years?'

Suki breathed out on a sigh as she shook her head, trying very hard not to read too much into his words.

'I still want you, Suki,' he said simply. 'More than I've ever wanted a woman before.'

'And am I supposed to thank you for making that astonishing declaration?'

He frowned, then shook his head. 'I'm not expecting your gratitude.'

'What, then? Just what are you expecting?'

He gave a restless shrug of his broad shoulders and as always when he tried to put his feelings into words his accent deepened and he became more Italian by the second. 'I've gone about this whole business badly, I know that. I have been impertinent, tactless even—saying that I wanted you to become my mistress. Even the word lover offended you. But how else can I say it, Suki? A relationship? How do your men usually put it?'

And with that last remark he damned himself. Her *men*! Good God, but it would amuse him to know that there hadn't been any! Not a single one! Wouldn't that feed his monumental ego even further?

She clasped her hands together so that he would not see that they were shaking with anger. Because for some reason the fact that he was dressing up his desire to bed her with this pseudo-respectable proposal of having 'a relationship' annoyed her far more than anything he had said to her before. At least when he had asked her to become his mistress he had been up front. What a hypocrite!

'"A relationship"?' she repeated faintly. 'I'm not sure exactly what you mean. Perhaps you could elaborate a little, Pasquale. How often would we see each other?'

She saw the gleam in his eyes as he anticipated victory. 'As often as our schedules allow. I'm away a lot, as you know, so our meetings will be somewhat erratic. Of course, now that you're under contract to me at Formidable it's going to be easier to *make* the time. Can you imagine how difficult it would have been if you'd still been jetting all over the place?'

How cold-blooded he sounded, she thought furiously, her blood boiling with rage. And then he smiled. He actually had the nerve to smile! What was more, it was the smooth, cruelly confident smile of a man secure in the knowledge that he'd got what he wanted.

Her!

'Tell me,' said Suki, choosing her words carefully, 'do you have girls in *all* the major cities?' She saw him frown, as if she'd puzzled him. 'Am I to be your girl in London?' she persisted coolly. 'And if that's the case, do I get exclusive access—or am I expected to share you? I suspect that Stacey might be rather put out.'

The anger on his face was so stark and menacing that she might have been intimidated under normal circumstances, but these *certainly* weren't normal circumstances.

'*What* did you say?' he asked, in a dangerously quiet voice.

But his anger was only matched by her own. She

felt reckless with it, drunk with it. 'I wondered whether *Stacey* might mind,' she reiterated.

'Stacey?' He spoke the word as though it were foreign to him.

'Yes, Stacey! I don't know how broad-minded *you* might be, Pasquale, but I'm afraid that I really couldn't tolerate a threesome—'

'A *threesome*? Is that the kind of man you think I am?' he stormed, and if she had thought that she had seen him angry before that was nothing to the look of dark rage on his face now. 'A promiscuous man?'

'And is that the kind of woman you think I am?' she countered heatedly. 'The kind who could be cold-bloodedly propositioned like that? I'm surprised that you haven't had your damned lawyer draw up a contract with all your terms of agreement!' She got to her feet unsteadily. 'I'm sorry, but the answer is no. And now I think I'd better leave, before we say anything else we might regret.'

He was on his feet in an instant. All the anger had vanished from his face; she could read nothing in the implacable mask he now wore. 'Very well,' he said. 'I'll see you out.'

Perversely, stupidly, it hurt like hell that he was prepared to let her go so easily. He would never, she realised with a sinking heart, beg her to stay. He was far too proud a man to do that. 'Please don't bother—'

'I *said*,' he repeated, with soft menace, 'that I'll see you out.'

The silence which accompanied their walk into the

main hall grew more awesomely oppressive by the second, and when he reached out to open the lift doors he turned to her, and his dark eyes pierced her with their intensity.

'Goodbye, Pasquale,' she said shakily, hating the finality of that tiny word, knowing instinctively that once she walked out of that door he would not pursue her again.

'Goodbye, Suki,' he said softly.

There was something so bitter-sweet and so unbearably poignant about the way he said it that for a moment Suki hesitated, torn with emotion, knowing that she must leave, and yet dreading the moment when she finally did.

And he was as motionless as she, as though he too wanted to prolong the moment, his gaze steady and intent while the air around them began to buzz with tension. She could see the pulse that was beating a rapid tattoo at his temple, and she found herself unable to tear her eyes away from him.

It was the softness in his face, and an imagined tenderness about his eyes, which was her undoing, and her own face softened in response. And when he commanded, in a quiet, low voice, 'Kiss me, Suki. Just once. Kiss me goodbye,' she couldn't have resisted him even if she'd wanted to.

Just one kiss, she told herself as wordlessly she went into his arms, and he drew her close, his embrace locking around her tightly as though he would never let her go.

'*Dio mio,*' he muttered in hoarse disbelief as he

cupped her face between his hands to stare at her for a long moment, before lowering his head to take her mouth in a sweet, sweet kiss which she knew the moment it started could have only one possible conclusion. And when he raised his head at last there was a soft smile playing on his lips as he took in her dazed expression.

'That wasn't—fair,' she said shakily.

'What wasn't fair?'

'Kissing me.' She swallowed. 'Like that.'

'Like what? Like this?' And he bent his mouth to hers again, renewing the pressure and leaving her breathless and trembling in his arms. 'Like that?' he mocked gently.

'Yes,' she said helplessly.

'Who ever said anything about being fair?' he murmured into her hair as he held her tightly against him.

'But you promised,' she protested drowsily against his shoulder, aware of the slow, steady thudding of his heart which beat in unison with her own.

'I had my fingers crossed,' he told her shamelessly. 'And what price a promise if it means I stop fighting for what is worth fighting for?'

He stared down at her with a burning question in his eyes. 'Suki?' he asked unsteadily. 'If you don't want to, then just say so. I do not take what is not freely given.'

She knew what he wanted: her assurance that this was what she wanted, something indeed that she gave freely, not something he had coerced her into.

She shook her head. 'You know I want you, damn you,' she said in a trembling voice, and she read the raw exultation in his eyes as he brought his mouth down onto hers. And if there had been any lingering doubt in her mind it was banished with that kiss.

He wasn't at all how she'd thought he would be. She had imagined urgency in his embraces, an impassioned but brief coupling as he sought to douse the fires of his desire which had been raging in his blood for so long.

But it was not a bit like that.

Even with her inexperience, she sensed his restraint as he continued to kiss her, as though he couldn't get enough of her lips, as though he were drowning in their sweetness. And his obvious approbation gave her the courage to cast her inexperience aside, to stop *thinking* and to allow her heart to govern the movements which she found were purely instinctive.

Her hands crept to the broad, muscular bank of his shoulders, curving possessively around his neck, and then she allowed her fingers to roam in glorious abandon in the rich lushness of his hair.

He made a small sound of assertion as he brought her even closer into his body, so that they fitted as perfectly as a hand inside a glove, and she was made achingly aware of the hard throb of his desire which pushed insistently against her.

His mouth was now kissing the soft skin at her neck, and her head was tipped back to allow him access to as much of her flesh as possible. She felt him pulling the T-shirt away from the waistband of her shorts, felt his hand skating slowly beneath towards her acutely aroused breasts, tantalising and tormenting her by refusing to caress them.

She gave a helpless little whimper as she felt his fingers brush lightly over the silk of her bra, then capture one nipple and play with it almost idly, until she felt her knees begin to give way.

He drew his mouth away from hers, and she shuddered at how bereft that abandonment made her feel.

'Now,' he asserted, in a harsh kind of voice.

'Yes, now,' she affirmed shakily. 'Yes, Pasquale, yes...now.'

Without another word he swept her up into his arms and carried her through to the bedroom, where he laid her on top of the vast bed. The curtains were drawn and the room was dim as he peeled off her T-shirt and let it flutter to the floor.

His eyes were blazing as he gazed at her breasts almost dazedly. 'Oh, *cara*,' he murmured before he bent his head to sweetly suckle one nipple, the silk of the bra growing wet and clingy beneath his mouth.

Suki was lost in a world of feeling. Hot, erotic sensations sprang into life in her body. Her breasts were heavy and swollen as he freed them from the restraint of the flimsy little bra she wore and explored their generous curves with enticing movements of his hands and mouth.

He slid the shorts off, then pulled his own T-shirt over his head, his eyes never leaving her face as he unbuckled his belt and unzipped his jeans. And when she saw the magnificent power of him springing free as he removed his briefs she felt like a delicious voyeur and she slowly ran her tongue over her bottom lip, deliberately provocative, saying nothing, promising everything.

He was naked when he came to lie beside her, studying her face intently as he stroked each breast in turn, watching her reaction as his hand moved slowly all the way up the slender length of her leg, pausing to stroke enticing little circles at the soft skin of her inner thigh, which had her moving around in restless frustration, until he took pity on her and his finger moved inside her panties, finding her moist and hot and wanting, wanting, wanting…

'Tell me what it is you like, what it is you want,' he whispered against her mouth as she moved her hips restively. 'I'll give you anything, *cara*, anything you want. Just tell me.'

She scarcely heard his words, she was so caught up in the magical movement of his hands and his lips against her skin. 'Just you,' she said huskily. 'Only you.'

He seemed to lose something of his restraint then, skimming the panties off with a breathless haste it thrilled her to witness, and it didn't even embarrass her when he took a small packet from the locker and began to undo it. She watched as he protected himself—and her—from any repercussions of their lovemaking, and was unable to repress the distinct and totally illogical pang of disappointment which his action produced.

But she forgot everything as he came to lie on top of her, his mouth whispering something incomprehensible into her ear as he entered her with one fierce thrust.

He suddenly stilled as he felt her stiffen from the brief pain which pierced her, her fingernails automatically digging into his back, and she felt the muscles beneath tense up.

'*Madre di Dio!*' he husked in a strangely gritty tone.

Had he guessed? she wondered. Of course he had guessed—but what now? Men as experienced as Pasquale probably wouldn't welcome a virgin in their beds. So what—*what* if he stopped?

Oh, he couldn't.

He couldn't.

The pain a distant memory, Suki began to move her hips, guided by some infinitely welcome instinct, so that on a shuddering sigh he began to move again, more slowly now, and then deeper—deeper and fiercer, each powerful thrust taking her closer and closer to something so exquisite, so unbearably exquisite that she was afraid to acknowledge it for fear that it might prove to be some impossible dream.

And when it did happen it took her completely by surprise. She gave a strangled little noise of disbelief as it began, his name wrenched from her lips on a sob as the first heavenly wave of bliss came, then another, and another—the contractions gradually becoming ripples which stilled into a lethargy that begged for sleep. And Pasquale tensed on one last frantic movement as he climaxed, a small cry escaping his lips as he buried his face in her hair.

They lay tangled together for what could have been seconds or minutes or even hours. Suki felt the beat of her heart gradually slowing to normal. Her head resting against his neck, she was feeling as warm and indolent as a cat stretched before a fire, and yet her thoughts lay in confusion because the situation was completely outside her experience. She had no idea what Pasquale would say or do next. Would he be mockingly triumphant that she had done just what she had vowed not to?

But he surprised her—as he always seemed to be surprising her. He propped himself up on one elbow, a look bordering on regret shading his dark eyes.

'So, Suki,' he said, softly, 'you let me find out in the very worst way possible that you were a virgin...'

The very *worst* way? How horribly censorious he made that sound. Biting her lip, Suki turned her face away from him, but with a gentle hand he moved her back towards him.

'Don't you know that I could have hurt you?' he whispered. 'Hell, Suki, I *did* hurt you, didn't I?'

'Not really. Only a little.'

'I would have been so much more gentle with you had I known.'

'Why? Do your virgins usually announce the fact to you proudly?' she fired back, and closed her eyes before she did something as stupid as crying.

He said something soft and profound beneath his breath, but still she kept her eyes tightly shut. 'Suki?'

'What?'

'Open your eyes and look at me.'

'No.'

'*Yes.*'

Reluctantly, she did as he asked, her chin rising defiantly. 'Why?'

He smiled, the most lazy, relaxed smile she had ever seen him give, and it melted her resolve immediately. 'Would you like me to show you what it can be like when it doesn't hurt at all?'

And, with his naked flesh pressing against hers, his mouth against her neck and his fingers brushing lightly from breast to thigh, there was only one thing she could possibly say. 'You know I would,' she answered, her voice shaky, her body greedily anticipating what was to come, while her mind mocked her. Because, despite all her good intentions, it had been as easy as breathing to end up in Pasquale's bed...

So this is what being a mistress is all about, thought Suki as she sat wearing a bra and a pair of French knickers in Pasquale's bedroom one morning, staring at herself in the mirror. From the bathroom came the sound of the shower running and Pasquale was singing something softly in Italian. He sounded happy, but of course he was happy. He was always happy after they'd made love. Which made him happy ninety per cent of the time, she thought waspishly.

Not that she was really complaining about *that* particular aspect of the relationship. They kept *mean-*

ing to go to the theatre, for a drive out into the country, but they never seemed to make it beyond the bedroom. And she adored making love just as he did. It was just…just…

Suki began to brush her hair, unable to rid herself of the niggly feeling of dissatisfaction.

Yet surely she had everything she wanted? Pasquale was kind, attentive, witty, funny. He made the most beautiful love imaginable. So *why* was it not enough?

The answer was simple: because he hadn't said one word to her that didn't indicate that she was anything more than the latest in a long line of lovers, and she couldn't help the insecurity which made her wonder when she was likely to be replaced. And consequently, instead of flowering and blossoming within the relationship, she sometimes found herself displaying a remoteness which she used as a shield to protect herself against future hurt.

After their first night together, he had asked her to move in with him, a request he had since repeated daily, but on this she had been adamant.

'No, Pasquale,' she had answered coolly, and had seen the dangerous glitter in his dark eyes.

'But why not?' he had demanded.

'Because I value my independence!' she'd lied, knowing that the real reason was that the less she gave, the less she would be hurt.

'You drive me mad! Crazy! Do you know that, Suki?' he'd exploded, in what was these days a rare display of temper, his accent deep and pronounced.

'The first woman I've ever asked to move in with me, and you say no!'

'Well, you know what they say,' she'd answered elusively. 'That the grass is always greener on the other side!' And she had drifted off into the bathroom, hearing his low growl of rage.

'Why are you pulling such an angry face?' came a low voice, and Pasquale's reflection loomed behind her in the mirror, his hands dropping to her shoulders. 'And why do you sit around in nothing but your underwear?' he murmured on a kind of groan. 'So that I want to take you back to bed and—'

He looked swiftly down at his watch and shook his head impatiently. 'There isn't time. I have this wretched meeting to attend.' He dropped a soft kiss onto one bare shoulder, and Suki's heart clenched as she covertly watched the dark head. Oh, how she loved the wretched man! No matter what she told herself, nothing could change that.

'There's always later,' she murmured, tipping her head back so that he could kiss her mouth.

'I'll be home at one,' he said huskily. 'Will you be here?'

'I might.'

'Promise me, *cara*.'

'I'll be here,' she said, smiling, unable to resist him.

'I'll take you out for lunch.'

'That'd be nice.'

He kissed her goodbye and she went back to her flat and changed. Answered a few bills. There was no Formidable job until Saturday and yet she wished that she had something to occupy her mind. She sometimes felt as though she was standing in the wings watching a play of her own life, only taking central stage whenever Pasquale was around.

She arrived back at his suite at five to one, wearing one of his favourite outfits—a simple white button-through sundress—with nothing but a pair of white lacy panties underneath.

She picked up a book and, curling her feet up beneath her, settled down to read it while she waited for him.

And waited.

And waited.

At two-thirty he still wasn't there, and so Suki rang down for a sandwich, then left most of it untouched.

She began to worry. What if he'd had an accident? She didn't even know where he'd gone, for heaven's sake—other than he was out on business—and that could mean almost anything.

She was a jittery mixture of anxiety and anger by ten to four, when the phone rang. She snatched it up as if it were a lifeline.

'Pasquale?' she said.

There was a pause, and then a female voice said, 'Miss Franklin?'

'Yes.'

'Pasquale—Signor Caliandro—asked me to call you to tell you that regretfully he is being held up longer than he anticipated.'

'May I speak to him, please?' asked Suki.

'I'd rather not disturb him,' came the cool reply.

'I see.' Did the woman sound mildly amused, or was that simply Suki's paranoia? She took a deep breath. 'Thank you so much for informing me.'

'My pleasure.' There was a click as the line was disconnected.

Suki almost threw the phone down and began to pace up and down the vast sitting room with its amazing views over the Thames.

How dare he? she thought furiously. How *dare* he keep her waiting then have some female, some *minion*—or *was* she?—telephone her almost three hours later to tell her that he would be late? What kind of person did he think she was that he could treat her in such a way?

Suki was brought up short. A mistress, that was who. That was how men treated women who had no place in their lives bar in the bedroom. Oh, yes, they gave them great sex—but zilch in the way of respect.

She could never remember having been so angry in her whole life; she was literally shaking with rage. Then her gaze came to rest on Pasquale's wallet lying on the coffee-table and inspiration came to her in a flash. Well, if he wanted to treat her like a mistress, then she'd jolly well *behave* like one!

Unrepentantly, she skimmed through it until she found what she was looking for, and then she slammed her way out of the suite and downstairs to order herself a cab.

*   *   *

She arrived back at six, struggling under the weight of all the carrier bags she'd accumulated. She took them straight into the master bedroom, stopping short when she saw that Pasquale was lying on the bed, wearing nothing but a pair of jeans, surveying her from between narrowed eyes.

'Well, hello,' he said, in a tone she couldn't quite decipher. 'I was wondering where you'd got to.'

Suki dropped the carrier bags on the floor and looked down at him, her mouth compressed into an angry line. '*Were* you?'

'Naturally,' he said blandly, but his eyes were very watchful. 'Where have you been?'

'What right do you have to ask me where I've been, when you never bother to tell me where *you're* going?'

'That's because you never ask me. In fact you show no interest whatsoever in what I'm doing, do you, Suki?'

'Because I'm your *mistress*!' she yelled. 'And mistresses *have* no rights, do they? Outside the bedroom, of course.'

A nerve began to flicker dangerously in his cheek. 'Are you going to tell me where you've been?'

'Yes, I'll tell you! I've been out...' She paused deliberately as she let his credit cards flutter in a plastic clatter onto the coffee-table. '*Buying,*' she emphasised.

'That's nice,' he said, in a voice devoid of any emotion. 'Buying what?'

Suki shrugged. 'Whatever took my fancy. I spent

hundreds of pounds and I used your credit cards. I do hope you don't mind—but that's what mistresses do, isn't it, Pasquale—go out and run up huge bills?'

She saw a spark of something raw and frightening in his eyes but when he spoke he sounded horribly calm. 'You think I treat you like a mistress, do you, Suki? Oh, no,' he said softly, shaking his head. 'But if you like I can demonstrate to you how a mistress really *should* be treated.' His eyes flickered over her body. 'Show me what you've bought,' he commanded in a velvety voice.

Suki swallowed. There was something in his eyes which vanquished all her anger, something in his voice which started an aching deep within her.

She shook her head, aware that she'd gone just that bit too far. 'I can settle up with you—'

'Show me,' he repeated softly.

Her heart pounding, she bent to the carrier bag and lifted out the first thing which came to hand—a short black dress in clinging Lycra.

'Put it on,' he said harshly.

'Pasquale—I didn't mean—'

'Put it on,' he interrupted brutally. 'Now.'

She stared into his hot, dark eyes and with faltering fingers she began to undo the buttons of her white sundress, then noticed that he was unbuckling the belt of his trousers...

'Pasquale!' she cried out in excited alarm.

'Take the dress off,' he said softly, and he continued to undress.

Trembling with hunger, she did as he asked, until

she stood before him wearing nothing but her briefs, and she blushed as he kicked his jeans off and she saw just how aroused he was. Quickly, she lifted up the black dress to put it on.

'*No!*' His eyes glittered, and there was a long, tense pause. 'Take off your panties,' he said deliberately.

'Pasquale…'

'Take them off,' he repeated.

She slid them down her thighs, so unbearably excited that she could hardly step out of them, so relieved, so exquisitely relieved when he reached out to pull her down onto the bed. He covered her body with his own and thrust into her without warning. It should have been shameful, humiliating—but it was the most exciting thing that had ever happened to her and, crying out, she couldn't prevent herself from convulsing helplessly around him and almost immediately she felt him shudder within the circle of her arms.

Afterwards there was complete silence in the room, save the sound of laboured breathing gradually returning to normal, and then Pasquale suddenly withdrew from her and rolled over onto his back.

He lay motionless, staring in silence at the ceiling, his face as forbidding as stone, his body tensed as if for a fight. It was as if she wasn't even in the room with him, let alone lying on the bed next to him.

And once the fire had died down in her blood Suki felt completely and utterly empty. *She* had become his mistress. He had not forced her; she had only herself to blame. And *she* had provoked him into that frantic, loveless coupling just now. What else would they provoke each other into before it was all over?

It was in that instant that Suki knew that she needed to get out of his life before she destroyed herself and her self-respect. She drew in a silent breath to prepare herself for a retreat with as much dignity as possible, knowing that she could not possibly get dressed while he lay awake. What if he tried to persuade her to stay? Used that formidable charm and power and sexual potency to make her change her mind?

No, she silently vowed. She didn't want words or awkwardness; she wanted *out*. Of his suite and his arms and his life. With a little sigh, she snuggled into the pillow, her breathing becoming slow and steady as she affected sleep.

She didn't know how long it took for Pasquale to fall asleep beside her. She could tell from the rustle of the sheets that twice he turned to face her, but he spoke not a word and she maintained her charade of serene sleep brilliantly.

It seemed like an eternity, but was probably only ten or fifteen minutes, before eventually she was rewarded with the sound of his slow, steady breathing, and she expelled a soft sigh of relief. She didn't dare risk getting dressed in the bedroom for fear of waking him, so she crept around like a thief, locating her clothes, which she literally threw on in the hall.

The lift was, thankfully, empty, and she raked a brush through her tousled hair and tried to wipe the smudges of mascara from beneath her eyes. But her appearance told the story of a woman who had just been thoroughly ravished, and it took every bit of pride she had to meet the knowing, rather amused stare of the man behind the reception desk.

'May I help you, miss?' he asked.

'You may,' she answered with dignity. 'I'd like some hotel notepaper and an envelope, please. Oh, and a pen.'

'Certainly,' he answered, and placed them on the desk in front of her.

She kept the note short and to the point. It said, 'You paid $5,000,000 for it; I hope it was worth it. Suki.' She placed it in the envelope, sealed it, and handed it to the receptionist.

'Please see that Signor Caliandro gets this, would you?'

'Yes, miss.'

And as she swung out of the hotel she realised that today, for the first time, Pasquale hadn't bothered to use any contraception...

CHAPTER NINE

THE old-fashioned doorbell clanged alarmingly and Suki screwed her nose up, tempted to ignore it, but it clanged again, and more insistently this time.

'I'm coming!' she yelled, and dipped her paintbrush into the jar of linseed, her eyes going ruefully to the large canvas she had been working on for the last fortnight.

Admit it, she thought. It's rubbish. Total and absolute rubbish. You've changed your whole life around so that you can pursue some crazy dream of painting, and now you discover that you can't.

And she knew why.

Didn't legend have it that a broken heart was supposed to inspire creative activity?

But not, it seemed, in her case. In her case it had simply deadened it.

The doorbell rang a third time.

'*OK!*' She pulled the door open and stared into dark and formidable eyes of jet, and for a moment she really thought that she might be about to faint.

'P-Pasquale...' she said tremulously, her defences immediately weakened by the shock of seeing him in the glorious, vital flesh. She took a deep breath. 'I don't want to see you,' she said tightly.

'Yes. You've made that fairly obvious,' he replied.

'*Pasquale!*' she exclaimed as he strode unasked over the threshold. 'Wh-what do you think you're doing?'

'I'm coming in. What does it look like?'

'You can't do that!'

'I just have,' he returned grimly. He turned to face her, his eyes skimming over her, taking in her pale, pinched face, the auburn hair worn in a functional french plait.

And she stared back at him, feasting her eyes on the man she had ineffectually forbidden herself to think about. The dark hair was ruffled, his chin slightly more shadowed than usual. The elegant silk tie was knotted casually, without its accustomed care. He looked like a man who had dressed in a hurry, and it made the bile rise in her throat as her jealous mind immediately leapt to one very painful conclusion as to why that might be.

'If you've come threatening litigation because I've broken my contract—' she began.

'No, Suki,' he interrupted coolly. 'That isn't why I'm here.'

Suki swallowed. Having over six feet of dark and brooding-looking male in the sitting room of the tiny country cottage she was renting made it look like a Wendy house. 'How the hell did you find me?' she demanded.

'It wasn't easy,' he admitted grimly, 'when you left town without a word, and so quickly. You made your disappearance fairly conclusive, Suki.'

'That's what I intended to do,' she returned coolly.

'Obviously.'

'So how did you find me?'

'Your agent told me. Eventually.'

'Carly told you? Why on earth should she do that, when I gave her strict instructions not to—?'

'I appealed to her better judgement.'

'You had no right to do that!'

'Wrong, Suki—I had every right, including the right which demands to know whether you are carrying my child.'

Suki's heart began to beat wildly in her chest. 'Pasquale, I—'

'Are you, Suki?' he demanded suddenly. 'Carrying my child?'

The world seemed to spin on its axis.

'Are—you—pregnant?' he said. 'Because I need to know.'

'No,' she answered quietly, swallowing back the sudden salty taste in her mouth. She had found out a week after she had left his hotel room and the discovery hadn't given her the relief she had expected to feel. Instead, she had spent the whole day crying, feeling that she had been robbed of something incredibly precious.

He let out a small sigh and Suki was appalled at how profoundly his obvious relief wounded her. Just what would he have done if she *had* been pregnant? she wondered angrily. 'Why do you want to know?' she asked.

His eyes narrowed as if her question had surprised him. 'Why?' he repeated mockingly, and Suki felt all her suppressed rage and grief and hurt begin to bubble up inside her.

'Yes, why? Do you normally have to follow your bed-partners up to find out whether you're going to be a daddy or not?'

He stared at her assessingly. '*Normally*,' he answered coolly, 'they don't run quite so swiftly from my bed.'

'I'll bet they don't!' she declared wildly, her face flaring with a hot, jealous flood of blood. 'Well, don't worry, Pasquale—this time you were lucky—'

'Lucky?' he interjected, that speculative look replaced by one of barely contained anger, and his voice sounded suddenly harsh with incredulity. 'Luck was not on my side when I failed to impregnate you. As was my intention,' he added deliberately, his eyes flashing a darkly arrogant challenge at her.

'Your—intention?' she repeated weakly.

His eyes narrowed. 'Naturally. I have never had unprotected sex with a woman. Except with you, Suki. And, believe me, it was no accident. It was a deliberate oversight. Although in the circumstances it was an easy oversight to make—you'd got me so hot for you that I could barely think straight.'

Disbelief warred with some deep, primitive longing as she struggled to make sense of his words. 'You mean—' the words stumbled out '—that you were actually *trying* to get me pregnant?'

'I was making love to you,' he corrected her. 'But

if in the process I made you pregnant, then yes, I would have been an extremely happy man.'

Her head was spinning. 'But why on earth should you want to do that?' she asked in bewilderment.

He studied her for a long moment, before nodding, as though he had come to a decision. 'I am not proud of my behaviour towards you, Suki. Without thought, I have robbed you of your virtue. I have falsely accused you of many things, and for that I am bitterly ashamed.'

Which didn't answer her question at all. 'But I still don't understand why you wanted to get me pregnant,' she said slowly.

He threw her an odd look. 'Don't you? Don't you really? Why does a man suddenly find that he wants to spend every moment, both waking and sleeping, with one woman? Why does a man want this certain woman, and only this one woman, to bear his children? It's called love, Suki.' His voice was very soft. 'And what does that man do when the woman he loves has made it clear to him that she does not feel the same way? I wanted you so badly that I was prepared to tie you to me in the most basic way there is—through procreation.'

She opened her mouth in disbelief, but no words came. He had just said that he loved her, and the words meant nothing. 'You're lying, Pasquale!' she accused shakily. 'You're lying to me!'

He shook his head. 'It's no lie, Suki. Don't you know that I love you? As I think I have probably loved you since you first came to my house as a teenager, standing in the sunshine with that mane of hair all fiery and magnificent and blazing. And the way you used to let your head droop and then slant those golden eyes at me made me have all kinds of wicked desires that kept me awake at night.'

He shook his head. 'But I didn't dare admit what I was feeling and so I fought it. Every damned step of the way. I was trying so desperately to look on you as the schoolfriend of my little sister, and feeling as guilty as hell because the more I saw you, the more I wanted you. It was far easier to learn to hate you after that night of the storm than to admit to the frightening alternative: that I was in love with you.'

It was lies, all lies, and Suki forced herself to quell the wild hope that his words inspired. 'But you threw me out,' she pointed out. 'Remember? Insulted me and treated me with the utmost disdain.'

'And don't you know *why*?' he demanded. 'You were still at school! You were only seventeen, for heaven's sake. I was older, experienced—you were a mere child—a guest in my house, and as such I was responsible for you—*morally* responsible and *physically* responsible. I had no right to abuse my position and power. I very nearly lost control that night—*I*—' he shook his head '—who had never lost control in my life. And I fooled myself, Suki,' he said savagely. 'In so many, many ways.'

'Fooled yourself?' she said, not understanding. 'How?'

'By allowing myself to pretend that I had not known that I was making love to you, that I was half-asleep and that I believed it was someone else. By allowing myself to believe that you were morally corrupt and a bad influence on my sister.

'It took me quite a while to admit that in my heart I had suspected all along that Francesca had been running wild at school since the death of our mother. My father made a mistake in sending her away to Switzerland—a mistake which I had sanctioned in allowing her to go there, since Father was too interested in his beautiful young wife to care much about Francesca's welfare.'

He shook his head, his expression pained. 'It made it easier for me to believe that her behaviour was due to *your* influence. I did that because it was the only way I could cope with the knowledge that I had almost made love to a girl of such tender years. And the only way I could prevent myself from taking you, over and over again, was to convince myself that I despised you. Because no matter how much I wanted you you were too young, Suki. Much, much too young.'

He paused, and the dark, beautiful eyes glittered like jet. 'But I never forgot you, nor stopped wanting you. And when I read about your supposed liaisons with other men it only served to reinforce my prejudice that you were a beautiful but faithless woman—'

'Someone like your stepmother?' she cut in shrewdly, suddenly understanding the influence of the role model that *he* had grown up with, and he nodded slowly.

'I'm afraid that I was guilty of the age-old mistake of dividing women into two categories and judging them.'

'And I certainly wasn't in the Madonna category?' guessed Suki drily.

He shook his head. 'Correct. I had started making plans to bring you back into my life, when my secretary told me that you'd secretly gone off for the weekend with her fiancé, who, incidentally, used to idolise you—'

Her head began to spin and Suki frowned, not understanding. 'You mean—you mean you'd started buying Formidable *before* you saw me in the South of France?'

He smiled. 'But naturally. Did you think otherwise?'

'Of course I did!'

He shook his head. '*Cara*, contrary to what the storybooks tell you, one cannot take over a corporation the size of Formidable overnight—it takes months of planning. As I said, I was eaten up with jealousy at the thought of you cavorting with Salvatore, and yet I was rejoicing in this early opportunity to see you again before I offered you the Formidable contract.

'And when I *did* see you I realised that I was still as vulnerable to your spell. And still I tried to resist. I tried to tell myself you were everything I despised in a woman. And at times I even convinced myself that I hated you. But at others...' His voice trailed off and he looked at her with intent, dark eyes.

'So you invested in Franklin Motors because—'

'Because I needed to have something to fall back on if you refused to accept the Formidable contract, which was not inconceivable.'

'You ruthless swine,' remonstrated Suki, but only half-heartedly. He had bought a company and invested in another because he loved her. She shivered in delight.

'But what I still don't understand,' he queried softly, and his eyes were full of genuine puzzlement, 'is that if I, as I now know I was, was your first and only lover, then why on earth didn't you sue all those damned newspapers for the lies they printed about you?'

Suki shrugged her narrow shoulders. 'I was persuaded not to—it would have been too much hassle, for one thing. Plus I had no desire to have some ambitious counsel try to pull me to pieces on the witness stand.'

He shook his head distractedly. 'I should have guessed, Suki. I should have *known* that there was something so fundamentally sweet and sound at the very core of you. You had far too much pride and dignity ever to have been promiscuous. One by one you gradually blew away my preconceptions, until all that remained was the certain knowledge of how deeply I cared for you.'

'But why didn't you just *tell* me all this?' she demanded. 'Why didn't you tell me that you loved me, instead of all this business about me becoming your mistress?'

He shrugged. 'Pride, for one thing. Because I was convinced that such a volte-face would be implausible after everything I had said and done. And because I was not sure how forgiving—if at all—your nature would be, especially where I was concerned. I was completely in the dark about your feelings for *me*, and that is why I thought it advisable to take things one step at a time.

'I thought that if I gave you time your feelings of anger towards me might one day change into something else. But it didn't work out like that. Instead of growing closer, we seemed to be growing more distant—'

'Because I *hated* being thought of as your mistress. It made me feel expendable—'

'Then why the hell didn't you tell me?'

'Pride too, I suppose—and I hoped that I wouldn't have to—that you might guess. Pasquale,' she said half-exasperatedly, 'didn't you even stop to think about why I had given you my—virtue?' She hesitated as she used his own word. An old-fashioned word. She liked it.

He lifted his hands in supplication. 'I was so crazy about you that I didn't stop to analyse it until after you'd gone, and when I did I realised that you would not have given me something so precious unless you cared about me...' His voice tailed off as his eyes asked a question.

She lifted a hand and laid it very gently on his cheek. 'I wish I *was* carrying your child,' she said softly. 'I wish it more than anything in the world.'

'Suki?'

She smiled at him. 'Yes, I love you. I've always loved you, you idiotic man—don't you know that? Pasquale—'

But she never got to finish what she'd been saying, because suddenly she was in the place she most wanted to be: in Pasquale's arms.

And he was kissing her as if he'd just discovered kissing and it was several breathless minutes before he lifted his head to stare down at her gravely.

'Those things I said about working women giving up their careers to look after children...'

'Mmm?' she asked dreamily.

'Forget them.'

'*Forget* them? That's very magnanimous of you, Pasquale,' she declared, her amber eyes sparking with mischief.

'I can't possibly dictate terms like that. I love you and I want you to be happy.'

'Enough to compromise your theories on child-rearing?'

The broad shoulders were lifted in the smallest of shrugs. 'Oh, yes, my darling. You are a successful woman, and your career is very important to you. I know that. I couldn't possibly ask you to give up everything you've worked for.'

She decided to put him out of his misery. 'Oh, yes, you could!'

'Hmm?' He bent his head to kiss the soft skin of her neck, then paused and lifted it up to stare at her. '*What* did you say?'

'That I agree with you,' she said complacently, amused by the perplexed look which appeared in his dark eyes. 'I think mothers should be with their children, if that's what they want to do. And I do.'

'That's not what you implied the other day,' he said drily. 'The other day you tried to tear my argument to pieces.'

'That's because the other day we were talking hypothetically,' she said firmly. 'And I was standing up for Francesca. Call it sisterhood, if you like. Seriously, Pasquale—I've been growing disenchanted with modelling for some time now. And you always told me that I ought to paint—well, that's what I'm going to do, and painting will fit in very well with family life. In fact, that's what I've been doing since I came to live here.'

For the first time in several minutes his eyes left her, and fell on the canvas she'd been working on when he'd arrived, and a shrewdly assessing look came into his eyes as he studied it.

'What do you think?' she asked suddenly.

'It—' He hesitated and winced very slightly. 'It isn't one of your—better pictures, *bella mia*.'

She gave a sigh of relief. He loved her! He loved her enough to tell her the truth! 'I know it isn't. In fact it's rubbish. My heart hasn't been in it because I've been so miserable—'

'And why have you been miserable, *cara*?' he asked innocently as he began to unbutton her shirt.

'You know very well why.' And she leaned back to make the unbuttoning easier.

'Tell me anyway?' he suggested as the shirt fluttered to the floor. 'Better still, why not show me? And afterwards we can discuss our wedding.'

'Our wedding? I can't remember you asking to marry me.'

'Easily remedied,' he murmured as he carried her off into the bedroom. 'Will you marry me, my beautiful golden-eyed girl?'

'You know I will, you arrogant brute!'

'But soon, *cara*. It must be soon,' he told her sternly. 'I am not prepared to wait for something that means so much to me. As I told you once before, I'm not a—'

'*Patient man!*' she finished, laughing up at him. 'And I am not a very patient woman, so will you please make love to me right now, Pasquale?'

He smiled down at her lovely face as he lay down beside her on the bed. '*Amore mio,*' he murmured softly, shaking his dark head in bemused wonderment, and he bent down and slowly began to kiss her.

Lucy Gordon cut her writing teeth on magazine journalism, interviewing many of the world's most interesting men, including Warren Beatty, Richard Chamberlain, Sir Roger Moore, Sir Alec Guinness, and Sir John Gielgud. She also camped out with lions in Africa, and had many other unusual experiences, which have often provided the background for her books. She is married to a Venetian, whom she met while on holiday in Venice. They got engaged within two days. Two of her books have won the Romance Writers of America RITA® award, SONG OF THE LORELEI in 1990, and HIS BROTHER'S CHILD in 1998 in the Best Traditional Romance category. You can visit her website at www.lucy-gordon.com

TYCOON FOR HIRE
by
Lucy Gordon

CHAPTER ONE

'WHAT are you wearing that thing for?'

Jennifer stood back to let her brother come into her house. She was already nervous about the evening to come, and his irritation only made things worse.

'I thought you bought a new dress for tonight,' he said. 'Dark blue satin, tight, slinky, very effective.' He cast a disparaging glance at her flowing evening gown of gold organdie with its demure neckline. 'You're going to a banquet, not a puritan convention.'

'I'm sorry, Trevor,' she said in a placating voice, 'but I just couldn't wear that blue satin. It's too revealing.'

'You didn't think so when you bought it.'

'Yes, I did, but I'd let you convince me it was my duty to go to this function. Since then I've got my sense of proportion back. I wish I could call the whole thing off.'

'You can't do that,' Trevor said, alarmed. 'How often must I tell you that appearances matter? Everyone knows you're representing the firm at the London Society of Commerce Banquet, and you have to be there.'

'But I was going with David.'

'And now he's dumped you—'

'He hasn't dumped me. We just—aren't seeing each other for a while.'

'Whatever. The point is you can't stay away and you can't go on your own. It would look like weakness. You've got to let the world see that you don't care.'

'But I do care,' she said sadly.

5

Jennifer had planned to attend the banquet with David Conner, the man she loved and had expected to marry. But he hadn't called her since their quarrel two weeks ago, and her heart was breaking. Her ideal evening would have been spent at home having a cup of cocoa and maybe even a good cry. Instead she was dressed up, ready to go out with a stranger.

'I hate all this business of putting on the proper mask,' she said. 'I always have.'

'Never let the enemy see you weakening,' Trevor said, reciting his favourite rule.

'And I hate having to think of everyone as the enemy.'

'It's how business is done. Come on, you've coped wonderfully well so far.'

'But you're not quite sure of me, are you? That's why you called in on your way home from work to make sure I hadn't got cold feet. Well, I have.'

Brother and sister were both part of Nortons Distribution, a trucking empire started by their grandfather, Barney Norton. They owned shares in the firm, and ran it between them since illness had forced Barney to retire. The difference was that Trevor lived and breathed business, while Jennifer had only gone into Nortons to please Barney.

Trevor was a thickset man in his thirties, no more than medium height, with a burly build. He might have been attractive if he hadn't frowned so much. Jennifer respected her brother for his dedicated work, but it was hard to like a man so short-tempered and critical.

'Be sensible,' he said now. 'Go and change into your glad rags.'

'I'm sorry, Trevor, but these rags are as glad as I'm going to get.'

He tore his hair. 'For Pete's sake! Tonight's a chance

to do some networking, make connections. Smile into their eyes, dance close. You've got the looks.'

It was true that nature had gifted Jennifer with the vivid beauty to play the role he'd outlined. Her large dark eyes dominated her oval face, and her mouth was deliciously curved in a way that could be more seductive than she was aware.

But nature had also missed something out. She completely lacked the ruthless drive and competitiveness that could have made her use her sexuality in the way Trevor expected. But he seemed not to understand this.

'You've got assets,' he said now. 'Flaunt them.'

Goaded, she said, 'Why don't you flaunt yours if it's so important to you?'

'Because mine aren't the kind that look good in skintight satin. The boardroom's my sphere, not the ballroom.'

'I must have been crazy to let you talk me into going to this do without David. And hiring an *escort*—even from a reputable agency. Think of it! Paying a man to accompany me!'

'I've told you: it's not like that,' he said impatiently. 'Jack's a good customer, and his grandson is an actor. A failed one, apparently, so he fills in with escort work. You did tell the agency it had to be Mike Harker, didn't you?'

'I asked for Mike Harker and nobody else. And before you ask, yes, I was careful not to let on that I've met his grandfather. As far as he knows it's an ordinary booking, so his pride won't be offended.'

'Good. Apparently he's touchy about favours, and it would have been awkward if he'd refused. What reason did you give for asking for him?'

'I said someone had told me he was very good-looking, and that was what I needed.'

'Fine. And you're quite safe. Jack assures me that Harker knows how to keep his hands to himself. Good grief! What's that?'

Jennifer followed his pointing finger. 'It's a cat,' she said, a tad defensively.

'Another of your waifs and strays, I presume?'

'I found Paws outside my back door, if that's what you mean.'

'Paws? You actually call it Paws?'

'She's a she, not an it, and her paws were the first thing I noticed. They're white and the rest of her's black.'

'Funny how every four-legged tramp seems to find its way here,' Trevor observed grimly. 'I should think the word's gone around the stray community. Drop in on Jennifer Norton. She's a soft touch.'

'Better that than a hard one,' she said quickly.

'As long as you don't bring that thing to the office, like you tried to with your last acquisition. We were just about to sign Bill Mercer up to a really profitable deal, and a damned snake slid out of your desk and nearly gave him heart failure.'

'It was a small grass snake, very sweet and perfectly harmless.'

'And then there was the gerbil—no, don't get me started on the gerbil. Anyway, it's not businesslike.'

'Well, I never was very businesslike, was I? Not the way you are, the way Barney wanted me to be. I shouldn't really be part of Nortons at all, you know. I'm not cut out for the cut and thrust. Sometimes I think I should get out while I'm still in my twenties, and try something else.'

'You can't do that to Barney,' Trevor said, aghast. 'After all he's done for us! I agree, you're a fish out of water, but you've always been his pet, and if you defect it will break his heart.'

'I know,' she said with a helpless sigh, for this was the argument she'd used to herself a hundred times. She couldn't hurt Barney, and the knowledge was like fetters.

'If you'd just use your head a little more,' Trevor said now. 'Stop making decisions that you haven't thought through. You're far too impulsive.'

It was true. Jennifer was warm-hearted and spontaneous, and these qualities often conflicted with the demands of her work. She had brains, and she'd learned the business thoroughly, but people and animals would always matter to her more.

She didn't try to explain this to Trevor. She'd failed too often in the past. She merely contented herself with saying, 'Tonight you're the one who hasn't thought it through. The whole idea is mad.'

'Nonsense! Look, I've got to go. Chin up!'

He gave her cheek a peck and departed.

Left alone, Jennifer sighed. When they were younger she and Trevor had been close, but now that seemed a long time ago. When she tried to argue with him she was out of her depth. In fact, she increasingly felt that her life had been taken over by forces outside her control, and never more so than tonight.

Trevor had spoken of what Barney had done for them, and it was true that he'd taken them in when their mother had died, when she'd been twelve and Trevor sixteen. Nobody had known where their father was, since he'd abandoned his family some two years earlier. There'd been a divorce and he'd moved abroad with his new lover. There had only been their grandfather.

Barney was affectionate, but his idea of childcare had been to scoop them up into his hectic life, taking them with him from place to place. It had been interesting and fun, but there had been nothing to make Jennifer feel less of an orphan.

Barney couldn't replace the father who'd deserted her, but she'd loved him, and striven to please him. She'd worked hard at school, enjoying his praise when she got top marks, and gradually coming to accept that she would go into the business.

'I'm really looking forward to having you two as my partners,' he'd say happily.

Trevor had joined Nortons as soon as he'd left school, and Barney had started preparing for the day his beloved Jennifer would follow. She hadn't had the heart to tell him that she would rather work with animals. To disappoint him would have been to risk losing his love, and she'd long ago learned how painful that could be.

So she'd entered the firm and performed every task well, making him proud of her. When his health had failed, five years ago, Trevor and Jennifer had been ready to take over the reins, leaving him to a happy retirement. To all outward appearances she was a glamorous, successful businesswoman, but inside she felt trapped, and a failure.

Now here she was, ready to attend a function that didn't interest her in the company of a man she didn't know, more imprisoned than ever by the expectations of others. And wishing with all her heart there was some way of escape.

Steven Leary stopped outside the apartment door and looked at his shabby surroundings in dismay. Once his friend Mike Harker had been a wit, with matinée idol looks, destined for stage and film stardom. But that had been twelve years ago. Steven had kept in touch, but they hadn't met for five years. Mike's career had flopped, and he now lived in this dump.

The door opened a crack, revealing one bloodshot eye. 'Who are you?' came a muffled voice.

'Mike? It's me—Steven.'

'Hell. Steven?' Mike drew him inside and quickly shut the door. 'I was afraid you were the landlord.'

They exclaimed over each other, and studied the difference that the years had made. Mike was still handsome, although bleary eyes and a red nose spoiled the effect.

'Stay clear,' he said, waving Steven back. 'I'm a walking flu germ.'

'Did I pick a bad time?' Steven asked, indicating Mike's white tie and tails on a coat hanger. 'You look as if you're going to a première.'

Mike gave him a wry look. 'If I was into premières, would I be living here?'

Over coffee they exchanged awkward conversation. Steven felt embarrassed to ask *Are you still an actor?*, and even more embarrassed to talk about his own success.

'I remember when you joined Charteris Enterprises,' Mike said. 'I said you'd end up running the place, and you did.'

'It's no big deal,' Steven said, speaking less than the truth. Charteris was a huge, powerful conglomerate, and its achievements were his pride and joy.

'You ought to be in bed,' he told Mike.

'I have to go out. I survive by working for an escort agency, and I've got a job tonight.'

'You're a gigolo?' Steven exclaimed, aghast.

'No, dammit, I'm not a gigolo! It's perfectly respectable. If a woman has to go to some function and she hasn't got an escort, she calls my agency and hires me. I just have to be attentive and make the right impression. She goes home to her bed and I go home to mine.'

'Which is where you should be right now. You can't escort a woman in this state. You'll give her flu.'

'And she'll give me money, so that I can stop avoiding the landlord.'

'Tell your agency to send someone else.'

'Too late.' Mike went off into a coughing fit.

'What's she like?'

'Dunno. Never met her. Her name's Jennifer Norton, and that's all I know. It's a commercial function, so she's probably a hard-faced business-type—mid-forties, too busy making money to have a real relationship, so she calls Rent-A-Man.'

'Get to bed,' Steven said firmly. 'I'll go in your place.'

'But they said she asked for me specially.'

'I thought you didn't know her?'

'I don't. But apparently someone recommended me.'

'Could she have seen you on television?'

'No such luck!'

'So she doesn't know what you look like?'

'No way. But she wanted a real looker.'

Steven grinned, not in the least offended. 'And I'm Frankenstein's monster?'

'Cut it out! You always had more than your share of girls, I remember. Can't think why, when you treated them so badly.'

'I never laid myself out to please them, if that's what you mean. Couldn't see the point. My dad used to say women were like buses. There'd always be another one along soon.' He gave a crack of laughter. 'Mind you, he got well clear of Mum before he said it.'

It was true that Steven didn't have the perfect, regular features that distinguished Mike, but many women found him vitally attractive. He was tall, dark, and powerfully made, with broad shoulders, and the set of his head gave him an air of natural authority. His lean face could scowl or laugh with equal fervour. Thick brows shadowed brown eyes radiating a fierce energy that gave his face its striking character. His mouth was wide and generous. It could form a grin that was predatory, even wolfish, but his smiles were delightful. When in a light-hearted mood he could be charming.

A man who stood out in a crowd. A man that another man, or a woman, would think twice before crossing. Perhaps a man to be feared. But not a man that a woman would choose as a gallant escort.

'You can't go and that's final,' he said. 'I'll use your name, and I'll be on my best behaviour. I'd better dash home for my evening rig.'

'No time. She's expecting me in twenty minutes. You'll have to wear mine. Luckily we're about the same size.' Mike coughed again. 'I hope you haven't caught my flu.'

'I never catch anything,' Steven said. 'I'm invulnerable. What are you looking at out of the window?'

'That shiny monster, with this year's registration, parked under my window. If it's yours you'll never pass as a penniless actor.'

'Thanks for the tip. I'll park a few streets away from her house and walk. Now get to bed.'

Her escort was late, which was fine by Jennifer. It gave her time to feed Paws and let her out one last time.

'Hurry up,' she said. 'He'll be here soon—if I'm un-lucky.'

Paws reappeared two minutes later, wet from a pud-dle, and promptly demonstrated her loyalty by leaping into her new mistress's lap.

'Oh, no!' Jennifer wailed, surveying the marks over her dress. 'I can't believe you did that!'

She made a dash for the bedroom, tore off the muddy garment, and began rummaging through her other eve-ning wear, desperately hoping that her worst fears weren't going to be realised.

But they were. Of two other possible gowns, one was at the cleaner's and one had a small tear. Bit by bit her options narrowed down until there was only the dark blue satin left.

'You ungrateful animal!' she chided Paws. 'I took you in, and now look what you've done to me. Oh, well, I suppose there's no help for it.'

Reluctantly she drew on the dress, which was even more daring than she'd realised when she'd bought it. To her horror, the lines of her underwear showed. There was only one thing to do, and that was remove every stitch underneath.

When she'd finished she had the perfect, smooth lines that the dress demanded. Its tight contours flattered her tiny waist and flat stomach, but the neckline was scan-dalously low. She possessed the generous bosom to carry it off, but still, it was going to take nerve. And her nerve was fast slipping away.

Her rich, dark brown hair was swept up in an ele-gantly ornate style. To go with the dress she donned a necklace and earrings made of glittering diamonds. Now she looked like a sophisticated young woman who could cope with anything life threw at her. She only wished she felt like one.

She finished just in time. The doorbell was shrilling. She put her head up, took a deep breath, and went to answer. And as soon as she opened her front door she knew that she'd made the mistake of her life.

The man's looks were striking, if not classically handsome. He radiated an air of arrogance and fierce will. In the very first moment, as they stood looking at each other, Jennifer realised that he was appraising her, his eyes taking a leisurely tour of her form.

She began to be self-conscious about the revealing dress. His gaze made her feel naked, and he was clearly enjoying every inch of her, which made her indignant. After all, he was her employee. Worse still, she saw an ironic gleam in his eyes, as though he understood her thoughts and was amused by them.

In short, she'd expected a tailor's dummy and gotten a man instead.

Embarrassment flooded her. It hadn't occurred to her that she was exposing herself as a woman who had to pay for an escort. But he saw the truth. She found her voice. 'Good evening, Mr Harker. You're a little late, but no matter.'

'My apologies,' he said, in a voice that didn't sound apologetic. 'I had an emergency to deal with, but now I'm all yours.' He spread his hands in a gesture that took in his own appearance. 'All present and correct,' he announced. 'Fingernails specially scrubbed for the occasion.' He offered them to her view, but still with the teasing air that unsettled her.

'Oh, my goodness!' she exclaimed suddenly. 'Those cufflinks.'

She guessed that his 'dress' cufflinks were all a failed

actor could afford, but they looked cheap and nasty, as if he'd bought them off a market stall.

'They're my best,' the man said brusquely. 'What's wrong with them?'

'Nothing, I—' Jennifer struggled to find a polite way of saying what she meant. It was hard. 'They're not quite—I mean, they don't really go with—perhaps I could suggest—just a moment.'

She hurried to her room and found the cufflinks she'd bought for David's upcoming birthday. They were silver, studded with tiny diamonds, and they'd cost her a fortune. She suppressed the little pang they gave her and closed her fingers tightly over them.

Her escort's strongly marked eyebrows rose in surprise when she asked him to hold out his hands. She removed the cheap items and fitted the luxurious cufflinks in their place. Glancing up, she found his eyes on her, and their cool mockery sent a wave of heat flooding through her body.

He regarded the diamonds on his cuffs, and his eyes gleamed as they appraised the diamonds about her neck and on her ears. 'I'm glad I go with your jewellery,' he murmured.

She refused to respond to his mockery. 'Here are the keys to my car, Mr Harker. Shall we go?'

As she opened the garage door on her sleek, four-wheeled beauty, she began to have qualms. 'Perhaps I'd better drive,' she said. She held out her hand for the keys, but Steven didn't move.

'Get in the car,' he said, with a quiet firmness that astonished her. 'I'm here to escort you, and I'll do the job properly. It wouldn't look good for you to be driving. People might guess that you've had to hire me.'

She bit back a retort and got into the passenger seat.

He began backing the car out as expertly as if he did it every day. She wondered where he'd learned that deft handling of a powerful vehicle. It had taken her a week before she was as skilled.

'Which way?' he asked.

'Central London. Go to Trafalgar Square and I'll direct you from there.'

When they were on the road he said casually, 'So, what story do we tell people?'

'Story?'

'About us. If someone asks, we have to say the same thing. When did we meet?'

'Oh—last week.'

'That's a bit recent. Why not last month?'

'No,' she said quickly. 'Not as long ago as that.'

'I see. You were going out with someone else then? Why aren't you with him tonight?'

'Because we—we had a disagreement.'

'Who dumped who?'

'We separated by mutual consent,' she said stiffly.

'You mean he walked out on you?'

'I mean no such thing.'

'Will he be there tonight?'

'Possibly.'

'Then you'd better tell me his name, just in case.'

'His name is David Conner,' she said stiffly.

'Have you worked out how we met?'

'No—I don't know—I'll think of something,' she said distractedly. She was growing more unhappy by the minute.

'I'm surprised to find you so disorganised. We're nearly at Trafalgar Square. Direct me.'

She complied, adding, 'We're going to Catesby House for the London Society of Commerce Banquet. *Careful!*'

'Sorry! My hand slipped on the wheel,' Steven said hastily. In fact, he'd had a nasty shock. There would be people there who knew him. He made a rapid decision.

'You'd better know,' he said, 'my real name isn't Mike Harker.'

'You mean it's a stage name?'

'No, I— Never mind. My name is Steven Leary. We're nearly there. Quickly, tell me something about yourself.'

'My name is Jennifer Norton. I'm the granddaughter of Barney Norton of Nortons Distribution—'

'Nortons Distribution?' Steven echoed. 'Trucks and depots?'

'Yes,' she said, surprised to find him so knowledgeable. 'Our organisation is the best of its kind in the country, and we're rapidly expanding in Europe.' She suddenly remembered who he was. 'Never mind that.'

'Yes, don't say anything too complex,' he said affably. 'My one braincell might not be able to cope.'

She refused to let him needle her. 'Take this next turning and you'll find a car park.'

As he switched off the engine Jennifer went to open her door. 'Wait,' Steven ordered calmly. He walked around the car and opened the door for her, holding out his hand to assist her. 'After all, this is what I'm here for,' he said, with a grin.

'Thank you,' she said, placing her hand in his.

She half missed her footing as she stepped out, but his fingers tightened, holding her steady, and she had an unnerving sense of vibrant power streaming through him and communicating itself through the contact of their skin. For a moment her heart beat faster.

She turned to reach back into the car for her velvet stole, but he was there before her, whisking it out and settling it around her bare shoulders. She couldn't suppress the tremor that went through her at his touch, and involuntarily she glanced up to meet his eyes. She found them fixed on her with a look that brought the colour flooding into her cheeks.

'You're beautiful,' he said seriously. 'In fact, you're sensational. I'll be a proud man, with you on my arm. No, don't say it!' He held up a finger to silence her, although she was too taken aback to speak. 'You don't care whether I'm proud of you or not. It's not part of our bargain. Well, I don't care whether *you* care or not. I'm telling you, you're a knock-out!'

Something was making it hard for her to speak. 'Thank you,' she stammered at last. 'It's nice to know that my escort approves of me.'

'I don't approve of you,' Steven said wryly. 'I disapprove of this whole situation. A woman who looks like you shouldn't have to hire a man, and if she does there's something badly wrong in her life. But you're gorgeous, sexy, and an incitement to every man to do something he'll regret. I only wish I had time to explore that contradiction.'

'My contradictions don't concern you,' she said, her cheeks flaming.

'They would if I decided to let them,' he said carelessly. 'What a pity that I don't have time!' He drew one finger slowly down her cheek. 'We should be going inside.'

'Yes,' she said, remembering, with an effort, why they were there. 'We should.'

Jennifer had attended many functions at Catesby House, and was familiar with its plush red and gilt interior, sweeping stairway and glittering chandeliers. But tonight she seemed to be seeing everything for the first time. The lights were more dazzling, the colours of the other women's dresses more vivid, and the black and white of the men more intense than she remembered ever noticing before.

She went to the cloakroom to deposit her stole. As she emerged to where Steven was waiting for her at the foot of the staircase she had the chance to observe him from a distance, against other men.

The comparison was all in his favour. He was almost the tallest man there. Certainly his shoulders were the broadest, his air the most impressive. But what struck her most was the confidence and authority that radiated from him. He looked like a predator, appraising lesser beings prior to devouring them. She'd seen that aura before, in men who headed great corporations. How did an unemployed actor come to have it?

Actor. Of course. He'd assumed the right role. Anxious to have a good atmosphere between them, she approached him with a smile. 'Congratulations,' she said warmly.

'I beg your pardon?'

'You've got right into the part. You look as if you belong here.'

'Thank you,' he said with suspicious meekness. 'I'm rather nervous among all these important people.'

'They're not really important. They only fancy they are because they've got money. Most business folk don't matter half as much as they think they do.' With a flash of mischief, she added, 'Just look down your nose at them, and they'll take you for one of themselves. I'm expecting you to be a big success.'

His lips twitched. 'You don't feel you got cheated on the deal, then?'

'On the contrary, I think I might have a bargain.'

'Maybe I didn't do so badly myself.' He offered her his arm. 'Shall we go?'

Together they climbed the broad stairs and entered the huge ballroom that was already crowded. Steven's sharp eyes saw at once that Jennifer outshone every other woman in the room. She knew how to choose perfume too. The elusive aroma that reached him was warm, with the faintest hint of musk. It wasn't the perfume of a young girl, but a woman, with all that implied.

He wondered what kind of lover had touched her heart. Had she chosen a giant among men? And what was she like when she was with him? Did her curved mouth grow tender and her dark eyes glow with desire?

They moved through the crowd, smiling and uttering greetings. Several people knew him, and Steven had a nervous time steering her away from them. He would be lucky to get through tonight without discovery, he realised.

'Come to the bar,' he muttered. 'There's something we need to talk about while I get you a drink.'

'I'll have an orange juice, since I'll be driving home.'

'Two orange juices,' Steven told the barman. He grinned at Jennifer. 'Just in case you change your mind.'

'Meaning you think you can change it for me?' she challenged him.

'Is that what I meant? Thanks for letting me know.'

His eyes were teasing, and Jennifer couldn't help smiling back. 'That's exactly what you meant,' she said. She turned back to look at the room. And then the smile froze on her face.

David was standing a few feet away from her.

CHAPTER TWO

JENNIFER had wondered if David would be here. Now she realized that she'd always secretly expected him. Her heart skipped a beat at the sight of his perfect features under thick, wavy, fair hair.

He looked in her direction and Jennifer saw the shock in his eyes. In another moment he would hold out his hands to her and all their differences would be forgotten. But he stayed frozen, his mouth opening and closing. He seemed confused. Then a young woman laid a hand on his arm, and he bowed his handsome head attentively towards her.

Jennifer stood there, stunned. David had turned away from her. There was a bleak, blind look in her eyes, and she forgot everything else, including Steven, watching her face closely.

Perhaps, she thought, David too had hired a companion. But a glance at the young woman banished that thought. She was mousy, and didn't know how to make the best of herself. This wasn't a professional. She was 'real'.

Jennifer's insides twisted at the thought that David had found someone else so soon. Then the girl smiled at him. It was a gentle, heartfelt smile, and it made her face charming. Jennifer was unable to control her little gasp. Steven heard it, and his eyes narrowed with interest.

'So that's him,' he murmured in Jennifer's ear.

'Him—who?'

22

'The pretty boy with the dull girl.'

'I don't know what you mean by pretty boy—'

'He's like a sugar figure on top of a wedding cake.'

'Can we drop this?' she asked with an effort.

'But why? I'm only here to show him that you don't give a damn. So let's show him—unless you're scared?'

'Of course not,' she said quickly.

'Then take the bull by the horns.'

'You're right.' She advanced on David with her hands outstretched. 'David! How lovely to see you.'

He too recovered himself, and she knew he hadn't expected to find her here with another man. 'Jennifer,' he said. 'What a—a lovely surprise.'

'But you knew I planned to come.'

'Yes—er—yes, of course. It's just that—let me introduce you to Penny.' He hastily drew forward the young woman, who gave Jennifer a nervous look, followed immediately by her delightful smile.

'This is Steven Leary,' Jennifer said. As the men shook hands she began to feel more confident. At least David knew she wasn't sitting forlornly at home, waiting for the phone to ring, and he need never know how often she'd done just that.

She slipped her arm through Steven's and he responded on cue, smiling into her eyes with a theatrical intensity that was almost fatuous. She had a mad desire to giggle, as though the two of them were engaged in a private joke that nobody else understood. Not even David.

He was frowning uneasily, as though the sight of her with another man displeased him. But then Penny claimed his attention and he turned away. Jennifer kept her head up and her smile in place, but it was hard.

Fifty round tables filled the room, each seating eight

guests. Jennifer didn't know whether to be glad or dismayed to find that she was at the same table as David and Penny. They were almost opposite her, so she could see how gallantly he drew out her chair. He was always an attentive dinner companion, Jennifer thought wistfully. It made him charming to be with. She averted her eyes.

'Tell me about David Conner,' Steven said. 'What does he do?'

'He owns a small firm making machine tools,' Jennifer said.

'Did he start it himself?'

'No, his father left it to him.'

The meal kept them occupied for a while. Steven played his part to perfection, attending to all her wants and smiling. Then there were speeches. Jennifer was facing the top table, but David and Penny had to turn around, so she could watch them without being seen. She noticed that David didn't rest his hand on his companion's arm, but sometimes he would lean close to speak to her, so that their hair touched.

The speeches ended and the mood became relaxed. People began drifting from table to table. One or two dropped by to talk to her. She did some useful networking, and when she'd finished she noticed that Steven was sitting with David and Penny. David was talking earnestly, and Steven was listening with a frown of concentration that made Jennifer wonder if he were concealing boredom.

'How about asking me to dance?' she said.

'My lady has only to command,' Steven replied, and led her onto the floor for a waltz.

'You don't know what a rare pleasure it is to dance

with a woman tall enough to look me in the eye,' he observed. 'Usually I get a crick in my neck.'

'I thought I ought to rescue you from David.'

'Afraid all his serious talk would be above my head, huh?'

'What did you tell him about us?'

'That I was your toyboy, of course.'

'Can't you be serious for a minute?'

'I'll tell you this seriously. I'm not sure I ought to help you get him back. You might end up married to him, and how would I ever forgive myself?'

'What do you mean?'

'He's not the man you need. You'd always be fighting with him for the mirror.'

'What nonsense!'

'It isn't nonsense, Jenny—'

'Don't,' she said quickly. 'Only David calls me Jenny.'

'It's the wrong name for you anyway. Jenny is a little brown wren, and you're a bird of paradise.'

'Don't be so sure,' she said lightly. 'I might turn out to be a cawing rook instead.'

He broke into laughter. It was a rich, pleasant sound, and several people glanced at them, including David. Immediately she turned up the wattage on her smile, focusing on Steven's face.

'OK,' he said, understanding at once. 'If that's how you want to play it—' He tightened his arm in the small of her back, drawing her against him, and an ardent look came into his eyes. 'You're gorgeous. I hope David appreciates you.'

'Of course he does.'

'Has he mentioned marriage?'

She hesitated. 'In his own way.'

'What does that mean?'

'In actions,' she said reluctantly, 'not words.'

'Don't fool yourself, Jennifer. That "actions not words" argument is how women convince themselves that a man has said something when he hasn't. You want him to propose and he won't. Is that why you quarrelled?'

'Never mind.'

'Of course I mind. Until midnight I'm your new lover, madly jealous of the man you're in love with. You *are* in love with him, aren't you?'

'Completely.'

'More fool you! What *was* the quarrel about?'

How could she stop this man? He seemed to have an hypnotic power that made it natural to tell him whatever he wanted to know.

But it was hard to analyse the quarrel because she wasn't sure what it had been about. They'd been discussing a problem David had had with his firm. To her the solution had been obvious, and she'd been happy to help him. Suddenly she'd looked up to see him watching her strangely.

'You know more about this than I do, don't you?' he'd asked quietly.

Even then she hadn't seen the danger, but had answered cheerfully. 'It's being with that old rascal, my grandfather. Some of it rubs off. Look, darling, all you have to do is—'

But he'd stopped her there, accusing her of trying to take charge. She'd denied it indignantly, and things had escalated. By the time they parted they'd covered so much ground that the original disagreement had become lost.

'It had nothing to do with marriage,' she said now, at last.

'I'm glad. You're worth a better man than David Conner.'

'Don't say that!' she protested quickly.

'Well done! I like you with that glowing light in your eyes. Don't keep trying to watch him. You'll spoil your effect. Concentrate on me. I think you're a knock-out, plus you've got courage and spirit.'

'Do you always talk to your clients like this?'

'My—? Well, it's true that I don't do this often,' Steven said, recovering quickly from his slip. 'I tend to tell people the blunt truth instead of murmuring sweet nothings. Smile at me. He's looking.'

Jennifer offered up her most dazzling smile and he returned it, gazing deep into her eyes. 'That's fine,' he murmured. 'Mind you, you're more impressive when you're annoyed.'

'If you dare to tell me I look beautiful when I'm angry I'll—I'll step on your toe.'

'I promise not to say anything so corny.'

'Good.'

'Even though it's true.'

She saw his lips twitch and couldn't stop herself from responding. The next moment she was joining in his laughter. 'Oh, go to the devil!' she said lightly.

'Certainly. With you in my arms I'll waltz to the mouth of hell and back.' His eyes flickered in David's direction, and he murmured through his smile, 'You've got him worried.'

'Who?'

'David. Don't tell me you've forgotten the poor sap?'

'Of course not,' she said, too quickly. It was true that

she'd been so intrigued by this man that David had briefly slipped from her mind.

'Let's give him something to really worry about,' Steven suggested. He drew her closer still, looking down deep into her eyes. 'I love the cut of your dress,' he whispered.

She knew he meant her low neckline, and to her dismay she started to blush. She was one of those lucky women who could blush attractively, her cheeks going a delicate pink—something the man holding her close noticed with interest.

'You're the most beautiful woman here,' he told her.

'Stop saying things like that,' Jennifer whispered.

'You're paying me to say them,' he reminded her.

She caught her breath with shock. She'd been caught up in this man's seductive spell, her senses vibrating with the power that streamed from him. And it was all a delusion. She'd bought his compliments, and they meant nothing.

'Well, since you're under my orders,' she said in a shaking voice, 'I'm telling you to stop.'

'You hired me to make David Conner jealous, and that's what I'm going to do.'

'I hired you as an accessory, to be useful to my firm,' she said quickly, remembering what Trevor had said.

'Nonsense, that's just the "party line". It's David you care about. Though just why is a mystery to me.'

He raised her chin with his fingers. She couldn't resist him. Suddenly her heart was beating madly. She tried to ignore her own sensations and remember only that she was playing a part. But she could hardly remember the part, or why she was playing it. It was like floating in a dream.

This arrogantly assured man had the nerve to brush

his fingertips over her lips. Jennifer drew a shuddering breath, astounded by the feelings coursing through her. This must stop. She must *make* him stop. But she did nothing. Nor could she speak.

She felt his touch drift across her mouth, along the line of her jaw and down her neck. Then his hand was cupping her head, drawing it closer as he lowered his lips to hers. Jennifer had a devastating sense of losing control. Everything about this evening had been a shock, and most shocking of all was the pleasure that possessed her as soon as his mouth rested on hers.

She lost all sense of time and space. She could no longer hear the band, or see the other couples circling around them. She was moving through the heavens in a dance that would last until the end of eternity. Her heart was beating wildly and she could hardly breathe.

'You must let me go,' she whispered.

'If I had my way I'd never let you go,' he growled. 'I'd whisk you out of here to some place where they couldn't find us, and discover what kind of a woman you really are. The answer might come as a surprise to you too.'

'How dare you?'

'Strange, isn't it? But I already know you as David Conner never will. I know what I want from you, which I'll bet is a damned sight more than he does.'

To her dismay the words 'I know what I want from you' sent a thrill through her. There had been a steely resolution in his tone that she'd never heard before from any man. She loved David for his gentleness and sweet temperament, but in a corner of her heart she had to admit he lacked decisiveness.

Not that decisiveness was all-important. She'd always

told herself that. But in the arms of this purposeful man she felt a unique quiver of response that alarmed her.

She heard him mutter a soft 'Damn!' and came out of her dream to realise that the music was ending. The dancers were slowing and she was in Steven Leary's arms, seeing the shock in his eyes, knowing that it mirrored the shock in her own. And nothing would ever be the same again.

For the next hour Jennifer functioned on automatic. Her mind was still whirling from the devastating encounter with Steven, and her flesh too seemed to be in turmoil, tingling with the memory of his touch.

Out of the corner of her eye she saw him waltzing with Penny. At last he appeared at her side again, taking her hand and leading her to the bar, where he procured her an orange juice. 'You must be ready for some refreshment,' he said. 'So am I. I've been working for you.'

'I saw you dancing with Penny,' she said, taking his meaning. 'How did you find her?'

'She moves too correctly. I prefer a woman who dances with a man as though she wants to make love with him.' His eyes challenged her.

'I can imagine,' Jennifer said, speaking awkwardly to conceal the fact that waves of heat were chasing themselves through her. 'Is that the only fault you can find with poor Penny?'

'She says "Yes" and "No" and keeps missing the step because she's trying to keep her eyes on David. She's his secretary, by the way, and he only invited her this afternoon.' He heard her quick sigh of relief and said mischievously, 'It looks as if he left it until the last minute, hoping you'd call. He doesn't understand you because he's full of himself. He's happier with a girl who isn't as pretty as he is. You two were bound to break up.'

'David and I haven't broken up—not finally.'

'You have if Penny has anything to do with it. She's keen on him.'

With a flash of spirit she said, 'I can take him back any time I want.'

'But is he worth taking?'

'Yes,' she said defiantly.

'All right. Come on.' Steven led her over to where David and Penny were talking. Charmingly he drew Penny away, leaving David and Jennifer together. David drew a deep breath.

'How have you been keeping?' he asked politely.

I've been yearning for you to phone, and breaking my heart when you didn't, she thought. *I've cried when nobody was looking, and tried to understand what I did wrong.*

'Well, you know what it's like at this time of year,' she said with a laugh. 'The work just keeps crowding in and I haven't had a moment to myself. I expect it's the same with you.'

Let me see the old look in your eyes.

'Well, yes, I've been pretty busy,' he agreed. 'In fact, I've been away for most of the last two weeks. That's why I wasn't there if you called me.'

'No,' she said tensely, 'actually, I didn't.'

'Of course not. I didn't mean— Well, anyway...'

He finished with a helpless shrug and a smile. Jennifer caught her breath at that smile, which illuminated his boyishly handsome face.

'David,' she said impulsively, stretching out her hand to him. In another moment he would say her name, and their estrangement would be over.

'Don't stand about talking, darling!' Steven appeared out of nowhere and seized hold of her. 'The night is young. Let's dance!'

Before Jennifer could protest she was swept willy-nilly onto the floor, held firmly in Steven's arms.

'Why did you do that?' she protested. 'He was just going to— What do you think you're doing?'

'Saving you from making a terrible mistake. I was watching, and he wasn't "just going to". You were just going to fall at his feet.'

'That's none of your—! I wouldn't have done any such thing.'

'Your face said differently. Is that all it takes? He gives that little boy smile, and a sensible woman goes ga-ga?'

'Let me go at once. You're right out of order.'

She tried to struggle free but he drew her closer, holding her tight so that his lips were close to her ear, and his body moved against her. 'You should be thanking me, you ungrateful woman! If you'd caved in at the first test your relationship would never have recovered.'

'What do you mean, "test"?'

'It was your first meeting since the quarrel, and you were the one who blinked. I'll bet he was talking about himself. Not about you, or the two of you, but himself. He looks the kind of self-centred idiot who thinks all roads lead back to him.'

She would have died rather than admit he was right. Her heart ached with disappointment that David hadn't come up to scratch, and it hurt that Steven had seen it.

'What is it with women like you that you have to fall for weak men?'

'He's not weak. He's not arrogantly macho, if that's

what you mean. Some men don't feel the need to be. It's a question of confidence.'

'And what did you do to damage his confidence?'

Jennifer drew a sharp breath. 'That's a lousy thing to say!'

'Too near the truth?'

Suddenly she'd had more than she could take for one night. 'I think it's time I went home,' she said.

'Right. Put your hand through my arm and we'll make a grand exit. Head up!'

Jennifer drove the first mile in silence before asking, 'Where shall I take you?'

'Just drop me at the next bus stop.'

'I'm prepared to drive you home.'

'Thank you, but the bus stop will do.'

'There's no need to be a martyr,' Jennifer said patiently. 'Tell me where you live.'

'Must we finish up with an argument?'

'What does it matter?' she said despondently. 'This whole evening has been a disaster.'

'Not the whole evening,' he reminded her. 'There were a few enjoyable moments—'

To her dismay she could feel her cheeks burning at the reminder. To make sure he didn't suspect, she spoke stiffly. 'Forget them, Mr Leary. I've already done so.'

'That I don't believe.'

'These things happen. People get carried away. It means nothing.'

'You act like that with every man? Shame on you!'

She could hear the grin in his voice and strove to keep her dignity. 'You know what I mean. The night's over and we'll never meet again.'

'Think so?'

'Not while I can prevent it.'

'A reckless man might interpret that as a challenge.'

'Don't try.'

'I'll bet you another kiss that you contact me before the week is out.'

'We're approaching a bus stop. Goodnight, Mr Leary.'

As she pulled in to the kerb Steven began to fidget with the diamond cufflinks. 'You'd better have these back.'

She didn't want them. She could never give them to David now. Weariness and disappointment made her say, 'There's no need. Keep them to console yourself for losing your bet. You'll get a good price for them.'

Steven already had the door open, but at this he stopped and regarded her coolly. 'Perhaps I'd rather wear them to remind me of you.'

'I'd rather you didn't,' she said, wishing that he would get out and leave her alone with her sadness. 'I want to forget everything about tonight.'

'And I don't mean to let you,' he said firmly, putting a hand behind her head and drawing her hard against him. It was a swift, decisive movement that left her no time to resist. Before she could think, his mouth was on hers, devastating her with the power and sensuality of his kiss.

He kissed her with fierce purpose. His lips were firm and warm, moving over hers insistently, allowing her no time to protest, to think, or do anything except respond.

'Stop this,' she said in a hoarse whisper.

'I don't want to stop,' he growled. 'And nor do you.'

She tried to deny it, to refuse him the easy mastery that he took for granted, but her blood was pounding and she couldn't think of the words. And besides, his mouth had silenced her again.

He kissed her as though he had all the time in the

world, teasing her with swift flickerings of his tongue against her lips. Those expert movements sent electricity sparkling and crackling along her nerves until every part of her seemed to be sensitised to him.

Her mind protested, but he'd found a way past thought, direct to her deepest, most sensual instincts. He was a master of the skills of the body, a master of provocation and incitement, and if she let him he would soon become her master too.

But the hand she raised to fend him off assumed a will of its own and touched his face instead. Perhaps her fingers curved about his neck and into his hair. She wasn't sure. She was beyond being sure of anything except that she was caught up in a bittersweet delight. She was mad to have let this happen, but it was too late now.

She felt his fingers drift lower to her tiny waist, sliding over the smooth satin that covered the womanly curve of her hip.

But something stopped him. She felt him grow tense, then draw back, releasing her lips abruptly. He was breathing hard and his eyes glinted. 'You madwoman,' he growled. 'Coming out with a stranger like this! You're not wearing anything under this dress. Are you crazy to do such a thing?' He gave her a little shake.

'This shouldn't have happened,' she cried. 'If you'd—you weren't meant to—'

'The hired help was supposed to keep his hands to himself, wasn't he?' he said angrily.

'Get out of this car,' she said in a shaking voice. 'Get out at once. Do you hear?'

'Yes, perhaps I'd better escape while we're both still safe.' He got out and closed the door, still looking at her through the open window. 'Until we meet again.'

'We never will.'

'Don't be stupid,' he said harshly. 'You know better than that.'

There was only one way to silence him and she took it, slamming her foot on the accelerator pedal and driving away. A glance into her rearview mirror showed him still standing there, watching her, a scowl on his face.

CHAPTER THREE

JENNIFER was late getting to her desk next morning. She'd overslept, after spending most of the night tossing and turning. She was horrified at the way she'd succumbed to the physical attractions of a man she barely knew, but he'd triggered sensations that had alarmed her.

She'd finally dozed off, and awoken with one certainty fixed in her mind. She must never, ever see Steven Leary again. He could make her act like a stranger to herself. Or rather, he could bring her up against the fact that she had no clear idea who she was.

She was Barney Norton's beautiful, successful granddaughter, and the apple of his eye. But she was also someone who took in waifs and strays, because she felt like a waif herself, and without them her life was lonely. She was a top businesswoman who was bored with business. And somewhere deep inside she was still the little ten-year-old girl whose adored father had walked out without a backward glance.

She'd thought of David, whose gentle manners and kindly nature she loved. Neither of her menfolk had appreciated him.

'He's very sound,' Barney had said, damning him with faint praise. 'Sound', in Barney's vocabulary, meant uninspired.

Trevor had put it even more bluntly. 'He'll never set the Thames on fire.'

But she didn't want a man who would set the Thames on fire. She wanted a man whose steadiness she could

rely on, and David fitted the bill perfectly. At least he
had, until their quarrel. But that was her fault, she assured herself. She'd offended him by the clumsy way
she'd tried to help. When they made up she would be
more careful.

Safe, dependable David had never tried to rush her,
never demanded. True, there had been moments when
she'd wished he could be a little more decisive, but he
was also vulnerable in a way that touched her heart.
Jennifer's nature had a bedrock of quiet strength, and
while she needed a man to hold onto, she also needed a
man who would hold onto her. She couldn't turn away
from anyone who needed her protection, and David had
only to smile and say, 'What would I do without you?'
to make her melt.

That was her touchstone, the reason she loved David
tenderly. It was why she would never love Steven Leary,
who hadn't a hint of vulnerability in his nature.

What had happened between them was something
apart, a warning that her sensuality could betray her into
the arms of the wrong man if she wasn't careful. But
she would heed the warning. Nothing was going to come
between her and David.

She'd reached the office in such a rush that she was
only vaguely aware that her staff were giving her curious
looks. As always, her first task was to check the firm's
share price. What she discovered made her stare at the
computer screen, frowning.

'That can't be right,' she murmured. 'Why should we
go up by that much since yesterday?'

But the same figures appeared again. Next moment
her phone rang. 'You'd better get in here and let me
know what's been going on,' Trevor growled, and
hung up.

Puzzled, Jennifer crossed the corridor to his office. 'I didn't understand any of that,' she said, closing his door behind her.

'I'm talking about you and Charteris Enterprises.'

'I've had nothing to do with Charteris Enterprises.'

'Oh, no?' Trevor said sarcastically. 'And you weren't with their managing director last night, I suppose?'

'You know where I was last night—at the banquet with Mike Harker. No, wait. He said his real name was Steven Leary.'

'He *told* you that? And you didn't hear alarm bells?'

Trevor shoved a newspaper across his desk. Jennifer's eyed widened at the picture of herself and Steven dancing smoochily. The caption gave details of the banquet, of herself, and of *'Steven Leary, Managing Director of Charteris Enterprises, who is also a major stock-holder and chief architect of its success.'*

'Now people think we're doing a deal with Charteris, and that's why our shares have soared,' Trevor told her.

'I don't understand this,' Jennifer said distractedly. 'You told me Mike Harker was a failed actor.'

'But that isn't him,' Trevor said through gritted teeth.

'Well, he's the man who turned up on my doorstep. This—I just don't understand. I danced with a dozen men.'

'Like *that?*' Trevor demanded, jabbing his finger at the picture. Jennifer drew a sharp breath as she saw what he meant. It had been taken at the moment when Steven had kissed her, and her response left no doubt about the matter. This was far from being just another dance.

She studied herself in dismay, her mind rejecting what her flesh remembered to be true. How could she have melted into his arms in that abandoned way?

And him? Had he too been lost? Or was he laughing

at a successful deception? And later— But she refused to remember later.

'I think I'd better have a talk to Mr Harker—or Leary, or whatever his name is,' she said grimly.

She called Charteris Enterprises. But she was stone-walled by Steven's secretary.

'Kindly tell Mr Leary that I don't know what his game is,' she said at last, 'but I'm going to find out.'

Steven had arrived at work to find the newspaper laid out on his desk and his staff ecstatic over his supposed coup. They'd known that Steven was negotiating to buy Kirkson Depots, a firm that operated in the same area as Nortons, but Kirkson was holding out for too high a price, and everyone now assumed that Steven had been playing a deep game.

He studied the picture, noticing how the clinging dress outlined Jennifer's splendid curves. She was looking up at him, her head thrown back in an attitude of ecstatic surrender, as though her partner was the only man in the world.

She'd wanted him to believe it was all an act, for the benefit of another man, and he'd been almost fooled— until the evening's final moments. Then the seductive spell she'd cast had swept him up. And not just him. She could deny it as much as she liked. He knew.

Alice, his secretary, looked in. She was thin, middle-aged and efficient. She also had a dry sense of humour that helped her survive as Steven's secretary. 'James Kirkson is here,' she said.

James Kirkson had come uttering words like 'com-promise' and 'rethink'. Steven kept his face blank to conceal his sense of triumph. In another few minutes

Kirkson Depots would be his at a bargain price. But he was interrupted by the phone.

'It's Ms Norton,' Alice informed him. 'She's very cross and she's on her way here.'

Steven glanced at Kirkson and made a sudden decision. 'When she arrives,' he announced in a loud voice, 'tell her I love her madly.'

'Very good, sir.'

Exactly fifteen minutes later Alice's door burst open and Jennifer whirled in.

'I'd like to see Steven Leary,' she said crisply.

'I'm afraid that's not possible. Won't you sit down?'

'I won't be here long enough to sit down. Your employer is a devious, conniving—'

'You must be Ms Norton.'

'I certainly am.'

'In that case, Mr Leary loves you madly,' Alice declared, at her most wooden.

For a moment Jennifer felt as though something had knocked the wind out of her. Her head swam, the world glittered, shooting stars rioted in space. Then her senses cleared and she realised that Steven was up to his tricks.

'Does he employ you to talk that stuff?' she asked through twitching lips.

'On this occasion, yes.'

'Whatever he's paying you, it isn't enough.'

'I agree. Can I get you some coffee?'

'What you can get me is Steven Leary's head on a plate,' Jennifer said crisply. 'Better still, I'll collect it myself.'

Alice moved, but she wasn't fast enough. Jennifer swept into Steven's office, already uttering the words, 'How dare you tell the press all that rubbish about us when you know perfectly well—!'

She got no further. Steven was out of his chair and across the room in time to cut off the rest. His mouth descended on hers in mid-word. His arms were like steel about her, preventing all struggle.

Jennifer's indignation fought with her instinctive response. The sense of sheer power holding her exhilarated her even while it made her furious.

He released her mouth just long enough to say, 'Business *and* pleasure, darling.' Lowering his voice, he said urgently, 'Kiss me back, for pity's sake!'

'*Not in a million years—*' She barely got the words out before he silenced her again. The world spun around her, making it impossible to think, or do anything except feel a fierce, sensual delight deep inside her. It was stronger than anger. For a blinding moment it was the only thing in the world.

But the moment passed and she was herself again. She freed her lips, feeling her heart pounding, hoping she wasn't too flushed. She looked into his face, expecting to find in it a look of jeering triumph, and was astonished to see an echo of her own reaction. Steven was breathing hard and his eyes were glittering.

'Jennifer,' he said in a husky voice, 'let me introduce you to—where is he?'

'Mr Kirkson slipped out while you were occupied,' Alice informed him, from the doorway.

'Damn!' Steven said explosively, releasing Jennifer with unloverlike haste. 'He was on the verge of caving in.' He glared at Jennifer. 'Thanks a lot!'

'Are you daring to blame me?'

'If you hadn't barged in just then I could have bought Kirkson's for a knock-down price.'

'Kirkson Depots? So that was it all the time! You set me up last night.'

'No way. It was an accident.'

'Ho-ho-ho!' Jennifer scoffed.

'Don't you "ho-ho" me. You have a lot to answer for.'

'I—?'

'You've just wrecked a deal that would have made this firm a lot of money.'

'A deal that you wouldn't have been in a position to make if you hadn't deceived me.'

'I did not deceive you,' Steven said through gritted teeth. 'Mike Harker's a friend of mine. He was half-dead from flu, so I took his place. That's all.'

Alice looked in again. 'There's a call for Ms Norton. I've put it through.'

Puzzled, Jennifer picked up the phone on Steven's desk, and found herself talking to her brother. 'Trust you to dash off like that without stopping to think!' he complained. 'Barney called. He's over the moon about the rise in our share price.'

'Oh, no!' she breathed. Ever since the firm had gone public it had been Barney's dream to see the price rise, and now it had happened. How could she tell him that it was all an illusion?

'He wants you to bring Steven Leary to dinner.'

'Now see what you've started,' Jennifer said to Steven. 'My grandfather wants you to come to dinner.'

'Fine! I accept.'

'And then this crazy story will get another head of steam. Where will it end?'

'Who knows?' he said wickedly. 'But it might be interesting to find out.' He took the receiver from her. 'Mr Norton, I'd be delighted to accept your invitation.'

Jennifer lifted the extension in time to hear Trevor say, 'My grandfather has invited us all to his house the day after tomorrow. He asks me to say that he hopes you won't mind being outnumbered.'

'I could bring my sister, to even up the numbers and protect me,' Steven suggested.

'Naturally we should be delighted to entertain your sister, Mr Leary, if you think she won't be bored.'

'Maud is a very serious person,' Steven said in a grave voice. 'She's dedicated to making money. I'm sure that you and she will get on well.'

'I'll leave Jennifer to arrange the details with you.' Trevor hung up.

Meeting Jennifer's indignant gaze, Steven said, 'I'm looking forward to meeting your family properly. I'll tell my sister.'

'Barney likes to start the evening at eight,' Jennifer said formally.

'We'll be there at eight. By the way, didn't you notice that I won our bet? I said you'd contact me in less than a week.'

'But you knew this was bound to happen. That's cheating.'

'You owe me. Pay up.'

'Certainly not.'

'I wonder if the press knows how Nortons treats its debts of honour?' Steven mused to nobody in particular.

The teasing gleam in his eye checked Jennifer's retort. She took a deep breath. She knew she ought to escape as a matter of sheer self preservation, but after all it *was* a debt of honour.

'Very well,' she said, trying to speak calmly. 'You may kiss me for precisely five seconds.'

'Oh, I don't think we need to drag it out that long,' he said, dropping a peck on her cheek. 'There. Now you can slap my face if you like.'

'What I would like to do is something for which there are no polite words. When I think of your behaviour last night—letting me think you were just an impoverished actor when all the time—and you took those cufflinks under false pretences. I think you should return them.'

'No can do. I passed them on to the real Mike Harker, with your message about the price he could get for them.'

'It's time for me to go,' Jennifer said, speaking with difficulty. 'I will see you at dinner.'

'I'll look forward to it.'

It was the merest chance that took Steven past Jennifer's house the following evening. He'd been calling on a valuable client, or he wouldn't have been in that direction.

It seemed a good idea to drop in on her. It would be interesting to see her in what he thought of as more 'normal' circumstances. It would be even more interesting to catch her off guard. It was a moot point which motive was the stronger, but since he was honest with himself he admitted he would enjoy taking her by surprise.

But fate turned the tables on him, because whatever welcome he'd expected it wasn't the one he got.

His ring at the doorbell brought the sound of feet scurrying urgently. The next moment the door was yanked open and Jennifer stood there, gabbling with relief.

'Thank heavens you're here, I was getting so worried. I don't think there's much time—oh, dear, it's only you!'

Women had greeted Steven in a variety of ways, ranging from 'Darling, how wonderful!' to 'How dare you show your face here again?' But 'Oh, dear, it's only you,' was new to him.

'Yes, it's me,' he said. 'I gather I'm not who you were hoping to see?'

Without answering she darted past him, down the garden path and into the street. She looked up and down, then, failing to see what she was looking for, did a little dance of frustration.

Steven barely knew her. She was dressed in old jeans and a shapeless shirt that concealed everything he'd hoped to see again. Except for her legs. She had the longest legs of any woman he'd seen, and the shabby denim that covered them couldn't entirely disguise their beauty.

Her face was bare of make-up. Her hair hung free and looked as if she'd been running worried hands through it. A greater contrast to the elegant woman of the banquet or the avenging angel who'd whirled into his office could hardly be imagined.

'This is terrible,' she wailed as she returned to the house and shut the door.

'Thanks,' he said, slightly nettled. 'I'm sorry I'm such a disaster.'

'It's not your fault,' she said, tearing her hair. It flopped over her forehead. She shoved it back but it flopped again.

'Who did you hope I was?' he asked.

'The vet,' she said frantically. 'Paws has just gone into labour.'

'Paws—?'

'My cat. At least, she isn't actually mine, but she wandered in and took over, and I didn't know she was pregnant, but she started acting strangely and I suddenly realised how fat she was—'

'Whoa! I can't keep up. What do you mean, "acting strangely"?'

'She keeps digging holes in the garden and trying to settle into them, and she's panting, as if she's in pain.'

'Where is she?'

'I managed to get her back into her box in the front room.'

He followed her pointing finger to where the cat was curled up in large cardboard box lined with cushions. Paws regarded him anxiously, and he dropped down beside her, feeling her abdomen gently.

'Yes, she's got at least four in there, I should say,' he agreed.

'You know about cats?' she asked hopefully.

'When I was a kid our neighbour had a moggie who littered every six months. For some reason she always came to our garden to give birth, so I got quite used to it. She always preferred newspaper.'

'Right.' Jennifer dived into the kitchen and returned with a stack of papers. Steven gently lifted Paws out into Jennifer's arms, removed the cushions and lined the box thickly with paper. When Paws was returned she sniffed around, then settled down, purring and looking up at Steven with a trusting expression.

'You know what she's thinking, don't you?' Jennifer said with a shaky smile. ''Thank goodness for someone who knows what he's doing!''

'As long as she's satisfied. But I'd be happier if you had a proper vet.'

'He should have been here ages ago. That's who I thought you were. Can you keep an eye on her while I call and see what's happened to him?' She vanished before he could answer.

'She's crazy,' Steven confided to Paws. 'How could she not have noticed that you're expecting? Hey, you're in a bad way.'

The cat was panting again, quick shallow breaths of distress, while a look of fierce concentration came over her face.

'Tell them to hurry up,' Steven called.

But Jennifer was finding the crisis growing deeper every moment. 'Nobody knows where he is,' she said, returning to the front room. 'He left the surgery half an hour ago so he should have been here by now, but he seems to have vanished into thin air—is Paws eating a sausage?'

'No, that's a kitten,' Steven said. 'It was born a minute ago. She's licking it to get it breathing properly.'

Paws's pink tongue was working quickly over a minute black object that wriggled and emitted tiny squeaks. Jennifer dropped to her knees with a smile of delight, and stretched out a tentative hand to scratch Paws's head.

Steven quietly rose and went into the kitchen, returning in a few minutes with a pot of coffee. Jennifer was still leaning over the box, so rapt that she didn't notice him, and he had a moment to notice the soft light on her face as she watched with breathless excitement.

'I should leave her for a bit,' he suggested. 'She's barely started the job yet. She needs peace and quiet.'

He helped her to her feet and drew forward a couple of armchairs so that they shielded the box. 'That'll give her the feeling of privacy.'

'When did you do this?' Jennifer asked, looking at the coffee.

'I've been blundering my way around your kitchen. It wasn't easy, but I finally twigged that tea is in the sugar canister, sugar's in the garlic tin and coffee's in the container marked ''Tea''. Finding biscuits in the biscuit tin threw me a bit, but I coped.'

He poured the coffee and set the sugar near her with practised gestures. 'I'm very domesticated,' he said, noticing her glance. 'My mother saw to that.'

'It's somehow the last thing I'd have expected of you.'

'It's fatal to judge by appearances. I guess we both know that. I never expected to find you the way you are.'

'What did you expect to find? I mean, why are you here?'

'I'm not quite sure. I had to see a client out of town, and the way home lay in this direction. I dropped in on impulse, and got the surprise of my life.' He saw her trying to peek around the armchairs.

'Leave her,' he said firmly. 'It'll be half an hour before the next one's born. By that time, with any luck, the vet will be here.'

But half an hour came and went with no sign of the vet. Another kitten appeared. Steven felt Paws's abdomen gently, and said, 'Two more to come, but things are going well.'

'I'll make a spot of supper,' Jennifer said. 'It's the least I can do for you.'

She went into the kitchen and set to work. Steven looked around at her home, trying to reconcile it with his previous picture of her. When he'd first come here the other night he'd been puzzled to find her living in a bungalow. A smart little flat would surely have fitted the elegant creature in the figure-hugging dress? There had been a sophistication about her that pulled against the cosiness of this little villa. He wondered if somebody had left it to her.

'How long have you lived here?' he asked, lounging against the kitchen doorframe.

She looked up from rummaging in a cupboard. 'I bought it a couple of years ago.'

'Were you living with someone?'

'I beg your pardon?'

'I mean a bungalow is a strange choice for a woman on her own.'

'Is it?' She seemed surprised. 'I just loved this place the moment I saw it. I knew I had to live here.'

She began slicing up peppers. Steven watched her for a moment before turning back to the room. Jennifer heard him murmuring to Paws, and realised that there was no easy way of understanding this man.

In the last two days she'd researched him, and come up with tantalisingly little. He'd built up a chain of small shops before selling them off and joining Charteris Enterprises ten years ago. Charteris was a huge firm that had been underperforming. He'd turned it around, cutting out dead wood, selling off some sections, and doubling profits.

Jennifer had formed the impression of a man dedicated to business: a hard man, keen, ambitious, his mind totally focused on his ends. One newspaper item had hinted at a succession of female companions, none of whom lasted long, but apart from that there was little to suggest that he had a personal life. Wheeling and dealing seemed to be his absorbing passion.

But how did that predator tie up with the man acting midwife to her cat tonight? She was becoming more curious by the moment.

Steven's curiosity was also growing. The more he found the less he seemed to know. On the mantelpiece was a photograph of an elderly man with a thin, pixie face. Next to it was a picture of a boy and girl, both in their teens, and one of a woman in her thirties who bore a marked resemblance to Jennifer.

'That was my mother,' Jennifer said, entering with cutlery and starting to lay the table.

'Where's your father?'

'The old man on the end is my grandfather. You'll meet him tomorrow night.'

'I guessed that might be him. What about your father?'

'This one is Trevor and me together when we were kids.'

'Where—?'

Jennifer had vanished back into the kitchen.

When she returned with food some minutes later Steven had turned out all the lights except a small table-lamp, and was kneeling down beside Paws, murmuring, 'That's it—clever girl—not long now.' He heard Jennifer and looked up. 'She's happier in dim light. Can you see what you're doing?'

'Just about. Don't worry.'

She set rolls and salad on the table, and went to fetch the steaks. Steven positioned his chair where he could take discreet glances at Paws without bothering her.

The phone rang. Jennifer snatched it up and found herself talking to the vet.

'I'm really sorry,' he said. 'My car's broken down, and it'll be at least an hour before I'm there.'

'Don't worry,' Jennifer reassured him. 'She's in good hands.'

'Thanks for the vote of confidence,' Steven said wryly.

'She's all right, isn't she?' Jennifer asked anxiously.

'Doing fine, as far as I can tell. She really means a lot to you, doesn't she?'

'Well, she's such a sweet little thing.'

'And she's your only companion in this empty place?'

'I told you: I love it here.'

'Are you and David going to live here when you're married?'

'I think we'd better keep off the subject of David.'

'Has he been in touch since the other night?'

'I said that's enough,' Jennifer told him with a warning in her voice.

'I guess he hasn't.'

Jennifer refused to answer. She wasn't going to antagonise him, for Paws's sake, but he'd touched a nerve. There had been no sign from David.

'Can I have some more salad?' Steven asked meekly.

'Certainly,' Jennifer said in a frosty tone.

'Go on,' he dared her with a wicked grin. 'Give in to your feelings. Chuck it over me.'

'The only thing I feel towards you at this moment is gratitude on Paws's behalf,' Jennifer said primly.

'You really do love that cat if you're prepared to forgive me for mentioning David.'

'Can we change the subject now?'

'All right. Tell me why there are no photographs of your father.'

'Because he walked out when I was ten years old and nobody's heard from him since,' Jennifer said flatly.

'I see. I'm sorry. It's none of my business. But I don't understand. I thought I knew about Barney Norton, but I never heard he had a son.'

'He didn't. My mother was his daughter, his only child.'

'Then how come your name is Norton?'

'It used to be Wesley, but when our mother died Barney took us in and changed our names to his.'

'Did he ask you first?'

'No, he just did it.'

'Didn't you mind that?'

'Not at all. Have some more coffee.'

She'd changed the subject on purpose. She found herself liking Steven now a lot more than she would have thought possible, but she couldn't have described to him the sensations of her teen self at gaining a new identity.

Jennifer Norton was Barney Norton's granddaughter, loved and wanted and sure of where she belonged in the world. Jennifer Wesley had been the girl who'd thought she was her father's pet until he'd dumped her without a backward glance. She'd cried through long nights for a betrayal she couldn't understand, for a wound that would never completely heal. No, she didn't want to be Jennifer Wesley again.

A glance at the clock told her that it was just the time David had used to call her. But that seemed a long time ago now.

The phone shrilled.

She was out of her chair and hurrying to answer with a speed that brought a frown to Steven's eyes. Watching her face, he saw how hope died as she heard the voice on the other end and it wasn't David's.

'I see,' she said brightly. 'Thank you for letting me know.'

She hung up and stood for a moment, coming to terms with the bleak emptiness inside. Whenever the phone rang it was always David—until it wasn't, and she became again the little girl who couldn't believe Daddy had gone for good because that was his key in the lock. But it was never him.

She saw Steven watching her and summoned up a

smile. 'That was the vet again, saying he's still trying to get here.'

'I see,' he said gently.

'Why are you staring at me?'

'Was I? I'm sorry. Let's have another look at the proud mother.'

Paws had produced a third kitten, and was about to have the fourth.

'I always made some warm milk about now,' Steven observed. 'After all that effort she needs something.'

'Warm milk,' she muttered, racing for the kitchen.

But the time she returned the fourth kitten had been born, and Paws was licking it vigorously. When she'd finished she accepted the milk, then settled down with a satisfied air of having done a hard job well.

'I think that's all,' Steven said, 'but it'll need the vet to be sure.'

'Look,' Jennifer said excitedly, 'the last one's got black fur and white paws, just like its mother.

'Paws Two,' Steven said with a grin.

'Maybe it's a boy. Then I ought to call him Steven.'

She sat down on the floor with her ankles crossed, gazing into the basket with an expression of total rapture.

'You stay there,' Steven said. 'I'll make coffee.'

'Uhuh!' was all the answer he received. Jennifer didn't mean to be impolite, but she was totally absorbed by the miracle. Steven crept away.

When he returned she was still in the same position, watching the new little family with delight. Steven regarded her, puzzled.

'This is what you really want to do, isn't it?' he asked, speaking almost in a whisper, so not to disturb the cats. 'Look after animals?'

'I suppose it is,' she said, accepting the coffee, and

also speaking in a whisper. 'Trevor says this place looks like a sanctuary sometimes, but I can't have too many animals because I'm away all day.'

'Being a tycoon.'

She made a face. 'I don't feel like a tycoon.'

'You don't look like one right now. Is this the woman who whirled into my office yesterday and told my secretary she wanted my head on a plate?'

Jennifer covered her eyes. 'Don't remind me of that when you've been so good to me.'

'But I love it. Alice says you sounded like a medieval tyrant saying, "Bring me the head of Steven Leary."'

'What I actually said was I'd collect it myself.'

'I wish I'd heard you,' he said with a grin.

'Steven, this is terrible. Officially I'm still mad at you for keeping me in the dark the other night.'

'That's OK,' he said with a grin. 'My back is broad.'

'But how can I be mad at you when I've just named a kitten after you?' she demanded logically.

'It's a puzzler, isn't it? Why don't you just change the kitten's name? Then we can be enemies again.'

'Do you want to be enemies?'

'It can be just as interesting as being lovers.'

'Friends, you mean.'

'I know what I mean.' His eyes were gleaming in the semi-darkness. Jennifer refused to rise to the bait.

'I shall never think of you as an enemy after tonight,' she said.

'Rash words. You don't know me well enough to be sure of that.'

'I suppose not. I probably never will.'

'With half London talking about our mad passion for each other?' he teased.

'They'll soon talk about something else. Scandals come and go.'

'Is that what we are? A scandal?'

'Food for the gossips,' she said firmly. 'They'll lose interest.'

'But will we?'

She knew they were straying into dangerous territory, but it was fascinating to sit here in the dim light, watching the gleam in his eyes. Of all the crazy ways to spend an evening!

And yet it was one of the nicest evenings she'd ever known. For all his flirtatious talk, her chief feeling was contentment. It was totally different from the dangerous sensations he'd inspired in her before, but just now it was what she needed.

The doorbell came as an unwelcome interruption. The vet stood there, apologising. Jennifer made the necessary replies and showed him indoors, to the box. Steven had already risen and was getting his things together. The pleasant evening was over.

'I'll see you tomorrow night, at your grandfather's house,' Steven said, making his way to the door. 'I'm looking forward to it, although I doubt if it'll be as interesting as tonight. Goodnight, Jennifer.'

'Goodnight, Steven. And thank you.'

CHAPTER FOUR

THE next day Jennifer spent the afternoon visiting a customer. She returned to her office to find a sheaf of telephone messages.

'David Conner called five times,' her secretary said. 'I don't think he believed me when I kept saying you were out.'

Since the banquet she'd thought a lot about David, wondering how he'd felt at seeing her. She'd resisted the temptation to call him on some pretext, and now her patience had been rewarded.

'David?' she said when he came on the line.

'Thank you for getting back to me, at last.' He spoke lightly, but with a slightly aggrieved note.

'I've been out. But I'm here now.'

'I thought we might have a drink, in our usual place.'

She hesitated. Steven and his sister were coming tonight, and she mustn't be late. 'It'll have to be a quick one.'

'Rushing off to a date?'

Her heart leapt. He minded. 'Of course not. I just have to get home.'

'The Crown, just for a few minutes.'

An hour later she slipped into The Crown, the softly lit cocktail bar where they'd often met before. It had worked. David wanted her back. Once tonight's dinner was over she could quietly disentangle herself from Steven.

David was at their usual table in the corner. He smiled

as she approached, giving her the gentle, uncertain look that always touched her heart. He stood to greet her and kissed her on the lips, but so quickly that she had no time to feel any thrill. There would be time for that later, she told herself.

They made small talk for a few minutes, avoiding both their quarrel and their last meeting. At last David said, 'Thank you for coming. I was afraid you weren't talking to me. I said a few things, that time, that were out of line.'

'I've forgotten it,' she said, smiling with happiness at being with him again.

'Have you? Isn't that why you were giving me the cold shoulder today?'

'David, I was out.'

'Sure that wasn't an excuse to avoid me?' he asked quietly.

'It was nothing to do with you.'

He gave a wry, disbelieving smile. For the first time Jennifer discovered that she could be irritated with David. His need for reassurance could be charming, but did he, perhaps, overdo it a little?

Steven's voice spoke in her head. *He looks the kind of self-centred idiot who thinks all roads lead back to him.* She bade the voice be silent.

'Honestly, David, I wasn't avoiding you. Our row's over and done with.'

'Of course. And you're sure you didn't tell your secretary to put me off?'

'I promise I didn't.'

'I wondered if I might be an embarrassment, now you've found someone else?'

He was jealous, she thought. He still loved her.

'*You've* found someone else yourself,' she said in a teasing voice, but inwardly agog for his answer.

'Penny? She's my secretary. She was just helping me out for the evening. You really pulled off a coup, arriving with Steven Leary.'

'You know him?'

'No—that is, I didn't know who he was that night, but since then one or two people have told me about him—'

He'd been asking about Steven. Heaven!

'You must be pretty close to have given him those cufflinks,' David observed.

She'd bought the cufflinks because David had admired them in a shop window. Obviously he'd recognised them. But she couldn't explain without revealing that she'd hired an escort, which she didn't want to do. While she was hesitating her mobile rang. It was Trevor.

'Where are you?' he demanded.

'Just having a quick drink. I'll be leaving directly.'

'I hope you hurry up. You know we have to get to Barney's for that Leary fellow.'

Trevor's hectoring voice carried. David stiffened and set down his drink. Jennifer hurriedly ended the call.

'I see,' David said heavily.

'It's not what you think. He and his sister are having dinner with us tonight.'

'How cosy.'

'It's just business, David.'

'Really?' he asked quizzically.

'Really. I must go now.'

He held her hand briefly and their eyes met. She leaned down to kiss him, enjoying the warm, comforting touch of his lips. How often in the last few weeks had she longed for it? Now it was hers again.

As David released her she had an odd sense of something missing, something that should have happened and hadn't. But it was foolish to judge David's kisses by Steven's. No one man kissed like any other, and this was her David, whom she loved. She pulled herself together.

'Goodbye, darling,' she said.

'Goodbye. Have a nice evening.'

'Without you?' she asked lightly. 'How could I?'

He smiled and brushed the back of her hand with his lips. Jennifer left with a light heart. She was a little surprised that he hadn't asked to see her again, but she decided that was probably because she'd hurried away before he'd had the chance.

Barney's house was a mansion on the edge of London. Jennifer reached it with enough time to bathe and dress for dinner. As she relaxed in the bath she glanced at the local paper that she'd found in the hall, and something she found there made her eyes open wide.

The gown she'd chosen was olive-green and coolly sophisticated, with a modest neckline just low enough for a simple gold chain, from which hung a garnet. More garnets glowed in her ears. She was triumphant with happiness that her estrangement from David was over, and that he cared enough to be jealous.

She went downstairs to find Trevor there, smartly and soberly attired, his stocky frame radiating gravity. He nodded approval at his sister's appearance.

'I'm glad I've got you alone for a moment,' she said quietly, handing him the local paper. 'Did you see this?'

'"Man fined for being drunk and disorderly",' Trevor read. 'What's so special about that?'

'Look at the name.'

He did so, then whistled. 'Fred Wesley!'

'Our father's name,' Jennifer reminded him.

'Probably just a coincidence. There must be a lot of Fred Wesleys in the world.'

'Suppose it isn't? Suppose he's hanging around here?'

'Jennifer, we haven't heard of him for years. We don't even know if he's alive. And we certainly don't want him turning up again.'

'Don't we?'

'You were too young to know what was going on, but he was bad news. According to Barney, he went after Mum because she had a rich father, and got her pregnant on purpose. When they were married he played around and lived off the money Barney supplied. I heard the rows. Know what he said to me once? "When you grow up, son, never forget that the world is full of women." I was fourteen. A week later Barney cut off the money and told him to get a job. So he moved out to live with his latest bit of fluff. Believe me, we don't want him back.'

'No, I suppose not,' Jennifer mused. She knew what Trevor said was true. Young as she'd been, she too had heard a lot of the rows. She gave herself a little shake. It was morbid thinking this way, and she wanted her wits about her this evening. But she couldn't resist asking, 'Did you ever learn Dad's lesson?'

'About what?'

'The world is full of women.'

'I've had a job to do,' Trevor replied austerely. 'It hasn't left time for the kind of liaisons our father regarded as normal.'

'Yes, you seem to have reacted against him and become a puritan,' she said with a touch of mischief. 'Dad would probably be ashamed of you.'

'I hope so. I'm certainly ashamed of him. I hope our guests aren't going to be late.'

'I wonder what Mr Leary's sister is like?' Jennifer mused.

'A businesswoman, according to him. Besides, her name is Maud.'

'What's that got to do with it?'

'There's something in the name Maud that inspires confidence,' Trevor said, in a voice that settled the matter for all time.

Upon reflection, Jennifer had to agree that he was right.

Barney appeared, dressed to kill. For a man who'd once been so formidable his physique was unimpressive. He was barely five feet six inches, and built on frail lines. His hair was white and thinning rapidly, his face was long and mild, and his eyes genial. A stroke, five years ago, had left him with a limp and an impaired memory. Only the gentle, kindly side of his nature was left, and tonight his eyes were gleaming with enjoyment at the prospect of a dinner party.

Right on cue the bell rang. Jennifer opened the door to find Steven standing there.

'Good evening, Mr Leary.'

'Good evening, Miss Norton.' His tone was admirably formal, but the gleam in his eye belonged to a pirate. 'May I introduce my sister, Maud?'

He stood aside, giving everyone a clear view of the young woman with him. There was a moment's stunned silence.

Maud Leary was in her mid-twenties and haughtily beautiful, in the style of an Afghan hound. Her height nearly equalled her brother's, although it was exaggerated by the way she wore her hair, pulled back from her face and drawn high up into a ponytail on the very top of her head. From there it fell halfway down her back.

Her floor-length dress was in the Grecian style, gathered under the bust and falling straight to the ground. It seemed to be made of metallic gauze, through which could be seen her slim, elegant form, apparently clad in nothing else, although Jennifer noticed the flesh-coloured body stocking.

Trevor drew a sharp breath. Glassy-eyed, he moved forward to greet the apparition, and found himself holding a gold-taloned hand, pointing down, as though its owner expected him to kiss it.

'How do you do?' he said hoarsely.

'How do you do?' she responded in a husky voice.

Steven met Jennifer's eyes and she smiled back, sharing his amusement. 'I can see it's going to be quite an evening,' she said in a low voice.

Steven grinned. 'I wonder if I was right to bring Maud.'

'You think he'll bore her?'

'No, I'm afraid she may eat him alive. It's her hobby.'

'Don't worry about Trevor. Nothing gets to him. How does she come to look so marvellous?'

'By devoting her life to it. She's a model.'

'You told Trevor she was dedicated to business.'

'No, I said dedicated to making money. She earns a fortune.'

'You know that's not how you made her sound.'

Steven's grin made his face suddenly delightful. 'I couldn't help it. Your brother's such a pompous ass that I'm afraid he brought out the worst in me. I'm sorry if that offends you.'

Jennifer laughed. 'It doesn't. I must admit, I've often thought the same.'

'By the way, how are the new mother and babies?'

'In the pink of health. They turned out to be three girls and a boy, all flourishing. The vet was very pleased with how well Paws had come through it. I didn't get the chance to thank you properly.'

'No need. All I did was sit there.'

'But you knew what you were doing, and I think Paws knew that. It made her feel secure. I just made her nervous.'

'As long as she's all right.'

They moved in to dinner. Barney had placed Steven on one side of him and Jennifer on the other. To her dismay, Trevor was next to Maud. Whatever would they talk about? she wondered.

But when she next looked they seemed to be absorbed in each other. Trevor was talking earnestly and Maud was answering in monosyllables. Jennifer caught snatches of his words: 'market share…forward price… Dow-Jones index…' Maud's huge eyes were fixed intently on his face, but it was impossible to tell if there was anything behind them. To Jennifer they looked totally vacant.

She turned her attention back to Steven and discovered him deep in conversation with Barney. They were sitting at right angles to the table, which made it easy for her to follow.

'You didn't know it, sir, but you were my mentor,' Steven was saying. 'When I was studying business there was one lecturer who took your career as a template. He knew every deal you'd ever made, and he analysed them all: all your sharp moves and the other guys' mistakes— which were mostly taking your words at face value.'

Barney roared with laughter. He was thoroughly enjoying himself, and Jennifer could see that he and Steven had recognised each other as kindred spirits.

The conversation became general. Trevor, incredibly for him, told a funny story about Jennifer's first days in the firm, and her early mistakes.

'That's not fair,' she protested, amid laughter. 'I don't do that sort of thing any more.'

'You're worse,' Trevor said. 'You still act first and think later. We call it Jennifer's "red mist",' he explained to Maud. 'It overtakes her without warning and makes her do mad things that I have to spend days sorting out.'

'That's a slander,' Jennifer cried, but inwardly she was delighted to see her brother loosen up and actually smile. In fact he was smiling a lot, mostly in Maud's direction.

It was a warm night, and when dinner was over coffee and liqueurs were served outside on the patio. Trevor was still talking to a fervently listening Maud. Barney had settled down to his favourite subject: his garden.

'I'd like to show it to you, but I'm a little tired. Jennifer, dear, why don't you do the honours?'

Steven took up his glass, and handed one to Jennifer. 'Let's go,' he said.

The garden was dotted with cleverly placed floodlights in various colours, so despite the darkness they found their way along the winding paths among the trees.

'This is an enchanted place,' was Steven's unexpected remark. 'I have a large garden myself, and one day I'd like to do something like this with it. But for the moment Maud is the one who looks after it.'

'She lives with you?'

'Kind of. She travels so much on assignments that it

isn't worth her having her own place, so she keeps a couple of rooms in my house.' He caught a fleeting expression on her face and added quickly, 'And if you're thinking that I come the heavy-handed brother, forget it. Maud looks like the fairy on the Christmas tree, but she's as tough as old boots.'

'I believe models need to be. They're also used to coping with boredom, aren't they?' Jennifer gave a chuckle. 'I expect that's coming in very handy just now.'

'I doubt if anything has prepared her for Trevor,' he agreed.

They drifted lazily along the half-lit paths towards the ornamental pond. It was long and narrow, with a rustic, lamplit bridge over the centre. Jennifer leaned over the railing, looking into her wine glass, listening to the sleepy grunts of the ducks below.

'I have the feeling David Conner has called,' Steven said suddenly.

'You're guessing.' She tried to sound cool, but she couldn't help the smile that touched her lips. Steven was watching her closely.

'I know that you're completely different tonight,' he said. 'The first time we met you were tense and uneasy. The second time you were hopping mad. Last night you were nice, but distracted. Now you're happy and charming. The reason's obvious.'

'Maybe.' She raised her glass in an ironic toast, not even realising that her eyes, gazing at him over the rim, were provocative.

'You shouldn't look at a man like that if you don't mean it,' Steven told her.

'I was only toasting your astuteness. You seem to be able to read me pretty well.'

'Not everything. I can't understand about Conner.

What does he have that transforms you from a nervous witch into a seductive siren?'

'So you think I'm a seductive siren?' she mused, laughing at him.

'You know what I think of you, Jennifer, just as I know that it's mutual. It's there despite the fact that we don't see eye to eye about a lot of things. It's there despite your lover. Is Conner your lover, by the way?'

The question caught her off guard. For the moment she was bereft of words, and Steven went on, 'I don't mean recently, since you quarrelled. Before that.'

'I won't discuss my love life with you—' she began.

'Seeing that you don't seem to have much of one that's a sensible decision. I'd like us to make love.'

His bluntness took her breath away. 'Well, we're not going to make love,' she managed to say.

'In a sense that's what we're doing right now, and you know it. Whatever we say on the surface, there's something else going on underneath, and it has to do with what we learned about each other that first night. Remember when we kissed goodnight? Can you leave it there? Because I can't.'

'You're wrong. David is all I could want. That's why I was heartbroken when I thought I'd lost him.'

'Yes, I remember some of the details of your—er— heartbreak,' Steven said wickedly. He eyed her indignant expression before observing, 'I believe this is the moment where you slap my face. Go ahead and get it over with— What's that?'

'Where?' she asked, trying to get her bearings after his abrupt change of subject.

'Over there.'

A murmur of voices came through the trees, and then

they saw two figures, one tall and willowy, the other broad and stocky, silhouetted by coloured lamps.

'Quick,' Steven said, seizing her hand and drawing her off the bridge into the shadows. Hidden by the trees, they watched as Trevor and Maud strolled over the bridge, Maud's hand held in Trevor's. His voice reached them. It was low, murmuring, intimate.

'Of course a referral to the Monopolies & Mergers Commission drives the share price down, and that's the time to buy, but only if...'

They passed on out of sight.

Steven and Jennifer stood in stunned silence. Then, in the same moment, they exploded into muffled laughter.

'I don't believe it,' she choked. 'Even of Trevor.'

Steven wiped his eyes. 'My poor Maud. She'll never forgive me for this.'

'Moonlight and flowers,' Jennifer said, going off into another gale of laughter. 'And all he can talk about is the Monopolies & Mergers Commission. Oh, heavens! I'll never be an aunt at this rate.'

The tension that had crackled between them was gone for the moment. Laughter had dissolved it into camaraderie—less thrilling, but just as pleasurable in its way. They began to walk on by the water, until they reached a rustic bench and sat there, watching the glow worms.

'I think it's time we discussed how to manage our separation carefully,' she said, 'so that nobody's shares dive.'

'Whoa, there! Who's talking about a separation yet?'

'But this can't go on.'

'It's not as simple as you think. We need to let people see us together at least once more. The day after tomorrow there's a shareholders' meeting for Dellacort Inc.

We've both got stock in the firm, so it'll be quite natural for us to attend together.'

'I don't know…' she mused.

'David is also a stockholder,' Steven said wickedly, 'so he'll probably be there. Think of the possibilities, Jennifer. He'll see us together, you'll tell him it's only business, while contriving, of course, to suggest that you're being evasive, and with any luck he'll send you roses that same evening.'

'You're too good at this,' Jennifer said.

'Manipulation is my middle name.'

His grin was irresistible, and Jennifer's lips twitched. 'Well, I was going to that meeting anyway,' she said. 'And if it has the right effect on David, I suppose I can help you out for a few more hours.'

'Jennifer,' he said admiringly, 'when you talk like that, no man could resist you.'

'Steven, I'll do one more thing, but that's it. Then we have to bring this to an end.'

'We'll see. I may have other ideas. Careful with your drink. You'll spill it on your dress, and that would be a pity, given the delightful way you're filling it out.'

'Don't change the subject.'

'Your charms *are* the subject, as far as I'm concerned. I lie awake dreaming about them. I've lost my appetite and become a shadow of my former self.'

'And pigs fly,' she said, meeting his teasing eyes. 'You're too full of yourself to lose food or sleep.'

'True,' he admitted, 'but I thought I'd say the right thing to show willing. And stop flirting with your eyes. I'm not David Conner, to be teased into delight.'

Jennifer chuckled. She felt happy and self-confident. 'Think I couldn't delight you if I set my mind to it?'

'Only if I decided to let you.'

'I'm sure you've already made that decision. You're not a man to let the grass grow under his feet.'

He raised his glass, acknowledging a hit.

'Did you decide to "let" me the other night?' she asked.

'The other night I was acting a role.'

'Not all the time. I was the one acting, for David's benefit.'

'Including that subtle way you caressed my cheek on the side he couldn't see?'

'You imagined that,' she said quickly.

'I'm a man of no imagination whatever. And what about David's partner? Was she acting too?'

'She's his secretary: helping out was part of her duties.'

'But she's there with him all day, every day. Nine till five. Later, if she's very keen on her work. Yes sir, no sir, three bags full, sir. You should be worried.'

'I know David better than you do.'

'You know nothing about men at all, Jennifer, or you wouldn't have come out into a moonlit garden with me. You'd have known that I'd never let you depart unkissed.'

She'd known exactly that, of course, but pride made her say, 'I'm going back to the house now.'

'Not until you've kissed me. I want to know if I've remembered it right.'

Jennifer tried to tear her eyes away from his, but he seemed to hold her in thrall. Against her will she felt her memory calling up sensations she wanted to forget. They weren't touching, yet she could feel him kissing her as he'd done the other night. The heat was rising in her body now, just as then.

Abruptly she rose from the seat and walked on. He

followed her and caught up, taking her hand in his. 'Listen,' he said softly.

Jennifer listened, and heard the piercing sweet trill of a nightingale.

'If I was making love to you,' Steven murmured, 'I'd talk about you, and the things we both feel, even though you deny them, and I don't believe in them.'

'That doesn't make sense,' she told him, speaking slowly, for she felt as if she were in a dream. 'How can you feel things you don't believe in?'

'It's alarmingly easy. You give me feelings that I know don't exist. If I thought they did, I'd be scared. Even knowing that it's all an illusion—you trouble me, Jennifer.'

They'd reached a large oak tree. Jennifer leaned against the trunk and watched the moon and stars gleaming through the branches. The whole universe seemed to reel overhead, while the breeze softly rustled the leaves.

'Perhaps you should be worried anyway,' she mused softly. 'Some illusions are stronger than reality.'

'You feel that too?'

'But they don't last. You'll return to earth.'

'Will you?'

'I never left it,' she said, knowing herself to be a liar.

He leaned his broad shoulders against the trunk, and stood watching her. 'One of us is a great self-deceiver,' he said. 'I wonder which.'

'We'll probably never know.'

'We'll know one day. Let's hope it isn't too late when it happens.'

He put his hands against the trunk on each side of her head. His body was pressing against hers very slightly, effectively making her a prisoner. She smiled up at him, still feeling in command of the situation. As he began to lower his mouth to hers she was ready for him.

But then something happened. The world seem to shift, altering her perspective, making her wonder what she was doing here, playing love games, when the man she really loved was somewhere else. It was David, with his sweet nature and gentle smile, who held her heart, because she held his. She doubted if Steven Leary even had a heart to offer.

As his lips were about to touch hers she turned her head aside with a swift intake of breath. Steven stopped, regarding her through narrowed eyes. He saw the slight tremor of her mouth and the glint on her eyelashes, and he understood. Abruptly he moved away.

'You really don't know the first thing about men, do you?' he said harshly.

Jennifer was about to defend herself, but he was already walking away.

Since their parents had died, many years earlier, Steven and Maud had been each other's only family. Despite the fourteen-year difference in their ages, they confided in and relied on each other. Maud admired her brother's brains and he respected her shrewdness.

'So that's Jennifer,' she said on the way home. 'She's delightful. There's a sort of radiance about her.'

'Yes, there is,' he said slowly. 'One call from her lover and she's a different woman.'

'But aren't you her lover?'

'Not yet.' Steven said. He fell into a brooding silence, oblivious of the curious looks Maud was giving him.

'Who's the other man?' she asked at last.

'A nobody called David Conner. He won't last.'

'But he's there now, getting in your way,' Maud said

with a chuckle. 'This is going to be fun. I used to think you'd never meet your match.'

'And I never will. Jennifer's quite a woman, and I'm looking forward to the next few weeks. But I don't think I have much to worry about.'

'Brother dear,' Maud purred, 'I may not be clever about things. But I'm very, very clever about people.'

'I've never doubted it.'

'If there's going to be a battle, I'm backing her. I'd rather like to see you writhing in the toils of love.'

That made him laugh out loud. 'Don't count on it. By the way, I'm sorry about tonight. If I'd know what Trevor Norton was like I wouldn't have let you in for an evening with him.'

'Oh, but I thought he was perfectly sweet.'

'Sweet? That pompous, half-baked, hidebound—'

'Steven, please! Don't insult the man I'm going to marry.'

CHAPTER FIVE

AS STEVEN had predicted, David was at the meeting. Jennifer saw him as she and Steven were leaving. She also saw Penny sitting beside David, who was laughing as though very well pleased with her company. The sight gave her a pang.

'Let's go and have lunch,' Steven said, squeezing her hand slightly.

The conference centre's restaurant was airy and spacious, with a glass roof that flooded the elegant grey decor with light. Steven led Jennifer to the best table in the place, beside a window where they had a view of a fountain display in a courtyard. A waiter held out a chair for her, but Steven waved him aside and manoeuvred her to the other side of the table. It was clear that he knew exactly what he wanted, down to the last detail. Jennifer found her own view of the other tables rather restricted, while Steven could see everything.

'I can't see,' she protested.

'Don't worry, I'll tell you everything you need to know about the saintly David.'

'Don't call him saintly.'

'I thought I was paying him a compliment.'

'You thought nothing of the kind. You wouldn't feel flattered if I called you saintly.'

'I've been called many names in an enjoyably misspent life, but saintly wasn't among them.' His eyes, full of meaning, were on her face. 'Certainly never from a woman. Hasn't it occurred to you that we might really give David cause for jealousy?'

'He's already jealous, thank you.'

'He doesn't look it. He's just walked in with Penny on his arm. Don't turn around. Remember, you're lost in the charm of my society.'

'Am I indeed?'

'If you want to get him back, yes. The waiter's showing him to a table—no! Conner's pointing to this part of the room—he wants to be where he can see us. That's encouraging.' He saw Jennifer's indignant glare. 'I'm only trying to be helpful,' he said blandly.

'I mistrust you most when you look innocent. Besides, I told you, he's already jealous.'

'How do you know? Did he come storming around to your home, threatening to put a bullet through us both if you ever saw me again?'

'Certainly not,' she said, laughing reluctantly.

'Then he threatened to put a bullet through himself? Yes, that's much more effective. Play on her heart, be a little pathetic. Works every time.'

'Surely that can't be experience talking?'

'I've never needed to employ pathos, and no woman has ever seen me at the end of my tether. But I've watched it done very effectively. All right, he hasn't thought of that one yet. I know—he threatened to ruin me financially?'

'David wouldn't kn—isn't that kind of man,' she corrected herself hastily.

'And he wouldn't know how,' Steven supplied. 'Exactly. All right, what *did* he do in his frenzy of jealous despair?'

'We met for a drink,' Jennifer said, wishing the words didn't sound so lame.

'And?'

'And what?'

'Don't stop just when it's getting interesting. What did he say? Or is it too intimate and passionate for my ears?'

'Quit trying to wind me up. Anyway, I told you all this the other night.'

'Do you mean we're still discussing that one little meeting?' he demanded, aghast. 'And there hasn't been another one since? My poor Jennifer! What did you do to get saddled with this booby? If I were in love with you, I'd have played merry hell by now.'

'How lucky for me that you're not!'

'Lucky for both of us if this is how you conduct a love affair. There's so much for me to teach you that I don't know where to start.'

'Don't bother. I can sort myself out with David without your help.'

'Fine, I'll come to your wedding—in about fifty years' time.'

'Perhaps he's just as you said—saintly?'

'What a bore he must be!'

'He's a gentleman, if that's what you mean.'

'Same difference!' He studied her for a moment. 'Do you know how lovely you are when your cheeks go that delicate pink?' He waited for her to answer, but she was determined not to.

'He's looking this way,' Steven said after a moment. 'He doesn't like seeing you with me any more than you like seeing him with Penny.'

'I don't give a rap about her; I keep telling you.'

'That's right. You keep telling me. He's turned away now. Their heads are together over the menu.'

'I don't wish to know that—'

'Kindly leave the stage,' he capped.

It was ridiculous. Jennifer tried to keep a straight face but she couldn't manage it.

'It's all right to laugh,' Steven said, watching her face appreciatively. 'Go on, give in to it. That's better.'

He could be disastrously charming when a certain gleam came into his eyes. Suddenly Jennifer was light-headed. The sun was shining on the fountains, the champagne glistened, and she was sitting with a wickedly attractive man who was giving her his whole attention. The thought danced through her head that she could easily become used to this.

Steven embarked on an anecdote about a mutual acquaintance. It was hilarious, and Jennifer rocked with laughter. He joined in and their eyes met. At once she knew it had been a mistake. He seemed to look deep into her, causing a feeling of agitation to start far down in her depths. It rose and spread until it pervaded her through and through. It glittered, too, like tinsel on a Christmas tree, so that her whole being was alive and joyful with the wonderful sensation.

Their lunch was served. She was vaguely aware that the food was delicious, but that sensation was lost in the greater pleasure of Steven's company. He focused his whole attention on her, as though nothing else existed in the world, and, although she knew that he was a clever man, and not to be trusted, she was flattered despite herself. Other women were staring at her with envy. The most attractive, dominant male in the room was absorbed in her, doing her honour, and the feeling was very sweet.

She caught him watching her with a half-smile, and raised her eyebrows in mute query.

'I'm admiring your power-dressing,' he explained, indicating her elegantly tailored charcoal business suit with the snowy white blouse and smart gold accessories.

'It's just as seductive as those daring evening gowns you wear, in a different way.'

'It's not meant to be seductive,' she said primly. 'It's meant to declare that I'm a serious mover in the commercial world.'

'And show off your legs,' he said irrepressibly.

She laughed, and ceded him the point. She was proud of her long legs, clad in dark silk tights that emphasised their perfect shape.

'And I'll bet your hands are manicured to perfection,' he went on. 'Let me see.'

'I wish you'd stop talking nonsense,' she said, but not too seriously, showing him her hand. He took it in his, and touched it with his lips.

'Gallantry from you is something I didn't expect,' she observed lightly.

'I'm acting as a good friend. David is glancing over here, wondering about us. He watches as I kiss the back of your hand—like this—but it doesn't worry him too much, because it's chivalrous, which he understands. But when I turn it over and kiss the palm—like this—then he starts to worry—rightly—because he knows my thoughts of you have taken another turn.'

Jennifer drew a soft, shuddering breath as his tongue flickered against her palm. Excitement raced along her nerves, pervading her whole body, making her heart begin to beat more powerfully and heat radiate out to her loins.

'He knows I want to undress you,' Steven murmured against her hand. 'He probably guesses that I've been thinking of it ever since the night we met.

'Steven—' she said urgently.

'What he doesn't know is exactly how I'd do it—bit by bit, very slowly, savouring, enjoying every last second, and making sure you enjoyed it too. You would, you know.'

'You are insufferably arrogant,' she whispered, speaking with difficulty through the thunder in her ears.

'Why? Because I know I could make you enjoy sharing passion with me? Don't you think you would?'

She couldn't answer. She was fighting the seductive pictures his words conjured up. She knew that, just as he'd said, she *would* relish letting him undress her, very much indeed. Then perhaps she would undress him in return, and discover all the things about his body that were now so tantalisingly hidden. Were his shoulders as broad and his stomach really as flat as she suspected? Were his hips as lean and narrow as in her haunted imaginings, and his thighs as powerful? Would she ever find out the truth?

At the same time she felt a rising indignation at Steven. He could make her want what she'd decided not to want, and it was unforgivable of him. He knew that this was a meaningless flirtation and she really belonged to David, but he shamelessly used the situation to make her doubt herself.

No! She corrected that quickly. She had no doubts. Her true feelings were all for David, and this was only a passing madness. When it was over she would be a better wife for having got it out of her system. If only it could be over soon! If only it would last for ever!

'What are you thinking?' he asked.

'Nothing—very much,' she said, startled.

'You were a million miles away in some mysterious world of your own. And you won't let me in, will you?'

'No, I can't let you in.'

'Is *he* there?'

'I don't know,' she said with a touch of wistfulness.

'I thought I knew once—but things have changed between us—'

'Jennifer, don't look like that,' he said suddenly. 'Not for another man.'

'David isn't ''another man''. He's the one.'

'Then heaven help us both,' he said, so quietly that she almost didn't hear.

Dismayed, she saw what had happened. The conversation had started as deliciously seductive teasing, but in a few brief seconds it had swerved and taken them to the edge of a pit.

Hurriedly she began to back away, pouring another glass of mineral water for herself, then for him, praising the food, asking questions about nothing. He answered briefly, as though his mind was elsewhere. When she ventured to look up she found him watching her, not with the mockery she'd half expected, but like a man who'd been caught on the wrong foot. After that neither of them said very much.

When they left Steven offered her his arm and they made their progress from the restaurant, still attracting glances from all around. Jennifer's last view was of David, staring at her as though thunderstruck.

The annoying thing about Steven, Jennifer discovered, or rather, one of the *many* annoying things about him, was the way his most outrageous words lingered in her mind, casting their light over the events of her life.

It had been easy to laugh at his comical forecasts of David's jealous behaviour, but when two more days had passed without a word from him it stopped being funny. She was glad Steven wasn't there, ready with a cynical laugh or a jeering word.

That set her thinking about him, and then she realised

that she'd never really stopped thinking about him. At every turn he'd been present, sometimes giving her the predatory look that warned her that whatever he did was for himself. At other times she would remember what she'd seen on his face in the conference restaurant, and hear him mutter, 'Heaven help us both!' That troubled her most. Of course she was well armed against him, and yet the glint of his eyes seemed to cast a spell over her. If she hadn't been in love with David…

David telephoned her to say he would be away for a week. He'd had to hurry to the south coast, where his mother was ill. Luckily she was making a good recovery, and he would call Jennifer again when he returned.

Steven invited her to a show, and she accepted. It turned out to be a 'play of ideas', most of which made her cross. Steven was more in sympathy with the author's views, and over dinner afterwards they began a lively argument that continued all the way home. By the time they parted some extremely frank things had been said on both sides. Jennifer couldn't remember when she'd enjoyed herself so much.

He telephoned next day and they had a drink in the evening. But she made an excuse to leave early. The truth was that she enjoyed Steven's company too much, and the sooner this was brought to an end the better.

She seemed to be split in two, her reasonable mind arguing against her senses. It was madness to be involved with Steven, no matter how seductive he seemed. She knew what a relationship with him would offer: all the thrill and excitement of a fireworks display, an experience never to be forgotten.

But fireworks sparkled and died. Too soon the show would be over, the field cold and deserted and the audience left to trail home alone. The little girl who'd once been cold and deserted was still sufficiently alive in her to make her reject that choice. She wanted roots, a solid life, a long-time commitment. In other words, David.

She would get this far in her musings before remembering that David was conspicuous by his absence. Had he called her at that moment she would have been his for the asking.

Then she would remember Steven's teasing smile, with its hint of devilment, and warmth would begin to steal through her body until she was lost in her awareness of him, forgetful of everything else. She would awaken from these trances shocked and fearful, resolved to be strong and put him out of her life. But somehow it never happened.

At last David called and asked to see her in their little cocktail bar. It was genuinely difficult for her to manage, and she warned him she would be late, but he seemed anxious.

'I really do need to see you. I'll wait until you can make it.'

She just wished Steven could have witnessed her triumph.

David was at their usual table. He stretched out a hand at her approach. 'I was afraid you wouldn't come,' he said, closing his fingers over hers. 'And it's so important.'

'What's important, David?' she asked eagerly.

'Martson Engineering.'

'Martson—?'

'They're giving me the runaround, just as you said they would. I hate to admit it, but you were right all along.'

For a moment she couldn't think what he was talking

about. Then she remembered that their original quarrel had started with Martson.

'I guess I should have listened to your advice,' David admitted. 'I brought the correspondence along.'

The papers confirmed what she'd tried to warn David about weeks ago—clumsily, as she now told herself. For why else would he have taken offence?

Suddenly David said, a mite too casually, 'I saw you at the Dellacort meeting. It seems to be getting serious between you and Leary.'

'There's nothing between us,' she said quickly. 'Someone got the wrong idea about us at the banquet and wrote something that made the shares move up. I'm waiting for the right moment to drop him.'

'You mean that's all?'

'That's all.'

'That's not what—hang on a minute! There's a man over there who owes me some money. I've been trying to pin him down for days. I'll be back. Don't go away.'

He moved off. Jennifer sipped her mineral water, looking slowly around the room, and gradually became aware that an extremely handsome young man was edging towards her table, wearing a look of faint apprehension.

'Ms Norton?' he asked at last.

'I'm Jennifer Norton,' she agreed.

'I tried your office, but you'd gone, and your secretary said you often dropped in here. My name's Mike Harker.'

'Good heavens!' Jennifer exclaimed.

'I guess you think I've got a nerve—'

'No, I'm just amazed to discover that you actually exist. Sit down.'

'Thanks.' He took the seat beside her.

'Have you recovered from the flu?'

'Oh, Steven told you about that. I wasn't sure how much you knew.'

'I found out the truth next morning.'

'He only meant to do me a favour,' Mike urged. 'I was at my wits' end, and he'll do anything for a friend.'

'Did he tell you how the evening went?'

'No. He was laughing when he got back, but he wouldn't tell me what the joke was. Did he annoy you very much?'

'I'm not blaming you. And I haven't complained to the agency, if that's what's worrying you.'

'No, it's not that. It's these.' Mike reached into his pocket and laid the diamond cufflinks on the table. 'Of course I couldn't keep them.'

'Why not? I gave them to you, indirectly.'

'But you didn't mean to, and they're too valuable for me to accept.'

'Please do,' she said warmly. 'I don't make gifts and then take them back, even under the oddest circumstances. I can't believe that you went to these lengths to find me.'

'I've been treading on eggshells, not knowing what I'd find. But it's all right. You're with that guy over there, aren't you?'

'Yes, I am.' Light dawned. 'But, Mike, if you'd thought I was getting involved with Steven, what would you have wanted to warn me about?'

A grin broke over his face. 'Well, you've met Steven—'

'That's why I'm asking.'

'Let's just say I'm glad you're not involved with him. Not that I've seen much of him in the past few years, but I don't think he's changed.'

'You go back a long way?'

'We were at night school together. That's where he did his business studies. He was always "love 'em and leave 'em". No woman could pin him down and he was proud of that. So of course they were all lining up for him. Can't think why. I suppose you couldn't blame him for likening them to buses.'

'Buses?'

'Always another one along soon.'

'Is that what he says?' Jennifer asked, wide-eyed and innocent. 'Fancy.' She felt as though her insides were tying themselves in knots at the unfortunate echo of those words. 'I used to know another man who said something like that,' she mused. '"The world is full of women." That was how he put it, but I guess it means much the same.'

'I don't think Steven intended it very seriously,' Mike said. 'It was more like a game to him. I wouldn't have told you, but you've got someone else, so it's all right.'

'Perfectly all right.' Jennifer added invitingly, 'So you can tell me everything. Steven was a devil in those days, wasn't he?'

'I'll say. He could help himself to any female. Pity, really. Do him good to get a knock. Hell, I shouldn't say that, when he helped me out, but it can really get under your skin. He's so damned sure of himself.'

'Yes, he is,' Jennifer murmured. 'Well, he'll probably take a tumble one day, like everyone else.'

'Not if he can help it. Steven says no woman's so special that a man need make a fool of himself.'

'He says that, does he?' Jennifer leaned back into the shadows lest her face betray her reaction to this conversation. She discovered that she was drumming her fingers tensely and made herself stop. None of this should come as a surprise. She knew what Steven was like, and besides, David was the one she loved.

'We went to a wedding once,' Mike recalled. 'It was an elaborate affair, with all the trappings, and he was horrified. He said weddings were a female conspiracy for making men look ridiculous, and he'd never let it happen to him. With anyone else you could say, "You're always ridiculous," or some such backchat. But not with Steven. Even then he was always on top.' He checked himself guiltily. 'Look, I've probably said more than I should—'

'Nonsense. What harm can it do?' she asked brightly.

'Your friend's coming back. I'd better go now.'

'Don't forget these.' She pushed the cufflinks towards him.

'If you're sure—thanks.'

David, who'd been nearing the table, watched him depart, and turned a quizzical look on Jennifer. 'Have you given a set of those cufflinks to every man in London, or just the ones I see you with?' he asked. 'Jennifer? Jennifer?'

'I'm sorry,' she said hastily, returning to reality.

'Well?'

'I beg your pardon?'

'Have you come to any conclusion?'

'Yes,' she said, her eyes alight. 'I've decided it's time I played a little game of my own.'

CHAPTER SIX

JENNIFER'S call to Steven was put through without delay.

'Jennifer,' he said cheerfully. 'What a nice surprise!'

'Shouldn't you be calling me darling?'

'No, there's nobody listening.'

She laughed. '*Touché*. How about dinner at the Ritz? My treat.'

'Fine. You observe that I'm admirably free from hang-ups about letting the woman pay. I'll even let you collect me and take me home afterwards.'

'Tomorrow night?'

'Great.'

'Steven, I have to admit I have an ulterior motive.'

'I knew you wouldn't disappoint me,' he said appreciatively.

'Can you help me out over a man called Martson? He's bad news, but I'd like to know just how bad.'

'He's a predator. He does all he can to weaken a company, then buys it on the cheap. But I know a few things that can be used against him. I'll have something for you by tomorrow.'

'I'm really grateful to you for taking the trouble,' she said meekly.

But she'd overdone it, because Steven immediately said, 'Jennifer, when you adopt that reasonable tone my antennae vibrate with danger. You're up to something.'

'Who, *me*?'

He laughed. 'I'll see you.'

Jennifer was delighted with the success of her little

stratagem. She would let Steven knock himself out finding the information she wanted, and then she would reveal that it had all been for David's benefit. That would
teach him to be so sure of his buses.

She was curious to know how his self-confidence
would stand up to the discovery that she'd played him
at his own game. And she would enjoy teasing him about
it. That was Steven's trouble. He hadn't been teased
enough.

She left work early next day, so that she could spend
a long time grooming herself for the evening ahead. She
had a new black dress, shot through with silver glitter,
and she didn't even try to pretend that it wasn't for
Steven's benefit.

The traffic was lighter than she'd expected, and she
reached his house twenty minutes early. It was a large,
modern building in an expensive, tree-lined avenue.

Maud let her in. She too was dressed for an evening
out, in a scarlet silk creation that outlined her slender
figure.

'Steven will be down directly,' she said. 'You won't
mind if I have to leave you alone for a moment?'

'I can see you're getting ready for a date,' Jennifer
said, studying the girl's beauty with a smile. 'He must
be really special.'

To her surprise Maud blushed. It wasn't a delicate
model's blush, but a fierce tide that went up to the roots
of her hair and clashed with her dress. Jennifer liked
Maud anyway, but she liked her even more for this chink
in her flawless armour.

'Yes, he is,' Maud mumbled. 'Very special. Excuse
me, I've got to go.'

From overhead came the sound of a door opening, and

feet coming downstairs. Jennifer heard Steven say, 'Maud, have you any idea where—?'

She turned quickly. Steven was standing halfway up the stairs, wearing trousers but no shirt. He halted abruptly when he saw her and she had a long moment to drink in the sight of his broad chest and muscular shoulders. Normally his sharp, well-cut suits disguised the power of his frame. Now, for the first time, she realised how magnificently he was built.

The world seemed to stop. Everything about Steven was vivid, from his heavy shoulders to the silky dark hair that covered his chest and swirled in a perfectly balanced pattern down to his waist, disappearing into his belt.

She'd tried to imagine him without clothes, but her thoughts hadn't come up with anything as splendid as this. Images chased each other, pell mell, through her brain. Mike had said, 'They were all lining up for him. Can't think why...'

But I know why, was the thought she couldn't stifle. *Lucky for me I've been warned. Another woman might have made a fool of herself over him.*

Steven's eyes showed that he too had been taken aback. They moved over her beauty with a look of appreciation, and he drew in a slow breath.

'I didn't know you were here,' he said at last.

'I'm a bit early. The traffic was light.' She had no idea what she was saying.

'I'll be with you in a minute.' He sounded vague.

Maud's eyes went from one to the other, while her lips twitched. But neither of them noticed her.

The scream of the doorbell broke the spell. Maud snatched up her wrap, muttered, 'Night, you two,' and hurried out.

As she opened the front door Jennifer caught a glimpse of the man standing there, and the joyful look on his face as he pulled Maud into his arms. Then the door shut them out.

Steven grinned at Jennifer's expression. 'That's how I felt, too,' he said. 'I'll be with you in a moment.'

He was back five minutes later in a snowy evening shirt whose elegant ruffles contrasted starkly with the harsh masculinity of his face. He looked ridiculously handsome.

And don't you just know it! she thought. *In fact, you're counting on it. Like buses, huh? What a shock you're going to get!*

He behaved beautifully, deferring to her at the car door, and not even trying to edge her out of the driving seat. Not until Jennifer was into the flow of the traffic did he drop his bombshell.

'I've changed my mind about the Ritz. I'd rather go to a nightclub.'

'But I've booked a table at the Ritz.'

'I'm afraid I took the liberty of cancelling that and booking us in at the Orchid Club.'

'Well, I suppose I might have known you'd do something outrageous and arrogant like that,' she said wryly.

'I suppose you might. Turn left up here.'

'If it's a club, won't it be members only?'

'I am a member. I'll be paying the bill too. In fact, I've taken over the whole evening. I do hope you don't mind.'

'You don't care if I mind or not. Steven, I don't want to go to a nightclub. It's too—' She nearly said intimate, but stopped herself. 'It's just not what I had in mind.'

'Don't be ungrateful after all the trouble I've taken to find out about Martson for you.'

'Really? Have you come up with much?'

'Enough to be interesting. Now can we go to the Orchid Club?'

'To the ends of the earth,' she said gaily.

'Be careful what you say. I may hold you to it.'

Jennifer laughed. Suddenly she felt wonderful. It was a glorious night. But that, of course, was because she was looking forward to taking the wind out of his sails.

When she saw the Orchid Club she knew Steven had out-manoeuvred her, which was impressive for a man who didn't even know the game they were playing. The nightclub was very exclusive, discreet and intimate. The doorman greeted Steven as a regular customer and gave Jennifer a swift, appraising glance that suggested she was the latest in a long line. This wasn't how things had been meant to go. But her moment would come.

Their table was in a dark corner, lit by one small lamp. Steven handed her to her seat and ordered wine, which the waiter brought.

'Well, here we are,' he said when he'd given their order.

'Yes, but—here.' She indicated their surroundings. 'This was supposed to be my treat.'

'What does it matter? I'm flattered by your eagerness to see me.'

'Don't kid yourself. It's your advice I'm eager for.'

'About Martson? He's an unpleasant character, but he's not in Nortons' league.'

'There are—reasons—why he's very important to me.'

He regarded her quizzically. It was so clear that he thought she'd made an excuse to see him that Jennifer began to feel a tingle of anticipation. She was going to enjoy this evening.

'Where's David tonight?' he asked suddenly.

Caught off guard, she stammered, 'I—I don't know.'

'Does he know where you are? Never mind. If he doesn't, he ought to. If I was in love with a woman I'd lock her up before I'd let her play the kind of game you're playing with me.'

'Maybe she wouldn't agree to be locked up.'

His answer was to take her hand and drop his head until his lips brushed the palm. 'Maybe I could make her want to agree,' he whispered.

She couldn't reply, although she knew Steven must be able to feel her pulses racing. He raised his eyes, giving her a look that devastated her.

'You don't know what game I'm playing with you,' she said at last.

'I know you're using me to make him jealous, and for the good of your firm. Are you saying there's more?'

She smiled mysteriously. 'There could be.'

'What a little devil you are! All right, I'll go for it. A touch of the devil makes a woman perfect. Are there any rules?'

'You'll find them out by trial and error.'

'And you?'

'I make them up as I go along.'

He released her hand and raised his glass to her, his eyes full of admiration. He thought he was treading a well-worn path, Jennifer mused. First the woman teased him, then she fell into his arms: it was so familiar to him. But tonight he was in for a shock.

'Why are your eyes gleaming in that delicious way?' he asked.

'Wait and see.'

'All right, Jennifer. It's your game. But I distrust you tonight.'

'I distrust you all the time,' she riposted. 'You must admit, it gives a certain piquancy to our dealings.'

'True. You never bore me for an instant. How are you going to surprise me?'

'If I told you that, it wouldn't be a surprise. Leave it for now. Tell me, is our little masquerade going well?'

'People think we're mad about each other.'

'No, I meant the market,' she said, with a little air of surprise. 'After all, that's what really matters.'

He grinned his admiration of this touch. 'Certainly it is. Well, Charteris's value has leapt up now the market's expecting us to tie up with you.'

'"Tie up with us",' Jennifer said thoughtfully. 'As in "eat us alive"?'

He laughed. 'I don't think I could put one across on you.'

'Oh, yes, you do. You also think you've got me fooled.'

He poured some wine into her glass, and wasn't looking at her as he said, 'Am I trying to do that, Jennifer?'

'Is there any woman you don't try to fool?'

'Is there any woman who doesn't want to be fooled?'

'Oh, yes. Right here. I value plain dealing.'

'Then you're different from all other women in creation.'

She leaned a little closer, over the table. 'I don't respond to flattery,' she said, in a voice so soft that only he could hear it.

He too leaned forward, until their hair was almost touching. 'Then I'll tell you, in plain, unvarnished words, that you're the most sensationally sexy woman I've ever known. I always study your clothes to guess how easy they'd be to remove. I know you don't plan to let me remove them—not yet anyway—but I can't help it. It's instinctive. When we talk I can't keep my mind on the words because I'm thinking how badly I want to see you naked, and to be naked with you, and all the things I want us to do together.'

The pleasure was rising in her at the delightful pictures he conjured up. But she refused to yield to it. Tonight, she was going to stay in control.

'Do you think you'll manage it?' she asked.

'Do *you* think I will?'

'Never.'

'Would you care to make a little bet on that?'

'The last time we made a bet you cheated,' she reminded him.

'And I'll cheat again if it'll get you into my bed. Why waste time with honest methods when cheating produces results?'

'But you're an honest man in business.'

'Perhaps business isn't so important.'

'Shame on you, Steven. Nothing is more important than business.'

Instead of answering he reached out a finger and drew it lightly down her cheek, then along the outline of her lips. The effect was so delightful that she took a long, quivering breath. 'You don't really believe that,' he murmured.

'No, but you do.'

'We could make something more important—if we wanted to.'

'Something?'

'Us.'

He was falling for it, she thought with an inner smile. Or rather, he thought *she* was falling for his sweet-talking ways.

'What do you say to that?' he asked.

'I say the waiter is standing just behind you,' she replied primly.

He grimaced before drawing back to sit watching her while the waiter served them. His eyes glinted in the dim light, reminding her of things she'd have been wiser to forget, or never to have known.

When they were alone again Steven regarded her quizzically, to see if she would take up the subject, but she refused to do so. Let him wonder!

'How are the little ones?' he asked, starting on his meal.

'We've passed two milestones,' Jennifer said, getting onto her favourite subject. 'They've all opened their eyes, and this morning the last one left the basket. That's the boy. He seems to be a late developer.''

'That's the one you named after me, isn't it?'

'I'm afraid so. Never mind. He'll catch up. The one who opened her eyes first is really advanced. She scampers everywhere, while the others just sit in the middle of the carpet and squeak. They're so sweet and tiny…'

He grinned at the sight of her face as she chattered on, her eyes alight with love for her tiny charges. That was a very special look, he realised. It was open, defenceless, vulnerable. Was there any human being she trusted enough to look like that? he wondered. Certainly not himself. David? He would have given a lot to know the answer to that question.

Jennifer had finished talking about the cats and remembered something else. 'Did I really see who I thought I saw collect Maud tonight?' she asked. 'Trevor?'

'You didn't imagine it. Those two are besotted with each other. Hasn't he said anything?'

'Not a word. Mind you, I haven't seen him except at

work, and recently he's been leaving the office early—
oh, of course!'

'No prizes for guessing whom he's been hurrying off
to meet,' Steven said, grinning. 'What about his mood?
There's no getting any sense out of Maud.'

'Well, he's seemed a bit preoccupied, but then he always has a lot on his mind.'

'It's my sister who's on his mind at the moment. Not
that he's got much to worry about. She isn't exactly
playing hard to get.'

'How long have you known?'

'Since the first evening. She told me on the way home
that she was going to marry him.'

'Love at first sight,' Jennifer mused. 'I never really
believed in it before. I guess Trevor's found what he
needs at last.'

'And what's that?'

'When our mother died,' Jennifer said after a slight
hesitation, 'we clung together. He was sixteen and I was
twelve, but I comforted him more than the other way
around. We were so close in those days. It was like we
were always holding each other's hands.

'But then he started to hang around with a gang, and
I guess he was too proud to hold my hand any more. So
he let go and never came back. But it was too soon. He
couldn't cope. I think he's been looking for someone to
comfort him ever since.'

'Surely Barney was there for you?'

'Not in that way. He loved us, but he was always
busy.'

'And what about you?' Steven asked, looking at her
curiously. 'Whose hand did you hold?'

'Nobody's, I guess.' Something caught in her throat
as the memory came back to her of long, lonely nights,

weeping for her mother, her father, or Trevor, or her grandfather—or anyone.

'Jennifer?' Steven said gently, studying her face with sudden concentration.

She came back to the present, adjusting a bright smile on her face. She didn't know that the smile was wonky and unconvincing, but she felt Steven take hold of her hand and give it a comforting squeeze. For a moment they sat in silence. There was nothing to say, but his hand was warm.

'You realise what you've just told me, don't you?' he asked gently. 'The secret of David Conner's attraction. You perceive him as solid and reliable.'

'He's always there when I need him—'

'Not now, he isn't. That's why you're clinging onto the thought of him like grim death.'

'I seem to be clinging to you,' she said awkwardly, releasing her hand.

'The fact is, you're afraid of being abandoned again. You're not really in love with him at all.'

'Why shouldn't I want to be safe?' she demanded.

'I could give you a thousand reasons, but I'll settle for this one. You want marriage, and the illusion of safety it brings. This is the real Jennifer Norton. Underneath that smart, sophisticated exterior is a little girl looking for a hand to hold in the dark.

'Well, I'm not a marrying man, but I'm better for you than Conner is because we understand each other. Jennifer, believe me, there's more safety in being with someone who thinks and feels as you do—even if only for a day—than in all the wedding rings in the world.'

She didn't know how to answer. Her heart was beating strongly, not with the sweet sexual excitement he could evoke in her so easily, but with a kind of alarm as he came so dangerously near to her innermost sanctum.

The next moment he invaded her secret world even further with the blunt words, 'Don't force the poor sap to marry you, Jennifer. You'll regret it all your life.'

'That's nonsense,' she said, speaking roughly to cover her turmoil. 'I couldn't force David to marry me.'

'I think you could, and I'll stop it if I can.'

'And dump me afterwards,' she challenged.

'Afterwards we'll toss our caps over the windmill. I don't think you've ever done that, and it's time you did. Maybe I wouldn't leave you. Maybe you'd leave me, and I'd come chasing after you.'

'I don't think so,' she said with a touch of wistfulness.

'Don't underestimate yourself. And forget Conner. He doesn't love you. Or if he does, it means his idea of love is as narrow as yours.'

'Steven, let's drop this,' she said in a warning voice. 'I mean it.'

'All right,' he said after a moment. 'But I'll just say this. Somehow you've got to sort out your demons, but Little Lord Fauntleroy isn't the answer.'

She choked with unwilling laughter. 'Don't call David that.'

'But you recognise him from the description?'

'You're impossible.' She was still laughing, annoyed with him for getting in under her guard with an irresistible joke. David didn't make jokes, she realised.

'What is your face revealing?' he asked, leaning towards her. 'I can't see in this light.'

'Good. The less you know about me, the better.'

'Don't tell me you're nervous? Of me?'

'No,' she said, too quickly. 'Not of you or any man.'

He said nothing, only watched her for a moment. He

was thinking how entrancing she looked when the colour came up in her cheeks, making her features even more vivid. Was she like that at the moment of true passion? he wondered. And how long would it be before he knew?

But he reined himself in. His pursuit of Jennifer had become an absorbing game, all the more fascinating because his quarry knew how to dodge and feint, how to lead him on, to draw back and send him after false trails. And—it amazed him to realise this—there was no certainty of success. He'd never yet wanted a woman that he wasn't sure of getting, and the novelty intrigued him.

'I'm glad you told me about your parents,' he said. 'It helps me see you more clearly. I'd thought of you as having an easy life, going into your grandfather's firm because it was fun.'

'I don't find it fun. I'd rather have worked with animals, but how could I tell Barney that?'

'Easily. If he really loved you he'd be glad for you to follow your own dream. He does love you, doesn't he?'

'Of course.'

'But only if you do what he wants?'

'That's not fair.'

'But do you believe it?'

'Stop trying to confuse me,' she said with a touch of desperation.

'All right,' he said quietly after a moment. 'I'm sorry.'

'Hasn't your work been fun for you?' she asked, determined to get him onto another track.

'Parts of it. Recently. Not at first.'

'I wish you'd tell me.'

He hesitated uneasily, and she guessed he didn't find it easy to confide in people, perhaps because he trusted nobody, except maybe Maud. She knew that if she could overcome this barrier she would be a step closer to the heart of the man.

At last he said, 'In a strange way, you remind me of my mother. She had a very hard life, but she never let it get her down. You were like that, going to the banquet on my arm, looking the world in the eye, not letting on how unhappy you were.

'There's nobody I've ever admired more than my mother. She faced all her misfortunes with courage, and humour. I just wish she'd lived long enough to see me make it. I'd have liked to give her some of the good things of life.'

'What about your father?'

'Died when I was fourteen. Mum was actually carrying Maud at the time. I'm the only father Maud's ever known.'

'Tell me more about your mother,' Jennifer begged.

'She was great. Not that I told her that at the time. After Dad died I became the man of the family. Mum still saw me as a kid. We had a few fights about that. I got a job delivering papers for the corner shop. When I found another one, stacking shelves in a supermarket on weekends, she had to admit I was a man.'

'She let you do two jobs? At fourteen?'

'I didn't ask her. I just did what I had to.'

'What about your education?'

'I managed. I left school early, got myself a market stall selling anything I could pick up cheap. When I'd made a small profit I got another stall.'

'How did you get from market stalls to Charteris?' Jennifer asked, genuinely fascinated.

'I took commercial courses at night school, and I moved into little shops that were near the end of their lease. In the end I owned three shops, but I wanted to play in the big league, so I sold up and got a job with Charteris. I ploughed the profit from the shops into Charteris shares, and in ten years I was running the firm. They didn't want to appoint me. They saw me as a jumped-up barrow boy—which I am. But there was nobody else who could drag them up to date.'

The completeness of his assurance almost took the words beyond arrogance. This man knew he was born to rule, and there was no need for further discussion.

'Over the years,' he went on, 'I've taken share options, bought more stock in Charteris whenever I could.'

'So now you have a power base.'

'Right. And money. Which matters. I've seen how terrifying the lack of money can be, how it eats you up and controls the whole of your life. I've lain awake, wondering if I could get this payment in in time to meet that bill, and, if not, how could I talk my way out of it? I've had people who thought they could put one over on me, because they saw me as just a kid. And I had to teach them the hard way that they were wrong.'

'The hard way?'

'There's no other way that works,' he said simply. 'If you're retaliating, you must do it so powerfully that the enemy won't challenge you again.'

He spoke in a matter-of-fact way that made Jennifer give a little shiver.

'I'm glad I haven't made an enemy of you,' she said.

He looked at her strangely. 'I'm glad you haven't, too,' he said.

CHAPTER SEVEN

SHE let him drive on the home journey, content to sit beside him in a pleasant glow.

'This will give me a chance to visit Paws and family,' he said. 'I'm curious to see how far they've come on.'

Jennifer's first act on getting home was to rush to the basket, but there was nobody at home.

'There's one here,' Steven called, scooping up a kitten from behind the sofa, 'and one over there.'

'Since they got out of the box I never know where I'm going to find them,' she said, laughing.

Paws appeared from the kitchen and joined in the hunt, and soon everyone was back where they belonged. Steven made warm milk for the cats and coffee for them. Jennifer was beginning to feel like a cat herself, a contented cat, stretching and luxuriating in the feeling that all was right with the world.

'By the way,' Steven said, 'we forgot something.'

'Did we?'

'Martson. You wanted to pick my brains about him, and we haven't discussed him at all.'

With a shock she remembered that this whole evening had been about putting Steven Leary in his place. It had been conceived as a light-hearted prank, but now it seemed silly and schoolgirlish. Tonight she'd learned things about him that intrigued her, and she'd let him see into her own secret heart where intruders weren't allowed. Now she no longer wanted to laugh at him, teach him a lesson, or do anything except kiss him.

'Do you want to talk about it now?' he asked.

'No—no, another time. It's not important,' she stammered, hardly knowing what she said.

'No,' he agreed, taking her into his arms. 'It's not important.'

She was beginning to be afraid of Steven's kisses. She wanted them too much. He was like an addiction, bad and dangerous for her, but impossible to resist. She'd push him away next time, but tonight she must kiss him back eagerly, burningly—just once more.

But as with all addictions there was no such thing as 'just once more'. For him too. One kiss became another and another, and suddenly he was raining kisses all over her face and neck.

'I want you,' he murmured, 'and I want you to want me.'

'You know that I—I don't know—Steven—'

Words dissolved into nothing as she began kissing him back urgently. Her head was full of pictures of Steven as she'd seen him at the start of the evening, stripped to the waist, broad-shouldered and muscular, the hair of his torso vanishing into his belt. The need to touch him had been growing in her from that moment until it was almost unbearable.

She saw his eyes, heavy with passion, gazing down on her with a strange, bewildered look, as if he found it hard to believe what was happening. 'You're always more beautiful than I remember,' he said thickly.

His hands moved on the flimsy dress. She knew that soon nothing would stop them. She was hurtling headlong towards something she desired with every fibre of her being, and yet...

The words that came out of her mouth were the last she'd expected to utter.

'Steven—Steven wait—'

She could sense the effort it cost him to leash himself back. 'What is it, Jennifer? What's wrong?' His voice was ragged with strain.

'I don't know—suddenly everything's going too fast—I'm not ready for this—'

She braced herself for his rage at being thwarted, but it didn't come. His face was very pale but he had himself under control. He even managed a kind of joke.

'Jennifer, your sense of timing is something wonderful. Do you think I can stop now?'

'I think you can do anything you set your mind to,' she said shakily.

'Oh, you clever, clever woman,' he breathed. 'Damn you for knowing the right thing to say!'

He released her slowly, painfully. As soon as she drew back from him he turned away, running his hands through his hair.

'I'm sorry,' he said distractedly.

He couldn't have said anything that would have surprised her more. Steven Leary had apologised. It was as if the stars had stopped in their tracks.

'It's my fault,' she said shakily, 'for not knowing my own mind.'

'Let's not argue about whose fault it is. I don't think I could stand that at this moment.' He gave an edgy laugh. 'It's not like me to misread things so badly.'

'You didn't,' she said haltingly. 'It was me—I just freaked out. I don't know why.'

'I'll go now if you want.'

'Yes, maybe you should.'

She longed to ask him to stay, but knew she mustn't. In another moment he would be out of the door and their relationship would be over, for she must never, never see him like this again.

The scream of the doorbell startled them both. They seemed to wake and look around them, wondering what had brought them here. Jennifer pulled herself together and opened her front door. A man and woman, both in their forties, stood on the step, with a girl of about ten.

'We're sorry to trouble you at this hour,' the woman said. 'We've been calling all evening, but there was nobody in. Brenda should have been in bed ages ago, but we didn't have the heart to make her go home, not if there was a chance of getting Snowy back.'

'Snowy?' Jennifer asked with a sinking heart.

'Because she's got snowy white paws, though the rest of her's black,' the little girl said. Then a joyous smile broke over her face, and she shrieked, *'Snowy!'*

She darted into the house to envelop Paws, who'd come dashing towards her. With a rueful smile Jennifer beckoned the parents in. Steven closed the door and stood quietly watching.

There were rapid introductions. Mr and Mrs Cranmer were armed with family photographs, showing Paws/ Snowy in the little girl's arms. There was no doubt that these were the cat's rightful owners. Young Brenda had already discovered the kittens and was cuddling them blissfully.

'We live four roads away,' Mrs Cranmer said. 'One of our neighbours said someone in this road had taken in a black cat with white paws, but she wasn't sure who. We've been knocking on doors round here, and someone said it was you. We were so worried when she disappeared so near her time. We had visions of her giving birth in a gutter with nobody to look after her. Thank goodness she was safe with you.'

'You must let us refund anything you spent on a vet,' Mr Cranmer insisted.

'The vet only arrived when the job was done,' Jennifer said. 'Steven did it all himself.'

Over coffee and cocoa they told the story of that night. There was much laughter, but Steven, watching closely, saw that Jennifer's smiles were a little forced. He met her eyes, his own full of warmth and understanding.

When it was time for the visitors to go Snowy jumped into Jennifer's lap and rubbed her head against her, purring noisily.

'She's saying thank you,' Brenda said wisely. 'She loves you.'

'I love her,' Jennifer said huskily. 'And I'm so happy that she's found her family again.'

'But you'll be on your own,' Brenda said. 'Would you like one of her kittens?' She held out the boy, whose markings were almost identical to Snowy's. 'I'll bring him round when he's old enough to leave his mother,' she offered.

Reluctantly Jennifer shook her head.

'I'd love to,' she said. 'But it wouldn't be kind to leave him alone in this house while I'm out all day. It was different with P— with Snowy. For her, even being left alone here was better than the street. But this little fellow has other options.'

'Don't you want him?' Brenda asked.

'Yes, I want him very much, but—' Her voice broke.

'We understand,' Mrs Cranmer said gently.

Steven watched as she closed the door after the family, and saw the way her shoulders sagged. She kept her back to him, then went into the kitchen and out of sight.

Steven called himself a taxi. While he dialled, he kept

his attention on the kitchen, and heard the sound of her blowing her nose.

'The taxi will be here in two minutes,' he said as she returned.

'Fine,' she said, smiling brightly, but he knew her brightness would fade the moment he'd gone. She would be really alone then, without the cats that had needed her, without David, without himself, without anyone. The thought of the loneliness she wouldn't acknowledge hurt him.

The words came out of their own accord. 'Spend tomorrow with me, Jennifer.'

'I—I've got meetings all day—' she stammered.

'Cancel them. Take the day off. Come with me to the seaside.'

'The seaside?' she echoed, not sure she'd heard him right.

'I want to take you to Huntley and show you where I grew up. Let's go mad.'

'Oh, yes, let's,' she said, suddenly as thrilled as a child.

'I'll collect you here at eight, tomorrow morning. Don't be late. Goodnight.'

When he'd gone Jennifer paced the floor restlessly, trying to organise her thoughts. She wanted Steven so much that she couldn't think straight, yet she'd refused to yield to her own desires.

Why had she panicked? Perhaps because her longing for Steven threatened to become stronger than she was, and disrupt the orderly life she'd promised herself long ago, when she'd been a lonely, abandoned child.

She'd only half expected him to be there next morning, but at five minutes to eight he was knocking on her door. She opened to find a man she barely recognised.

Steven Leary, in a check shirt and jeans? Steven Leary, without a tie? And smiling like a kid looking forward to a treat?

His look mirrored her own. Fawn trousers and a buttercup yellow shirt was an ensemble she would never have worn to work. Neither would she have knotted the rust silk scarf about her neck, or shouldered the gaily decorated canvas bag.

'Aren't you ready yet?' he demanded.

'Cheeky so-and-so! I need ten minutes.'

The words were mundane, but beneath them lay something else: question and answer. How is he/she looking at me now? What has changed between us?

But for the moment, at any rate, they could cover the tension with an air of normality.

'You're dressed just right for a day by the sea,' he said when she was ready.

'Well, I hope it's a proper seaside,' she told him severely. 'With a sandy beach, and a cove, with a whelk stall and a man selling ice creams.'

'I'm afraid the beach is shingle,' he said. 'But there was a cove and a man selling ice creams. I'm sure they won't have changed.'

'When I was a child our parents used to take Trevor and me to the seaside,' Jennifer said as Steven headed his car out onto the road. 'Those trips still have a golden glow in my mind. The sun was always shining, the ice creams were always delicious, and Trevor and I were always squabbling about whose sandcastle was the biggest.'

'I'll bet you won.'

'Not always. But he used to cheat.'

'By the way, speaking of Trevor, Maud didn't come

home last night—not for the first time. I think we should start preparing for the wedding.'

'You're not serious?'

'You don't know my little sister when she's made up her mind. She's awesome.'

Jennifer was about to argue when she recalled Trevor's face as he'd taken Maud into his arms. It had borne a look of total, humble adoration.

'You say she decided on the first evening,' she said, a little troubled. 'Then can she really love him?'

'Why else should she want to marry him?'

'Well—there comes a time in the life of every model...' Jennifer paused delicately.

'She's not marrying him for financial security, if that's what you think.' Steven kindly helped her out. 'She's got plenty of money of her own, I promise you. Why? Don't you believe in love at first sight?'

'Do you?' she asked, startled.

'I believe in something at first sight. As for love—' He shrugged. 'It's obvious what the word means to Maud, but for me—' He checked himself. 'I guess everyone sets their own meaning.'

'I don't think you do know how Maud defines it,' Jennifer said thoughtfully. 'Obviously she sees something in Trevor that's hidden from us. Maybe that instinctive insight is love. And trusting the other person enough to let them see the truth about you. If they've found it, I envy them.'

'But you've found it,' he pointed out. 'You and David.'

'David and I love each other, but you know it's not simple and untroubled, the way it seems to be with Trevor and Maud.'

'Perhaps if it's troubled, it isn't love at all,' he suggested mildly.

'I'm not giving up on it just because we have a few problems. Most couples do. We'll work it out. Is it very far to Huntley?'

'Sixty miles,' he said, accepting her change of subject without demur. 'It's just a little place, or it was when I last saw it. It wasn't a popular resort for family holidays because of the pebble beach, so it stayed quiet and uncommercial, and a lot of elderly people used to retire there. When I was a kid I thought it was too sleepy, but I'm getting to the age when I appreciate the peace.'

'Into the sear and yellow,' she said appreciatively, regarding his powerful body. 'Did you remember to bring your Zimmer frame?'

'Nope. I'm planning to lean on you.'

She watched his hands on the wheel, controlling the heavy vehicle without effort. They were shapely hands, muscular and beautiful, and last night they had held her with passion, demanding yet also giving, knowing just where and how to touch her. And yet she'd sent him away. Was she mad?

Before long she could taste the salty tang in the air, and knew they were near the sea.

'There it is!' she cried, as she'd done as a child. 'I just glimpsed it between those trees.'

The water was dazzling in the sunlight, and she knew a thrill of the old excitement. Soon the sea appeared again, this time for longer, and at last they were on the coast road, with the shore beside them all the way.

'There was a whelk stall just past here,' Steven remembered. 'No sign of that any more.'

But they found a good seafood restaurant and sat by the window enjoying the view.

'There are more people here than I recall,' he said. 'Huntley must have prospered. Good for Dan Markham.'

'Who's Dan Markham?'

'He owned the corner shop and gave me my first job, delivering papers. I still shudder when I think of getting up at six on those winter mornings. But he always gave me a hot drink before I went out with the papers, and another one when I got back. He was a great old boy.'

Jennifer had never heard him speak so warmly of anyone before. 'Tell me more about him,' she said, glad to keep him in this mood.

'He looked like Santa Claus, with a bushy white beard and a twinkle in his eye. And he was generous to the point of foolhardiness. He paid me more than the going rate, and he increased that when my mother died.'

'A rotten businessman,' Jennifer observed with a smile.

'Terrible,' Steven agreed. 'He'd give customers credit, and then write it off because they were nice people.'

'Shocking! I hope you lectured him about his inefficiency.'

'I did. I can hear myself now, fourteen years old and saying, "You've cut your profit margins to ribbons, Mr Markham." And he stared at me blankly, and said, "I don't know about profit margins, lad. I just buy and sell things." While his wife was alive she'd done the books. After a while I took them over. That was when I discovered how much my own mother had benefited from his charity.'

He finished drily, and for a moment his eyes were dark, as though even now the memory had power to hurt.

'I'll bet you paid him back every penny,' Jennifer said.

He gave her a sudden, startled look. 'Am I that transparent?'

'Well, I think I'm beginning to know you a little.'

'Yes, I guess you are. I calculated what we owed him, and I refused to take another penny in wages until I'd worked it off. He and I had some terrible rows about it, but I won.'

'Of course,' Jennifer murmured.

'I paid him back and I tried to teach him good business practice. But I never managed it. The place went downhill for years, and he simply couldn't understand why.'

Jennifer regarded him with fascination. Steven Leary did have a heart. Not the melting, sentimental kind, but a rough, powerful organ that behaved awkwardly but was honest and good, even kind. It was a heart she increasingly wanted to know about. Even, perhaps, to possess.

'Did he lose the shop in the end?' she asked.

'Nearly. Luckily someone stepped in and hauled him out of the mire.'

'No prizes for guessing who.'

After a moment he gave a grin with a touch of sheepishness. 'Yes, all right. It was me. I happened to be passing near Huntley a few years ago and dropped in to see him. He was about to be forced out, and I'm a man who likes to pay my debts, so I made him a loan.'

'Did he ever manage to repay you?'

Laughing, he shook his head. 'I had to write it off,' he admitted. 'The paperwork was just too much trouble.'

'Don't make excuses. You were fond of him. Sheer human weakness.'

'I don't have any human weaknesses,' he defended himself. 'Not the amiable kind, anyway.'

'Paws could say a thing or two about that.'

'Helping Paws that night was sheer practical efficiency to stop you having hysterics.'

'You're a fraud. Underneath that steel exterior—'

'Beats a steely heart,' he interrupted. 'Don't go crediting me with melting qualities. I owed that old man. End of story.'

'If you say so.'

When they resumed their journey the road turned inland for a spell, then abruptly back to the coast.

'These apartment blocks are new,' Steven observed. 'Ugly great things! Good grief!'

Jennifer followed his gaze to the horizon, where a huge ferris wheel had come into view between the apartment blocks. Noisy music floated in their direction, and bright lights flickered.

'That monstrosity is new,' Steven groaned. 'It looks like the developers have moved in.'

Closer to Huntley it became clear just how much the developers had taken over. Modern buildings were everywhere, garishly lit shops lined the promenade, and the little town was crowded with people.

'It's not the place I knew any more,' Steven said heavily. 'But why has everyone suddenly come here?'

They had one answer a few minutes later, in a huge casino that overlooked the sea.

'It pulls them in from miles around,' the doorman confided. 'Open twenty-four hours a day. Always something going on. The kids love it.'

'I'll bet they do,' Steven said in horror.

'Good investment,' Jennifer reminded him.

'Not in my backyard,' he growled without irony. 'I just hope it did old Dan some good.'

He set off in search of the corner shop, and to

Jennifer's relief they saw a bright, cheerful shop bearing the name 'Markham's Newsagent'.

'He made a success of it finally,' Steven said with relief.

'Thanks to you.'

'Let's go and give him a shock,' he said, seizing her hand and almost running inside.

A sleek young man was in attendance behind the counter. 'What can I do for you, sir?' he asked, smiling blandly.

'Is Dan Markham around?' Steven asked.

'Dan—? Oh, you mean old Mr Markham. I think he went to Canada.'

'He's on vacation in Canada?' Steven echoed in dismay.

'No, he sold up.'

'Sold up? But the name—'

'Oh, yes, it's still called Markham's because that's what people are used to, but actually the shop's owned by a chain now. They bought it from Dan Markham.'

'You mean they drove him out,' Steven said grimly.

'Didn't have to. He was only too eager to sell. The bloke he owed money to had just written off the whole debt—more fool him! A week later Dan sold this place. He said he was glad to take the money and run.'

'I see,' Steven said slowly. 'Yes, I see.'

He walked slowly out of the shop.

Jennifer followed him anxiously. Steven's face was pale, as though he'd received a shock, and she discovered that she could feel sorry for him. In the context of his whole life this was so trivial. And yet...

She tried to tuck her hand into his arm. He didn't throw her off, but he barely relaxed enough for her to manage it. He was walking along the street with his head down, scowling, seemingly lost in his own world of anger and dismay.

'It matters, doesn't it?' she asked sympathetically.

'Yes, it matters,' he said heavily. 'I don't know why but—hell, yes, it matters.'

His arm relaxed a little more and she was able to tuck her hand in properly. 'Let's go for a walk.'

They crossed the road and strolled down onto the beach. Some hardy bathers were bobbing about in the water, but on the whole the beach was sparsely populated. These days people came to Huntley for the gambling and the garish entertainments, and the peaceful haven that had lived in Steven's mind had vanished for ever.

They rounded a small headland and found themselves in the little cove she'd wanted. There was nobody else in sight and they were well clear of the bathers by now. Steven stopped abruptly and, seizing up a handful of pebbles, began to hurl them savagely into the water. Each one went further than the last, as though he was trying to work off his feelings.

'"More fool him!"' he echoed bitterly. 'More fool *me*!'

'Why does it matter so much?'

'A week! He must have known he was going to sell. He played me for a sucker.'

'Looks like he learned something from you after all, then.'

He scowled at her, but a moment later he put his arm around her shoulders. She slipped her own arm about his waist and they walked on, hearing the shingle crunch under their feet. Neither of them spoke for a long time, but she was content to leave it at that. Time slipped past and she realised that they'd travelled a considerable distance. The town lay behind them and they were alone on the beach, with only the waves for company.

With nobody to see, she put her arms about his neck and looked him in the face. 'Don't be hurt,' she said softly.

But he was, and it was worse for him because he wasn't used to the pain of disillusion, and didn't know how to cope. She felt a rush of tenderness for him, and was instantly disconcerted. This was what she felt for David, and it was perilously close to love. She'd promised herself not to love Steven Leary.

His next words troubled her even more. 'I'm glad you were with me when I found out.'

She heard the faint, worrying echo of other, similar words, spoken at another time, by another man. But the echo faded before she could place it.

Steven drew her close, not kissing her, but holding her as if for comfort. She hugged him back fiercely, longing to take all his troubles onto herself. How naturally his head seemed to fit on her shoulder.

'OK. I've worked off my temper now,' he said at last with a rueful sigh. 'Sorry to drag you so far. I'm acting like a jerk, aren't I?'

'No way. But can we get the bus back? I'm about walked out.'

He took her hand. 'Come on. Let's get out of Huntley all together. I don't care if I never see the place again.'

CHAPTER EIGHT

THEY got a bus back to town, found the parked car and headed out.

'Well, that wasn't the day I'd planned,' he said wryly as he drove. 'But it was instructive.'

He pulled in to an old-fashioned pub with a thatched roof and outside tables shaded by big coloured umbrellas. They ate at a table near the duck pond, tossing titbits to the quacking inhabitants.

'Look at it another way,' Jennifer said gently. 'You were fond of him, and you owed him. You paid your debts by giving him a prosperous retirement. Why shouldn't he have it his way?'

He nodded abstractedly and ate in silence for a while. At last he said, 'You're right, of course. Who was I to demand that he pickle himself in aspic for my sake? He was an old man. He must have been fed up with working by then.'

'But it's not the same, is it?'

'No, I still have this irrational feeling that he betrayed my trust—which is nonsense, I suppose.' He gave her a wry smile. 'My trouble is that I like arranging people's lives. And mostly I get away with it, which makes me worse.'

'And you're worse still when you don't get away with it?' she teased.

His smile became a broad grin. 'I'm hell on earth when I don't get my own way,' he admitted. 'I don't know why I'm making so much of it. I suppose he was a benchmark in my mind: someone to trust in a wicked world.'

'Don't you trust anyone else?'

'Yes, you,' he said unexpectedly. He watched her startled face and said, amused, 'That stopped you in your tracks.'

'You couldn't have said anything that would have surprised me more.'

'I trust you completely. Despite our battles I think you're the most totally honourable person I've ever known. I think—in fact, I know—that you'd never play anyone false who trusted you.'

That Steven Leary, of all people, should pay her such a tribute left her speechless. There was a warm note in his voice that she'd never heard before, and a new look in his eyes as he took her hand gently in his. 'Jennifer—'

'Steven, please! My life is complicated, and you complicate it more.'

'Because of David?'

'Well—yes. Aren't I playing him false?'

'No. You and David are moving naturally and inevitably to the end. You're not suited, and you're both beginning to see it.' When she didn't answer he intensified his hold on her hand and asked, 'Did you call him last night, after I'd gone?'

'No,' she said quietly.

She should have called David, who was waiting anxiously to know about Martson. But she hadn't been able to force herself to do it.

'Did he call you?'

'No. Don't ask me about David, Steven.'

'I can't help it. I'm jealous. Maybe I have no right, but I'm jealous of every man who's known you in the

past, who's touched you, who's kissed you, who's—
devil take it! I can't go on like this.'

'Perhaps we should stop seeing each other?'

'Do you want to do that?' he asked quickly.

Slowly she shook her head. But the way she'd tricked
him into last night's meeting suddenly seemed terrible
after his homage to her honesty.

'Steven—there's something I should tell you—about
why I called you yesterday—'

'Hush!' He touched his lips with his fingers. 'There's
no need to tell me anything. I know you better than you
think.'

'Maybe you don't know me so well.'

'I know the important things, like the truth of your
heart. You called me for—reasons of your own, shall we
say? Some things should remain unspoken.'

He thought she'd dreamed up an excuse to seek his
company, she realised. But then, hadn't she?

She couldn't say any more. She was falling under a
spell, feeling that his heart was finally opening to her.
She'd just risked throwing that away, but she didn't dare
risk it again. It was too precious. And it was such an
innocent little deception, made in another life, when
she'd been a different person. The woman who was falling in love with Steven Leary had only been born a few
moments ago. She would bury her secret deep, where it
could never threaten them.

They spoke little for the rest of the meal. She was
content simply to sit there in the setting sun, enjoying
his company and the feeling that they were growing
closer. He was arrogant, prickly and awkward, rude
when it suited him, unreasonable, demanding and difficult. But the unexpected glimpse of his vulnerability
she'd been granted today had touched her heart. Briefly,

he'd needed her, and he hadn't been afraid to show it. From there, everything else had followed, until now she stood on the threshold of a new and wonderful future.

His barriers were coming down for her and, most remarkable of all, he seemed content to have it so. When he glanced up suddenly and smiled, there was acceptance in his eyes, and a curious puzzled look. She understood that. She felt exactly the same.

They went home slowly. Once, when they paused at traffic lights, he took her hand in his and squeezed it briefly, then drove on without a word. She felt aglow with happiness. Passion was sweet, but just as sweet was this growing closeness.

When the car stopped he said, 'I still haven't explained that Martson file to you. I left it in your house this morning. I'd better come in and tell you now.'

'Martson?' she asked in a daze. 'Oh, yes, Martson.'

She hadn't remembered. Everything but Steven now seemed so far away. As they went inside, each movement seemed heightened, the edges sharper. The sound of her key in the lock seemed enormously significant, and so did the click as he shut the door behind them and stood looking at her. It was dark by now, but her curtains were still open, letting in enough light to show her his eyes, full of a confusion that she'd never seen before. She too was confused, and could only whisper his name. The next moment she was in his arms, feeling his lips on hers.

It was a different kiss from any other he'd given her. Before she'd always felt the hint of ruthlessness, the possessiveness that fuelled his nature. This time she sensed a hunger, almost a plea, and her heart responded to it.

'You know I want you, don't you?' he murmured against her mouth.

'Yes—' she gasped. 'But—'

'Hush.' He brushed his lips across hers to silence her. '"But" is for cowards. You're no coward, Jennifer. You're strong enough to do what you want. There's only yes or no to this question.'

He was kissing her between words, teasing her with his lips, sending flickers of feeling along her ragged nerves. She tried to think, but he was purposely denying her the chance, invoking the desire that gave him the hold over her that he wanted. Jennifer clung to him, longing for the strength to break away, and longing, too, to stay in his arms for ever.

'Dump David and have an affair with me instead,' he murmured.

'An affair?'

'You don't need marriage, Jennifer, any more than I do. Let's light up the sky, go everywhere together, let the world know how we feel about each other.'

She drew back and gave him a challenging look. 'Maybe we feel different things.'

'We feel the same. It's just that I'm honest about it and you're not. We both know the score.'

'Who's keeping score?' she asked quizzically.

He laughed and nuzzled her ear. 'Do you know how badly I want to take you to bed at this moment?'

'Is that your idea of a romantic approach?'

'It's an honest approach to a woman who said she liked plain dealing.'

'Yes—yes, I do.' She couldn't remember saying it.

'You're not in love with me any more than I am with you. Are you?'

'No,' she said hazily. 'I'm not in love with you.'

'Yet we belong together: you know we do. I'll never

make you pretty speeches but I'll match you passion for passion, risk for risk. Together we'll set the sky ablaze.'

This time his kiss had a fierce, driving purpose, as though he'd cast aside doubt and was sure of victory. 'You belong to me,' he growled. 'Don't you? *Don't you?*'

She tried to answer but her senses were reeling. The word 'yes' hovered on her lips, and in a fit of madness she wanted to cry it aloud, to say that she was his and only his. Then a new life would begin for her, full of excitement and joy, full of wild and whirling passions. In another moment she would say the fatal word, and damn the consequences.

Somewhere in the background she heard the phone ring.

'Hell!' Steven muttered.

'Leave it,' she whispered. 'The answering machine is on.'

Sure enough, after a couple of rings the machine clicked in and they heard her voice suggesting the caller leave a message. Then David spoke.

'Jennifer, I've been trying to get you all day. Have you had any luck with that stuff about Martson yet? You said you had the perfect way of finding out about him, and the sooner I know the better. You know how important it is to me, darling.'

She felt Steven stiffen in her arms, and a look came over his face that almost made her cry out to see. His hands fell to his side.

'My God, but you're clever!' he said softly.

'Steven—no! It's not like that!' she said in horror.

'It's exactly like that.' He was frighteningly pale. 'You made a sucker out of me. Don't deny it. After all, it's your victory. You should be proud of it.'

'No,' she said wretchedly. 'Please—listen to me.'

'That was why you called me and asked me out, wasn't it?'

'Steven—'

'Wasn't it?'

'Yes, but—'

'And I fell for it. What a laugh that must have given you! I forgot about David, and that was stupid of me, because it's all about David, isn't it?'

'I didn't do it for David,' she cried. 'I did it for me. I wanted to take you down a peg. And, if you must know, I was going to *tell* you that the information was for him, just for the pleasure of annoying you.'

'Oh, please, you can do better than that!'

'It was stupid and I changed my mind. Today—'

'Don't mention today unless you want me to do something we'll both regret,' he said with soft savagery. 'When I think how I— *Damn you!*'

She tried to turn away from the fury in his eyes. She thought she could see pain there too, but it was hard to be certain through his anger. But she'd barely moved when he seized her shoulders and pulled her around to face him.

'Look at me,' he grated. 'Look me in the face, if you can. I thought you were an honest woman, Jennifer. I should have remembered that there's no such thing. Every woman tells a lie each time she opens her lips, and when she's kissing a man, that's when she's lying the most.'

Without warning he jerked her against him, and his mouth crushed hers in the most ruthless kiss he'd ever given her. It was compounded of desire, pain, and cold, vengeful fury. His rage alarmed her, but side by side with fear was a primitive thrill at his forcefulness. Almost in spite of herself, her lips parted and her body moved invitingly against his.

'How can any woman kiss like this, and yet it's all deception?' he growled against her mouth.

'It wasn't—' she gasped.

'Shut up! Do you think I want to hear anything you have to say?' His mouth smothered hers again, plundering, conquering, overwhelming. Fires raged through her.

'Your heart's pounding,' he mocked. 'I'll bet you even know how to fake that.'

'Steven, please—'

'Such a clever little liar! And all for what? For that mediocrity who sent you to do his dirty work. Did he think about how far you might have to go to get what he wanted? Did he care? Hell would freeze over before I'd let *my* woman run into danger for me. Or didn't you have the sense to realise you were doing something dangerous? Did you think you could jerk me around like a puppet without facing the consequences?'

Suddenly Jennifer's strength returned. Thrusting hard against him, she managed to free herself.

'I'm not afraid of you,' she flashed.

'Then you're a fool.'

'It was a silly schoolgirl trick, and I gave up the idea last night. I haven't thought about David all today. There's been no place for him in my thoughts because you—you and I—couldn't you feel that today was different—?'

'Yes, it was,' he said harshly. 'It was the day I finally saw right through you.'

She drew a sharp, painful breath. 'I want you to leave now, Steven.'

He picked up the Martson file and turned to leave.

Then he stopped, gave a short, scornful laugh, and tossed it at her.

'Take it. You worked hard enough for it,' he sneered. 'I hope Conner appreciates that. Always assuming that you tell him everything, of course.'

The door closed quietly behind him.

'Darling, you're wonderful. However did you get hold of this?' David was rustling through papers as he spoke.

'I just asked someone who's good at this kind of thing,' Jennifer said vaguely. 'As long as it's useful.'

'I'll say. There's some very sensitive material in here. Well done.' David leaned over and kissed her.

They were in his office. Jennifer had driven straight there next morning to hand over the file. She'd gone through it herself first, and knew that Steven had pulled out all the stops to do her a favour. The knowledge filled her with guilt.

Penny entered with coffee. When she'd poured it she gave Jennifer a respectful smile and withdrew.

'Penny looks a bit pale today,' Jennifer observed. 'Is she ill?'

'No, no, she's fine,' David said hurriedly. 'Actually, you're looking pale yourself.'

'I was late getting in last night.'

'That's right; I left a message on your answering machine. Did you get it all right?'

'Yes, I got it,' she said quietly.

If she was looking drawn it was because she hadn't slept a wink after Steven left. She'd tossed restlessly, and at four in the morning she'd risen, made herself some tea, and sat watching the dawn.

Normally clear-headed, she now found that she couldn't sort out her thoughts or her feelings. Anger and misery struggled for supremacy, with neither winning for very long. One moment she was furious with Steven for the things he'd said to her, the next she was full of remorse for what she'd done to him. There was an ache in her heart that wouldn't be argued away.

Yesterday she'd caught a glimpse of the man deep inside him, the man he usually tried to keep hidden. He'd opened up a little, just enough to hint at the depths of his complex personality. The night he'd tended Paws had told her that he could be kind. Now she knew that he could also be generous and sentimental, both traits he was ashamed of. And he could be more easily hurt than he wanted anyone to know.

She'd asked, 'Don't you trust anyone else?' and he'd answered, 'Yes, you,' taking her breath away. His tribute to her honesty had opened a pit at her feet. She'd tried to avoid it. It was sheer ill luck that he'd discovered her little deception—and read more into it than she had ever meant.

Again and again Jennifer went over their quarrel. Steven had been bitter, and bitterness had expressed itself as anger. Had there been an undercurrent of unhappiness, or had she imagined it? And what had lain behind his implied threat of retaliation?

She returned to her office, and for the rest of that day she became tense whenever the phone rang. But it was never Steven. Not that day, nor the next. Nor the next week.

Now that she'd been given the key, Jennifer could see the changes in Trevor. His grimness had vanished, and he smiled easily. He even laughed sometimes. He was a supremely happy man, and it had transformed him.

Even his business dealings were different, showing a

flair and adventurous spirit that had never been his before. Jennifer watched him with pleasure, but she said nothing about the night she'd seen him with Maud. He too never mentioned it, and she wondered if he even knew she'd been there. He might have seen her car outside the house, but she guessed he was past noticing anything except the woman he loved.

Then Maud herself called and invited Jennifer to lunch, naming an Italian restaurant instead of the nouvelle cuisine establishment Jennifer would have expected. There was a further surprise when Maud piled her plate high, and tucked in with gusto.

'I thought models ate like birds,' Jennifer said.

Maud shook her head. 'Most of us eat like horses,' she said. 'Besides, I'm eating for two now.'

'You mean—?'

'I'm pregnant,' Maud said triumphantly.

'But you've barely known Trevor a month.'

'We didn't waste any time,' Maud explained, patting her stomach with a smile.

'But your career—'

'I've had that. It was very nice, but I want something else now. I think part of me was secretly waiting for Trevor.'

'Maud, are you actually—in love with him?'

'Of course I am.' The young woman looked shocked. 'He's gorgeous.'

'Gorgeous? Trevor?'

'He only needs someone to love and understand him.'

'He has a family.'

'But he's always felt left out by you and your grandfather.'

'I don't understand.'

'Trevor's jealous because you've always been

Barney's favourite. He adores your grandfather, tries his best to please him, but he can't break into your charmed circle.'

'He told you all this?'

'Of course not. The poor darling wouldn't know how to put it into words. But I've watched, and seen his face.'

'Are you saying this is why Trevor's been so grumpy?'

'He felt second best. But not any more.' Maud patted her stomach again. 'With us he's always going to be first.'

Jennifer smiled, truly delighted for them. 'Does he know about the baby?'

'Not yet. I'm going to surprise him tonight. I want to get married very soon. My wedding dress is really stunning, but I need to wear it quickly, before I start to put on weight.'

'Your—wedding dress?' Jennifer asked, dazed.

'I'm a very organised person,' Maud explained unnecessarily.

She knew Maud had told Trevor about the baby when he reached work humming next day. She followed him into his office.

'Can I do something for you?' he asked, with the friendliest smile he'd given her for a long time.

'You can tell me all about last night,' she said at once, adding significantly. 'I had lunch with Maud yesterday.'

Immediately a silly great grin took over his face. 'We're going to get married,' he said, and hugged her.

'I'm so glad,' she told him sincerely. 'As long as you're happy.'

'*Happy?* I didn't know what happiness was before. When I think—she's so perfect, and I'm so ordinary…'

He wasn't just saying the right thing, Jennifer realised. Trevor had never known what the right thing was. His humble words came straight from the heart.

'She's what I always wanted,' Trevor said. 'Someone who'd be mine, and there for me. After Mum died—I got lost somehow.'

'I know,' she said.

'But now I'm not alone any more,' he said simply. 'I guess you've felt alone too.'

She nodded, and smiled at him. He smiled back. They were brother and sister again.

She made some coffee and they sat talking for an hour, as they'd never talked before. Jennifer regarded her brother tenderly, delighted by the transformation in him. There had always been a nice man underneath somewhere. It had taken love to reveal that man.

This was how love ought to be, she realised: something that brought out the best in you. It should mean knowing your own heart with total certainty, not being tormented by doubt, feeling tenderness for one man, but responding helplessly to another. Love, clear and direct, making the world simple, answering all questions. Why, oh, why couldn't it be like that for her?

If anyone had told her that two nights later she would be sitting in the Savoy, celebrating her engagement to David, she would not have believed them.

CHAPTER NINE

THE day started like any other. The first sign of the earth-quake to come was when David dropped into her office, looking agitated, to tell her that he'd just left Steven.

'He sent for me to say Charteris could offer me some work.'

Jennifer frowned, wondering what mischief Steven was up to. She soon found out, as David described the shocking, incredible turn the conversation had taken.

'It was a wonderful deal for me, but just when I was really fired up about it he said there was a condition.' David took a deep breath. 'I have to give you up.'

'*What?*'

'He just came right out with it. "Stay away from Jennifer Norton', he said. I thought people only acted like that in gangster movies.'

'Are you telling me,' Jennifer had said slowly, 'that Steven Leary dared—actually *dared*—?'

She could hardly speak from anger. Since the night of their quarrel her feelings towards Steven had been softer, sympathising with the pain she'd caused him. But now all that was swept away in the shock of discovering how ruthless he could be. This was Steven's revenge, a stark demonstration of power that he mustn't be allowed to get away with.

A strange look came over her face. Trevor would have recognised it and warned that it meant 'Jennifer's red mist', the herald of a wild, impulsive action that she would regret five minutes later. Her next words seemed to come out of their own accord.

'David, we have to stand up to him. Even if this hadn't happened, we'd have been thinking about the future soon.' She grasped his hands in both hers. 'Now it's time to tell everyone—and I mean *everyone*—that our marriage is going to take place, whether Steven Leary likes it or not.'

She saw the shock in his face, and for a moment almost expected him to demur. But then he said politely, 'Of course, darling. As you say, it was just a matter of time...'

Her anger carried her through the next hour, breaking the news to Trevor and Barney, calling the evening paper and inserting an announcement in time for that night's edition.

But then David departed and she was left alone, in turmoil over the effect of her hasty words. David offered the security that had always been her first need. Steven had tempted her with another life, a life of risk, where you could win or lose everything on the toss of a word. But the word had fallen against her, and it was too late. Too late.

That evening she and David dined at the Savoy, and it was everything a betrothal celebration should be, with candlelight and roses. Jennifer tried to enjoy herself, and stifle the little voice that said this was too perfect—no, not perfect, too correct—as though it were happening to a precisely written script. Tonight was what she'd longed for. And it was all wrong.

To her dismay David insisted on champagne, although white wine always gave him shattering headaches. An onlooker might have thought there was a touch of defiance in his manner, as though he were trying to convince himself of something.

'To us!' he said, raising his glass in salute.

'To us!' she responded, clinking her glass against his.

As she'd feared, the champagne gave him a migraine. His eyes were soon dark with pain and his smile became forced.

'I think we should be going,' she said gently.

He agreed gratefully, and she shepherded him out to get a taxi. It was too far to David's flat, but her own home was nearer. She could put him to bed and let him sleep off his pain.

They reached her bungalow in a few minutes, and she helped him inside. In the bedroom she pulled off his clothes and rolled him into bed. He looked up at her from the pillow, keeping a tight hold of her hand.

'You take such good care of me,' he whispered. 'Thank you, darling.'

She was swept by tenderness for him. 'I'll always take care of you,' she promised.

He smiled faintly, and closed his eyes. Jennifer released her hand and pulled open a drawer to take out a nightdress. Then she slipped away, closing the bedroom door quietly behind her.

She made up the bed in the spare room and, moving quietly, slipped into the bathroom for a shower. Perhaps the warm water pouring over her body would wash away the strange feeling of dissatisfaction on what should have been the most wonderful night of her life. She'd won the prize that had eluded her so long, and she'd shown Steven that he couldn't dictate to her. Yet she couldn't shake off her unease.

She stepped out of the shower and towelled herself vigorously. The nightdress was white and filmy, and it whispered over her head and down to the floor. In her haste she'd chosen the wrong garment. This one was designed to tease a man into removing it, not for a woman who was heading for the spare room because her lover had a headache.

Suddenly her body was alive with the desire for tender, feverish hands, touching her all over, caressing her intimately, evoking her answering passion. She closed her eyes and gradually a face formed in her dreams…

With an exclamation of dismay she opened her eyes again. How dared Steven intrude at such a moment? What business did his face have in her mind, as though the mere thought of passion evoked his image? He wasn't the man she loved, or the man she was going to marry. Yet there was no getting rid of him.

She put her head around the door for a last look at David. He'd pushed the duvet cover back and lay on the bed naked. He was beautiful, she thought, and stood watching him admiringly. But after a while she realised that her admiration was pure and dispassionate. Not a single lustful thought disturbed her.

But that was because he was ill, she thought hastily, and heard again Steven's mocking voice. 'You'd always be fighting with him for the mirror.'

She began to back out, leaving the door open in case David called out in the night.

A sharp buzz on her doorbell made her jump. Hastily she took her robe from behind the bedroom door, pulled it on over the flimsy nightie and went to answer.

Steven Leary stood on her doorstep, his eyes dark and fierce, his mouth twisted in grim, bitter lines.

'What are you doing here?' she demanded.

'Let's talk inside,' Steven said, urging her irresistibly back inside and closing the door behind him.

'We have nothing to talk about. Get out at once.'

'I'll go when I'm ready. You may not have anything to say, but I have plenty. Let's start by discussing your weird sense of humour.'

'Where you're concerned, I have no sense of humour.'

'Well, I think it's pretty funny of you to get engaged to that no-hoper and leave me to find out from the newspaper. I wonder when you were going to tell me.'

'Why should I tell you? It's none of your business.'

'You know better than that.'

He pushed past her into her front room. Jennifer had never seen him like this before. Instead of his usual immaculate appearance, his tie was missing, his shirt torn open at the throat, and his hair was awry. Strangest of all was the savage look in his eyes as they rested on her. For once, Steven wasn't in perfect control.

'I ought to shake you,' he said savagely. 'All right, we quarrelled, and maybe I said a few things—but to get back at me like *this*—!'

'Get back at you!' she echoed angrily. 'You think that's all my marriage is? A kind of revenge?'

'Don't talk to me of your marriage,' he raged. 'You have no more intention of marrying David Conner than I have. You got up this phoney engagement to pay me back. OK, I was clumsy. I should have known he'd go running to you and that you'd get so mad at me that you'd do something stupid. But this? Are you out of your mind?'

'You're wrong, Steven. This was always going to happen one day. I'm in love with David. You've known that from the first evening. And he's in love with me.'

'I know you've had some mad idea that he's the man

to solve your problems, and he's been dazzled by you like a rabbit caught in headlamps. I should have allowed for that. I didn't. I screwed up. But this is where it stops. The joke's over.'

'It's no joke.'

'Grow up, Jennifer! You can't marry him. And you don't seriously mean to. You did this to put me in my place. All right, you succeeded. I give in.'

Inexplicably, for a woman who'd just engaged herself to another man, a pulse started beating in her throat. 'And what—exactly—does "give in" mean?'

He turned a haggard face on her. 'Isn't it obvious?'

'Not to me.'

'I came here seeking you out, didn't I? I don't chase after women, begging favours, but I've come to ask you—plead with you—to stop this nonsense now, because otherwise—'

'Otherwise?' she asked, scarcely able to speak.

His face tensed. A man who'd found himself on the edge of a precipice might have looked as Steven did at that moment. 'Otherwise my shares will take a drop,' he finished curtly.

Jennifer stared at him, rigid with shock. 'What?' It was barely a whisper.

'Your sudden engagement can do me a lot of harm in the market.'

'I don't believe I'm hearing this,' she cried wildly. 'I don't care about the market! I'm marrying David because I love him.'

'Nonsense! You're marrying him because you lost your temper with me,' Steven retorted with devastating accuracy. 'And he's marrying you because you told him to.'

'That—isn't true,' she stammered, trying not to see

David's face in her mind, pale with shock as she arranged their marriage.

'Don't ask me to believe he proposed to you,' Steven said witheringly. 'He has too much sense of self-preservation for that. You said, ''We're not going to let him dictate to us, are we, David? We're going to get engaged just to show him.'' The poor sap never knew what hit him.'

'You have no right to say that.'

There was a burning look in his eyes that made her feel that her robe was transparent. 'I have the right to say anything that will get you out of this mess. Does he know how you come alive in my arms? Does he wonder why you're so dead in his?'

'You don't know how I am with David.'

'I know you don't burn up at his touch the way you do at mine, because no woman reacts that way to more than one man at a time. If it's there for me, it's not there for him.'

'You've changed your tune. Only a few days ago, in this very apartment, you accused me of faking it to fool you.'

'I was good 'n mad, and I had every reason. But when I calmed down I knew you couldn't pretend that much. One touch and we both go up like straw.'

'Stop it!' she cried, turning away and covering her ears.

He pulled her around to face him, giving her a little shake. 'Why? Does the truth hurt? Look me in the eyes and tell me it's not like that.'

'It's—too late—' she whispered.

'It's never too late as long as there's *this* between us,' he said, and pulled her into his arms.

Part of her had known this was inevitable from the

moment he'd arrived, yet she was still taken by surprise. If she lived to be a hundred it would still be a shock to feel his lips crushing hers and his arms like steel about her. Once he'd kissed her with tenderness, and the dawning of some feeling to which she hadn't dared to give a name. But now there was only the drive to enforce his own will. No tenderness, just the sheer blind power of a man who understood nothing else.

He wrenched off her robe, tossing it to the ground, and there was only gossamer silk between her nakedness and Steven's plundering hands. The nightdress might not have been there for all the protection it offered. Through it she could feel every light caress, every intimate touch. He was treating her without respect or courtesy, forcing her to acknowledge the desire that made a mockery of all other feelings. But her pounding heart told her that he was paying her the tribute of a fierce passion that was out of his control.

He was kissing her quickly, tracing a line along her jaw with his lips, then down her neck to her throat. 'It was always going to come to this,' he murmured. 'We took too long to face it—far too long—'

'David—' she whispered frantically.

'Forget him. This is what matters now. No woman has ever affected me the way you do.'

One of the straps of her nightdress snapped under the urgent movements of his fingers. He was kissing her neck, her shoulders, her breasts. Jennifer fought not to respond, but the feelings he could evoke in her were stronger than will. They could make her forget sensible resolutions and think only of him and how he could force her to want him. She was so totally absorbed in him that she wasn't even aware that he'd drawn her towards the bedroom, and through the door...

'*Jennifer*...'

She looked up into Steven's face, but he hadn't spoken. He'd become still and pale at the sound of the voice that had come from her bed. She felt him grow tense with shock. Slowly he drew away from her, his eyes fixed on the bed. David was just sitting up, a hand covering his eyes.

For a long moment the world froze. At last David dropped his hand, stared at them for a moment, then fell back again with his eyes closed.

'You deceitful little jade,' Steven said slowly. 'You did it again.' He was white with anger as he pulled her out of the bedroom.

Jennifer tried to clear her head. Her body was still singing from his touch, and she could hardly grasp the calamitous nature of what had happened. She flinched at the savage look in Steven's eyes.

'Steven, you don't understand—'

'What is there to understand? You knew how I felt about you and you let me make a fool of myself showing you. And all the time—you were laughing at me. *Again!*'

'I wasn't,' she cried wildly. 'It's not the way you think—'

'You'll be telling me next I didn't see David Conner in your bed,' he raged.

Her own temper rose to meet his.

'And so what if you did? He happens to be my fiancé. What man has a better right to be in my bed?'

'At one time I could have given you an answer to that. But that was before I realised you were stupid enough to take this farce seriously.'

'I'll do as I like,' she cried. 'How dare you come here dictating whom I may and may not marry? You were so sure of yourself. Snap your fingers and Jennifer would come running, because she couldn't possibly love another man if Steven Leary wanted her.

'But you were so wrong. Everything I've ever done has been for David. He's the man I love and nobody else could mean anything to me.'

'You've been playing with me...' Steven whispered.

'Yes, I've been playing, but so have you. You've got no complaint, Steven. You just found someone else who could play the game better. How does it feel?'

'Like being knifed through the heart,' he said quietly.

His answer shook her to the depths. For a moment his face was wiped clean of all except raw pain. She had a blinding flash of awareness, such as a fencer might feel when, after duelling for a few rounds, she discovered that the buttons had fallen from the foils. Suddenly it wasn't a game any more. The buttons were off, the blades were sharp, and the pain was terribly real.

She had one brief glimpse of anguish in his eyes. If it had lasted longer she might have reached out to him, but the shutters came down at once, leaving only bitter vengeance behind.

'There's an old saying, Jennifer,' he said in a voice of deadly quiet. '"Fool me once, shame on you; fool me twice, shame on me." I actually let you fool me twice, and I can't leave it there. Nobody treats me the way you have. Nobody deceives me, then casts me aside. I win every game.'

'You haven't won this one,' she flung at him.

'The game's not over yet. It won't be over until I've won and you acknowledge it.'

'You'll wait a long time for that.'

'If I have to wait for ever, my moment will come,' he said bitingly. 'But it won't take that long. You'll wish you'd never made an enemy of me. Remember I said that.'

He took a step towards her, and it was all she could do not to back away. There'd always been an underlying hint of menace about Steven, but now it was more than a hint. It was there, it was real, and it was turned against her.

'Get out of here,' she breathed.

'When I'm ready. I've something to say first. Go ahead and marry your pretty boy. You'll regret it in a week. And when he drives you crazy, with his weakness and petulance, remember how it could have been between us. You and I could have made the stars envious. And you threw it all away.'

Then he was gone, leaving her staring at the door, trembling with shock.

Jennifer was awoken by a light kiss on her forehead, and opened her eyes to find David beside her.

'I've brought you a cup of tea,' he said.

'Oh—thank you. How are you this morning?'

'Fine. Those headaches never last long, thank goodness.'

He was looking better, smiling contentedly. Which was odd, she thought, for someone who'd seen his fiancée kissing another man the night before. But perhaps he hadn't seen it. For much of the time his hand had been over his eyes. And sometimes, she knew, his mind blocked out the worst of his headaches.

She sipped the tea, and found it delicious. David had many domestic talents.

'You were right about the champagne,' he said. 'Luckily for me you were there.'

She wished he hadn't said that. Once she'd loved to

hear how he relied on her, but now it seemed to lay fetters on her. She'd got him into this situation, and she couldn't turn away from his need.

Then it came back to her, the thing she'd been trying to remember, on the beach when Steven had said, 'I'm glad you were with me when I found out.'

Need. The eager hold on a comforting hand. She'd associated those things with David, but they'd been there too in Steven. This was the elusive echo that had troubled her, and she'd remembered when it was too late.

She and David had breakfast together like an old married couple. Then she dropped him at work and went on to her own office, where Trevor was waiting for her. He spoke some conventional words about her engagement, but his eyes were troubled.

'You are happy, aren't you?' he asked at last.

'Deliriously,' Jennifer declared.

'It's just that Maud thought things were happening between you and Leary.'

'I was stringing him along for the firm,' Jennifer said. 'That's over now.'

'Your break-up with him has lowered our price, but only a little,' Trevor said. 'It'll climb again.'

But to everyone's dismay the price went into a steep drop that seemed to grow faster with every hour. 'Someone's unloading our shares,' Trevor said, aghast.

In despair Jennifer realised that Nortons was on a downward slide to oblivion. But suddenly the price halted, and began to inch back up.

'The rumour is that one man is buying us up,' Trevor said. 'And he probably owns enough now to demand a seat on the board. To make matters worse, Barney wants a board meeting this evening—and he's going to be there.'

Barney arrived ten minutes before the meeting was due to start, and surveyed the boardroom with its neatly arranged chairs about the oak table. 'We need an extra chair for our newest board member.'

'But we don't know who he is,' Trevor said patiently. 'And he isn't going to turn up because he doesn't know there's a meeting.'

'Anyone smart enough to pull this move is smart enough to arrive at a meeting nobody's told him about,' Barney declared firmly.

At precisely five minutes to six the three partners were ready. Barney took his seat in the high-backed chair at the head of the table.

'Mr Chairman, would you like to begin?' Trevor asked formally.

Barney shook his head. 'Let's wait just a little longer.'

Jennifer and Trevor glanced at the empty chair, almost expecting to see it inhabited by a ghostly presence, so strong was the force of Barney's conviction.

At that moment the large grandfather clock in the corner began to strike six. All of them sat transfixed as the sonorous sounds filled the room.

As the vibrations from the last note trembled into silence the door opened, and Steven Leary entered the boardroom.

CHAPTER TEN

IN THE moment of total silence Trevor jumped to his feet. Jennifer rose slowly. Only Barney stayed where he was, apparently unperturbed.

'Good evening,' Steven said. 'I hope I haven't kept you all waiting.' He spoke to them all, but his eyes were on Jennifer and they were made of stone.

'You mean it's you who's been buying us up?' Trevor demanded.

'Not him,' Jennifer said. 'Charteris.'

'No,' Steven said coolly. 'Me, personally. I now own a third of Nortons.'

You'll wish you'd never made an enemy of me. His words echoed in her head with terrible significance. Steven Leary had come for his revenge.

'I think we should welcome our new board member,' Barney said, smiling. 'The best way forward for us all is to try to get along.'

'I agree,' Trevor said.

'Don't either of you understand what's happening here?' Jennifer demanded wildly. 'You have to fight him or he'll swallow us whole.' She turned on Steven. 'Barney doesn't understand about you, and Trevor doesn't want to fall out with Maud's brother, but I see through you and I'll fight you.'

'You've made your position very clear,' Steven said. 'Now I wonder if we could get to business.'

He took his place at the table, leaving Jennifer stand-

143

ing there, aghast. It was clear the other two didn't see the danger.

But she'd known Steven as they hadn't. She'd felt the power of his arms about her, seen his face above hers, heavy with passion, then dark with rage. Once she'd seen it gentle, vulnerable, when he'd told her simply that he trusted her totally. Now trust had turned to bitterness.

Steven distributed some papers, pushing Jennifer's towards her without a glance. She studied them and felt a chill at the efficiency and thoroughness she found there. Glancing up, she found him looking at her. He'd followed her thoughts, and wanted her to understand that it was just as she'd feared.

Calmly he laid out his plans. He planned for the firm to do a lot of business with Charteris, which meant that Nortons would have to expand, at great cost.

'Once we've gone in this deep, Charteris will have us in its pocket,' Jennifer protested. 'They can force down our prices, then drive us under and buy us up cheap.'

'I suppose you'll just have to try to trust me,' Steven said coolly.

'Jennifer, my dear, it's not like you to be prejudiced,' Barney protested.

Even Trevor was making noises of approval as his eyes swept the pages. Jennifer knew she'd lost this round.

'There is one thing,' Trevor said as Steven prepared to depart. 'How did you know about this meeting?'

Steven gave a smile as cold and bleak as winter. 'When a man is determined to do something, then he'll usually manage to do it. And believe me, I'm very determined.'

His words were general, but his eyes were on Jennifer. The next moment he was gone.

* * *

A week later Steven's work was interrupted by a commotion in his outer office. He threw open his door, and, as he'd expected, he found a furious Jennifer.

'Come in,' he said distantly. 'I can give you five minutes.'

She hadn't seen him since the board meeting. He seemed thinner, and there were dark shadows under his eyes.

'It won't take me that long to tell you what I think of you,' Jennifer said. 'Of all the unscrupulous, devious—I've just been talking with Barney. How dare you tell him that I should postpone my wedding!'

'You can't start your honeymoon just as Trevor is returning from his.'

'I thought I knew how low you could stoop—'

'You were wrong,' he interrupted her coolly. 'You haven't begun to discover how low I can stoop. You may find out yet.'

'I'm not postponing my wedding at your command.'

'Then I'll just have to take a more active role in Nortons while you're gone.'

Jennifer froze as she saw the trap into which he'd lured her. 'You'll take a more active role over my dead body.'

'But you won't be there,' he pointed out.

'You devil,' she breathed. 'And to think that I—'

'That you what?'

She was struck dumb. There was suddenly nothing to say.

His secretary looked in. 'Your next appointment is here. Shall I ask him to wait?'

'No need,' Steven said. 'Ms Norton is just leaving.'

It was as though he'd switched her off. Jennifer

paused in the doorway for a last horrified look at him, but he'd turned away.

'I've postponed the wedding for a month,' she told Maud with a sigh. They lunched together regularly these days. 'I had no choice.'

'I don't know what you did to make him so bitter,' Maud said, 'but it really got to him. Mind you, after he tried to scare David off in that heavy-handed fashion I wouldn't blame you for anything. It's strange of Steven to be so clumsy. Usually his judgement and timing are spot-on. He must be in love with you after all.'

To Jennifer's dismay this suggestion caused a flutter of agitation deep within her. To hide it she said, 'What a dreadful prospect!'

'Oh, heavens! Not you as well!' Maud said plaintively. 'Between the two of you I'm getting squashed. What happened to make my brother go out of his mind?'

Jennifer told her everything, right up to the moment Steven had discovered David in her bed. 'He thinks I made a fool of him, and to him that's unforgivable. He won't stop until we're just a subsection of Charteris.'

'Actually, Charteris is a bit cross with Steven for not getting them better terms from Nortons. They think he takes Nortons' side too often.'

'How do you know?' Jennifer asked.

'Because he tells me everything. Naturally he swears me to secrecy.'

'And you promise?' Jennifer asked.

'Of course. Otherwise he wouldn't tell me, and then how could I tell you?' Maud asked logically. 'You mustn't let on to him that you know.'

'No chance of that, since we're not on speaking terms. I don't understand. What scheme is he working on now?'

Maud considered a moment, before saying, 'I'd better tell you something else. How do you think Steven got the money to buy thirty per cent of Nortons?'

'I've always wondered about that.'

'The bank made him a huge loan, but he had to put up his Charteris shares as collateral.'

'He did *what*?'

'He's in the same boat as you, Jennifer. If anything happens to Nortons he loses everything.'

Jennifer was stunned. Whatever Steven was doing, he was committed to it in deadly earnest. But he wasn't acting from love. She inspired his passion, but these days it was a cold, vengeful passion that left her apprehensive.

'Try to understand him,' Maud begged. 'Steven's been fighting most of his life, for Mum, for me, and only lastly for himself. He doesn't know anything else. He's forgotten how to say please.'

'It's nice of you to try,' Jennifer said wanly. 'But it really doesn't make any difference now.'

She drove home slowly, feeling as though life was closing in on her like a prison. Secretly she was glad of the excuse to delay her wedding. She would have escaped if she could, but the memory of David saying, 'You take such good care of me,' was with her always. She'd fought so hard to win him, and now his need seemed to shackle her.

Despite their quarrel she missed Steven desperately. It wasn't merely desire that united them. There was a tough, astringent quality to his mind that appealed to her. They could laugh together, and read each other's thoughts, because they complemented each other. She could have loved him, if only he'd loved her. But he'd gone out of his way to tell her that he wasn't in love with her and wouldn't make a commitment to her. It was his pride he was avenging, not his heart.

That last bitter scene in his office had been like a door slamming. The hurt was bad, but it would have been even worse if she'd been in love with him. It was some consolation that at least she was safe from that. She must cling onto the thought. Because otherwise life would be unendurable.

There was some justice in Maud's complaint that she was caught between the two of them. Mostly her brother stayed at work late these days, but that evening she found him at home in a black mood.

'For heaven's sake, do something,' she told him. 'Reach out to her, before it's too late.'

'It's already too late,' he growled.

'I lunched with Jennifer today and she told me what really happened the night you called at her flat.'

'What is there to tell? She was in bed with her fiancé.'

'But she wasn't. He had a migraine from drinking champagne and she took him home and put him to bed. She slept in the spare room.'

He gave a crack of ribald laughter. 'My God! Would you listen to that?'

'If Jennifer says it, I'm sure it's true.'

'True?' he roared. 'Of course it's true. It's just the kind of witless performance I'd expect from that ninny.'

'Well, I suppose the poor man can't help the way he's made.'

Steven got up and strode to the door, as though movement eased his tension.

'I'll tell you this,' he said contemptuously. 'If I was naked and lying in the bed of the sexiest woman I've ever known, I'd sure as hell think of something more inspiring to do than *have a headache.*'

The phone call that turned Jennifer's world upside down came in the middle of one afternoon.

A young man said, 'I'm Constable Beckworth. We have a man in the cells at Ainsley police station. He was arrested for brawling and he asked us to call you. His name is Fred Wesley and he says he's your father.'

Jennifer took a long, slow breath to counter the feeling of being punched in the stomach.

'Ms Norton?'

'I'll be right there.'

She was functioning on automatic as she drove to the station. Her father had arrived back in her life after sixteen years, and she couldn't think straight.

He was older, thinner, his hair grey and straggly. He looked like a man who'd lived rough for a long time. But he had the same perky grin that had won her heart as a child.

'The bad penny turned up again,' he said. 'Pleased to see me?'

'Let's get you out of here,' she said, avoiding the question.

They didn't talk on the journey, although he whistled at her shiny car. With his shabby clothes he looked incongruous against the soft leather.

He whistled again when he saw her home. But all he said was, 'Nice.'

'I'll get you a meal,' Jennifer said.

After so many years missing him, longing for him, wondering why he never made contact, now she felt all at sea. She didn't know what to say. He was a stranger—until he gave his cheeky grin again, and that made her smile. But at the same moment came a slight chill. She wondered how much he relied on that grin, and instinct told her that it was too much.

'How did you know how to contact me?' she asked as she moved about the kitchen. Fred stood watching her, a glass of wine in his hand.

'Saw a piece about the old man in a magazine,' he said. 'It mentioned "Trevor and Jennifer Norton".'

'He changed our names when we were children,' she said quickly. 'We had no say—'

'Don't worry. The old's boy's rolling in it, you get your hands on some.'

'That's not—' she began to say, but he'd already turned away and was studying her living room.

'Very nice,' he said, drawing the words out. 'Done well for yourself.'

'Why did you call me and not Trevor?' she asked as they sat down to eat.

'Don't think he'd have given me the time of day. We didn't get on well when he was a kid. But you and I were always close.'

'So close that you walked out on me and never got in touch,' she couldn't help saying.

'I was only thinking of you. Barney never liked me. I reckoned if I wasn't there your mum could go back to him and he'd see you all right.'

'So it was an act of generosity for our sakes?' she asked quietly.

'That's right. A father's love.' There was the grin again.

'Dad, don't,' she said tensely. 'I'm glad to see you again, but you don't have to feed me all that stuff.'

'Well, whatever. You did all right for yourself, and that's the main thing.'

'What happened to that woman you went to live with?'

'Oh, her! We broke up. Easy come, easy go.'

'Like buses,' Jennifer said quietly.

He roared with laughter. 'Hey, that's not bad. A bit like buses, yes. I tried my hand at this and that, but the luck was against me.'

'You might have stayed in touch.'

'Barney told me not to,' he said, just too casually. He saw her disbelieving eyes on him and shrugged. 'Well, you were better off without me. Look at this place. Very nice. Very nice indeed.'

Jennifer ground her nails into her palm, wishing he'd stop saying 'very nice'. She'd imagined this meeting for years, but now it was here and he was a man she didn't know and was finding hard to like.

She struggled with the feeling. His image had lived in her heart too long for her to dismiss it easily now. Somehow their reunion must be made to accord with her dreams.

Things would be better next day. A good night's sleep would change them both for the better. She made up the bed in her spare room, ensuring that he had every comfort.

He seemed glad of an early night. As she'd suspected, he'd been sleeping rough, and he'd drunk two bottles of wine with very little help from her. When he was snoring she called Trevor. Her brother exclaimed, but didn't react as caustically as he would once have done.

He arrived early next morning and the three of them had breakfast together, but Jennifer could see that Fred had been wise in not calling Trevor. Father and son had nothing to say to each other. Trevor was painfully stiff and polite. He mentioned his coming marriage, and after

a few conventional words Fred asked, 'Pick a girl with
a bit of money, did you?'

It was a measure of Maud's softening influence that
this question offended Trevor. He visibly winced, and
changed the subject. As he was leaving he said to
Jennifer in a low voice, 'I didn't like him years ago and
I don't like him now.' He touched her arm gently. 'If
you've got any sense you'll keep him at arm's length.
Don't let him hurt you.'

'He can't hurt me after all this time.'

'I hope not. I'm afraid you're about to get sentimental
about him.'

'Well, he is our father. I'm going to spend today with
him.'

She had been beginning to fear the worst, but the day
turned into an unexpected pleasure. Fred was on his best
behaviour, making her laugh and squiring her to lunch
with great charm. It was true that she picked up the bill,
but it was still enjoyable to be sitting there with him.
Somewhere deep inside her a tense knot of muscle began
to relax. It wasn't too late. The past could be repaired.

She kitted him out with some new clothes, including
a couple of suits, and had to admit that he looked splendid in them. They dined at the Ritz that night, and she
began planning how they would spend the next day.

'Why don't you go to work in the morning,' he suggested, 'while I go and see your mother's grave? We'll
meet up for lunch.'

Next morning she told him how to find the church-
yard, and arranged to meet him at the Ritz at twelve-
thirty. She left early for lunch and stopped off to buy
him a silk tie.

She reached the restaurant ten minutes early, and ordered an aperitif for herself and him. She pictured his

face when he arrived and found everything ready for him.

Twelve-thirty and no sign of him. He'd probably forgotten the time. She wondered which of his new suits he would be wearing.

Twelve forty-five. Perhaps her watch was fast. She checked with the waiter and found that it was actually twelve-fifty.

She ordered a mineral water and sipped it slowly, trying not to listen to the ominous murmur of fear in her heart. Of course he was coming. He would be here by one o'clock.

At one-fifteen she stopped pretending to read the menu. Perhaps something had happened to him. She ought to call home. She dialled on her mobile but there was no answer. Perhaps he'd got lost.

Perhaps he wasn't coming.

She dialled again. It might have been a wrong number. But again there was no reply.

Perhaps he wasn't coming.

She began to say it to herself: He's not coming. He's not coming. It throbbed through her head so persistently that she imagined she heard a voice saying the words. Then she realised that the voice was real.

'He isn't coming,' Steven repeated.

She looked up as he sat down opposite here.

'How do you come to be here?' she whispered.

'We share a family grapevine now. I know all about it. Did you really think he wouldn't let you down again?'

'It's—not the same.'

'Yes, it is, Jennifer. It's exactly the same. He's a man who runs out. He ran out on you then and he's run out on you now. I expect he's done pretty well out of you. How much did you spend on him?'

It was the truth, and she'd never run away from the truth.

'A lot,' she said. 'All right. So now you know. Will you please go away?'

'Not until I've said a few things.'

How could he torment her now? she wondered. However much he hated her, how could he do this?

'Please go away,' she said tiredly.

'This was always a mistake, Jennifer. He can't reach back into your childhood and make it right, and nor can you. What he did he did, and it helped to make you the person you are, a woman who needs safety and reassurance from a man—or thinks she needs it.

'But it doesn't have to be like that. You're stronger than you know. Strong enough to say good riddance to him.'

'You know nothing about it.'

'I know that you can put all that behind you if you really want to. Don't let this destroy you. You're strong enough not to.'

'I don't feel very strong right now,' she admitted. The tense knot was starting in her stomach again. 'I just want to—'

'Give up? Don't say that. Don't even think it. Stand up on your own. You can, you know. You don't need anyone as badly as you think you do. Not your father, not David, not me. Keep telling yourself that, because it's true. And maybe you'll still be in time to avoid the disaster you're walking into. That's all.'

He got up and walked away without another word, leaving Jennifer staring after him almost in shock. His words might have been meant as a sort of comfort, but he'd uttered them without once softening the harshness of his face and voice. He'd handed her the key to surviving this experience, but he'd done it without warmth. He was as hostile as ever but he'd given her the strength to overcome her pain. Or rather, he'd pointed out her own strength.

There was no sign of Fred when she went home. All his new possessions were gone, plus he'd taken her best suitcase to carry them. Her new chequebook had been removed from her desk. In its place was a note, saying simply, *Sorry, love, but you don't begrudge me, do you? Fred.*

For a dreadful moment she was swept back years. She was alone, with no points of reference in a hostile world, and a chill wind was whistling about her. She flinched back into herself, seeking refuge from that wind, longing for a place where she could crawl away and hide.

But Steven's voice pursued her. 'You're stronger than you know...stand up on your own.'

It was true. Steven had seen the truth about her more clearly than anyone else. And he'd come seeking her out to offer his fierce, uncompromising comfort, knowing that it would be her truest support.

She saw David that evening, and related almost the whole experience. But she didn't mention Steven.

'My poor darling,' he said, taking her hand. 'What a terrible thing to happen to you.'

'I don't know,' she said thoughtfully. 'In an odd way it was useful. It laid a ghost. Perhaps I'm better off without that ghost.'

'I can imagine what it must have done to you— brought back the past, traumatised you.'

'But does bringing back the past have to be traumatic? Maybe it happens so that we can deal with it and make it really the past? It's strange. I never thought of that before. But I should have.'

'Darling, you're so wonderfully brave about it,' David said tenderly. 'I wish I'd been there to help you.'

'I had help,' she murmured.

'I know I haven't been much use to you recently. I feel I've failed you. But not any more. From now on I'm going to be everything you've always wanted me to be.' He gathered both her hands in his. 'I'm here for you, Jennifer, and I always will be. Once we're married I'll never leave you. We'll be together all our lives. That's a promise.'

CHAPTER ELEVEN

MAUD was happy to exchange her glamorous life for domesticity, but she wanted to go out in a blaze of glory. Her wedding dress had to be expanded just an inch.

Jennifer went with her for the final fitting, and was full of admiration. The traditional gown was long and romantic, with a train and a veil streaming behind her.

Jennifer had been uneasy with Maud's request that she be bridesmaid, but Trevor had been eager for her to agree, and she had reluctantly done so. If Steven was to be her brother-in-law, she couldn't spend her life avoiding him.

Maud had chosen Jennifer's dress herself, with an unerring eye. The result was silk of the palest peach, cut and draped in a style that was sophisticated, elegant and faintly Grecian.

The reception was to be held in the huge garden at the back of Steven's house. When Jennifer arrived there early on the morning of the wedding the marquee was up and caterers were already scurrying back and forth.

There was no sign of Steven, and Maud confided that he'd gone out earlier, saying he would return later. Jennifer wondered if he was avoiding her.

Maud's favourite hairdresser arrived and set her hair in huge rollers. Then she put him to work on Jennifer, giving so many detailed instructions that he asked which one was the bride.

'I am, but I'm fine,' Maud said. 'I want Jennifer to look just right.'

She applied her own make-up with swift, professional movements, then worked on the bridesmaid's face herself. An uneasy suspicion was gathering in Jennifer.

'You're wasting your time making me look good,' she said. 'I'm marrying David, and even if I weren't, your brother is the last person I'd choose.'

'Funny, he says the same about you,' Maud said, putting the last touches to Jennifer's left eyebrow. 'Only more forcefully.'

When her hair was finished Jennifer had to admit that Maud knew what she was doing. Delicate, wispy curls floated about her face, giving it a flattering softness. The peach threw a warm glow on her skin, and her dark eyes seemed larger than usual, thanks to Maud's artful magic.

'I'm just dying for a cup of tea,' Maud said prosaically.

'I'll go down and get you one,' Jennifer offered.

It gave her the chance to practise walking in the delicate silver sandals that went with the dress. By the time she'd made it to the bottom of the stairs she was moving easily. She sighed with relief and looked up to find Steven standing there, his gaze fixed on her.

She'd been concentrating so hard that she hadn't seen him enter. Now she caught him off guard, and the look in his eyes, before he controlled it, showed her everything he would have preferred to keep hidden. She saw his shock at her transformation, and one moment of naked longing, before he brought down the shutters.

After a moment he spoke, through lips that seemed stiff. 'I didn't know you'd arrived.'

'Maud and I have just finished getting ready. I'm fetching her a cup of tea.'

'No time. The cars are here.'

'I'll tell her.'

Just a few banal words, but they left her feeling as if she'd been through a wringer. She wondered how she was going to endure today.

At last it was time to depart. Maud swirled down the staircase in a cloud of glory to where Steven was waiting for her in the hall below. Jennifer helped her into the car, carefully arranging the gorgeous dress so that it wouldn't crumple. Steven opened the front door and prepared to get in.

'You're supposed to sit with me,' Maud protested.

'It's better if your bridesmaid is with you,' he said in an expressionless voice, seating himself beside the driver.

On the short journey to the church Jennifer refused to look at his back. She was remembering what Mike Harker had told her. *Steven said weddings were a female conspiracy for making men look ridiculous, and he'd never let it happen to him.*

Today was the kind of occasion he'd meant, to be endured only for Maud's sake. No doubt he thought of herself as part of the conspiracy. He'd made it plain often enough that all he'd wanted from her was an affair.

When they reached the church Steven waited while Jennifer adjusted final details of the bride's appearance. At last he offered Maud his arm, and they began the procession to the church.

They were a few minutes late, and when the organ struck up Trevor looked around and smiled at his bride, in joy and relief. She smiled back, and their mutual happiness lit up the church. She had full and complete possession of Trevor's heart, Jennifer reflected, and she needed nothing else.

She remembered the night Paws had given birth, and

Steven joking about her sounding 'like a medieval tyrant saying, "Bring me the head of Steven Leary."'

But it was his heart she wanted. And nobody could bring her that because he didn't have one.

And yet he'd sought her out when her father had deserted her for the second time, offering her something that hadn't sounded like sympathy but which had done her more good than David's conventional comfort. Rough as Steven's words had been, they'd steadied her as surely as—she sought for the comparison and found the one that had been waiting all the time—as a hand held out in the darkness.

She bowed her head over her bouquet, suddenly swept by a tide of misery. She would never admit, even to herself, that she loved Steven. But the pain would go on and on, and she didn't know how she was going to bear it.

Inwardly she cried out at Steven for his heavy-handed attempt to part her from David. But for that she wouldn't have known the moment of rashness that had made her insist on the engagement. Now she was trapped, bound to David by his need of her—a need which, in honour, she could never betray—and by his conviction that she needed him.

Maud took her place beside her groom, and the service began. Steven gave his sister away, then stood back. He never once looked in Jennifer's direction, but she knew he was conscious of her, as she was of him.

At last the organ pealed out triumphantly. The bride and groom swept from the church, and the congregation followed.

At the reception Jennifer was joined by David, who kissed her cheek and told her she was beautiful. They sat together during the speeches, receiving several smiling glances from people who obviously knew that they were next.

Afterwards Trevor and Maud led the dancing on the lawn, shining with love and happiness. Jennifer danced with David, conscious that Steven, having avoided her until now, was watching her with burning eyes. She wondered if he would ask her to dance, or rather, demand a dance, since that was more his style.

But instead he took the floor with one of Maud's model friends, a young woman so stunningly beautiful that Jennifer couldn't bear to watch. She slipped away, hoping nobody would see her, and wandered across the lawn, into the trees.

But even here there was no peace, because it reminded her of the enchanted night when she'd wandered with Steven in Barney's garden. She'd laughed with him, and teased him in a way that now seemed the height of madness. Why had she never suspected the dangerous path she was walking? Because she'd been falling in love, and that was the most dangerous thing of all.

On the far side of the trees she came to a patch of land where workmen were busily clearing bushes and levelling the ground. Metal spikes had been driven into the earth, with light ropes slung between them, apparently outlining the shape of buildings.

'What's this?' she asked curiously.

One of the workmen stopped and gave her a friendly grin. 'Not sure, really. We've been told to clear the ground.'

'But these outlines?'

'They've been moved a dozen times, and I guess they'll move a dozen more. He keeps changing his mind.'

'But what's it going to be when it's finished?'

'Well, as far as I know—'

'What are you doing here?'

Jennifer turned to see Steven behind her, frowning.

'I was curious,' she said. 'You don't mind my looking at your garden, do you?'

'I don't like your being here,' he said curtly. 'It's not safe in those fancy sandals. The ground is uneven.'

He took her arm, steering her firmly away. She could sense his anger, and knew that concern for her safety was only a cover. This was a secret, something else from which she was shut out.

'Did you see your father again?' he asked as they walked back across the lawn.

'No. When I reached home he'd gone, taking my chequebook—which he made good use of.'

'Good,' he said coolly. 'You're better off now. But I dare say you don't think so.'

'Yes, I do. I'm grateful to you, Steven. You really helped me. I wonder why, when you hate me.'

'I don't hate you. Despite everything I respect and admire you. I thought it would help you see sense about Conner.'

'I'm still going to marry him. He needs me and he's good to me. If you could have seen him when I told him about my father—'

'I'll bet he offered you a life of tender protectiveness and cotton wool. You'll suffocate in a month.'

'I gave him my word.'

'Break it, Jennifer. Break every promise you ever made rather than go through with this and destroy us both.'

She gave a wan smile. 'I don't think you're that easily destroyed.'

'I want you. I've never made any secret of it—'

'Yes, and I know why. Another man's woman. A challenge to your possessiveness. But it's not enough. Just think of me as a bus, Steven. Passing by, and out of your life.'

'Out of my life? With my sister married to your brother? We'll never be out of each other's lives. In a few months we'll have a mutual nephew or niece.'

'Then I'll wave to you at the christening. And so will my husband. I'll be married to David by then.'

'The devil you will!'

'I will, because my word is my bond. That was the first thing Barney ever taught me. He said it went for life as well as commerce.'

He gave a bark of cynical laughter. 'I can just hear the biggest twister in the business saying that. How many times did *he* wriggle out of awkward commitments?'

'Nobody knows,' Jennifer admitted. 'But he always managed to look like the soul of honour while he was doing it. Steven, please try to understand. How can I desert David *now*, when I've just been reminded how cruel it feels?'

'Don't ask me to understand, because I can't. I'm not soft-hearted like you. I take what I want, when I can. I'll never go through this kind of fancy performance, but I could give you a life worth living.' His face was dark with suffering. 'I should say I wish you happiness for the future, but I can't tell such a lie. I wish you the same future as mine—a life of bitter regret and wondering what might have been. Goodbye, Jennifer.'

When the bride and groom had departed for their Caribbean honeymoon, and the guests were drifting away, Barney found Steven alone in the garden, deep in a very large whisky.

'I'm ashamed of you,' he declared.

'I'm not driving,' Steven said, surprised. 'This is where I live.'

'I'm not talking about the drink. I'm talking about you, giving in without a fight. And you have the nerve to say I was your mentor. You never learned that from me.'

'I've tried fighting,' Steven growled. 'But it doesn't get me anywhere. In fact, it was fighting that created this mess, according to Maud.'

'Wise woman. But you still aren't a credit to my example. And after all I've done to help you.'

'I know that. I'm grateful to you for warning me of that meeting.'

'But I did it for a reason, lad. I want Jennifer out of this engagement as much as you do, and I believed you were the man to do it. But you've fumbled it badly.'

'All right, what would you do?'

'Well, first, I wouldn't have got myself into this situation, but that's because I know Jennifer so well.'

'Of course, she's your granddaughter. If she was *my* granddaughter *I* wouldn't have got into this situation,' Steven complained.

'The way you're going, you'll never have a granddaughter,' Barney riposted. 'Not with Jennifer.'

'Well, that suits me fine. Because if you think I'd marry that pig-headed, obstinate—'

'Are you in love with her or not?'

'Yes, dammit!'

'Then we have to take firm, decisive action. All we need is David Conner's weak spot.

'Oh, I can tell you that,' Steven observed.

He did so. The old foxy gleam came into Barney's eyes. 'That's it!' he crowed. 'One last scam, just as I promised myself. Here's what we do.'

When he'd finished talking Steven poured himself another drink. 'It won't work,' he said. 'Even David Conner would never be that much of an idiot.'

'There's no end to the idiocies a man will commit when he's in love,' Barney declared. 'After all, look at you.'

Steven scowled.

CHAPTER TWELVE

'WILL you take this woman to be your lawful wedded wife...to love and cherish her—?'

Steven gave her a smile full of love as he said, 'I will.'

But then his face turned into David's, and Jennifer cried out that this was the wrong man. She would have run from the church but David clung to her.

She awoke to find herself sitting up in bed, shaking, with tears pouring down her face.

'Oh, God,' she wept, 'not again.'

She sat there in the darkness for several moments before she could find the strength to get out of bed. She was becoming desperate to avoid these dreams, but they pursued her every night.

She went into the kitchen to make herself some tea. As she worked she brushed away the tears, but more flowed in their place. At last she sat down, staring into her cup, and let the tears come as they would. It was better to weep now, when nobody could see her.

It wasn't always the same dream. Sometimes she began by marrying David, and he changed into Steven, who smiled and said, 'You didn't think I was going to let you marry another man, did you?'

That one was the hardest because it touched a nerve. Secretly she'd always expected him to stop the wedding. She knew that Maud had passed on the facts about the night he'd found David in her bed, and that he'd believed them, so surely they no longer had any quarrel? But he'd done nothing.

She wasn't sure what she'd expected, but she couldn't imagine him sitting tamely by while he lost the woman he wanted. Burn down the building, kidnap the groom, the bride, the whole wedding party. Steven was capable of all that before accepting defeat.

But he didn't want her; at least, not enough to make a commitment. That was the truth she had to face. At the very moment when she'd finally understood the depth of her love for him, he had shrugged and lost interest. For him, there would always be another bus along soon.

Now here she was, the night before her wedding, breaking her heart over the man who'd scorched across her life and vanished, leaving her desolate.

She hadn't seen or spoken to Steven for weeks. He'd sent a wedding gift of antique silver, accompanied by a formal note wishing her every happiness, and she'd written him an equally formal letter of thanks. After that there had been only silence.

She'd seen little of David, too, as he'd been away in Scotland, hunting suitable sites for Nortons depots. Barney had entrusted him with this mission as a way of welcoming him into the family.

Barney's reaction to her engagement had been strangely muted. He liked David, but he hadn't been eager for the marriage. She realised that he'd fallen under Steven's spell.

Even her brother was getting on well with Steven, whose hostility had faded in the face of Trevor's devotion to Maud. Trevor too would have been glad to see her marry Steven, but he'd welcomed David politely, and, by telephone from the Caribbean, had offered him the use of his new four-wheel drive car for the trip over rough terrain.

The whole Scottish idea had puzzled her. David's brief had been to investigate the islands, but to Jennifer these were the wrong places to site new depots. She had an uneasy feeling that Barney had created the job out of courtesy, apparently forgetting that David had a firm of his own to run.

He'd returned much later than expected, and with only vague explanations. At last, reluctantly, he'd told her the true reason.

'When I was on the isle of Arran, Trevor's car was stolen. The police expected to find it easily, because the last ferry had gone, and there was no way of getting it off the island until the next day, when they could mount a watch. But it seemed to have vanished into thin air. I kept holding on, hoping it would be found, so that I wouldn't have to return without it.'

'But you drove it home,' she said. 'So you got it back.'

'After a week it simply turned up in the hotel car park. It wasn't damaged. Nothing had been taken from it. Even the petrol tank was full.'

'But that's weird. What do the police think?'

'They're as baffled as I am. It had been wiped clean of fingerprints, so there were no leads. You don't know what a relief it was to be able to start for home and stop having to make unconvincing excuses for the delay. Luckily your grandfather didn't seem to notice anything odd.'

'Barney usually notices things,' Jennifer said, puzzled.

'Maybe he's being tactful. I've given him my report but when I ask him about it he just puts me off. I'm not sure he's even bothered to read it. He probably thinks I'm a complete no-hoper.'

'Of course he doesn't,' Jennifer said warmly. She felt

the old protective tenderness for this gentle man. But mingled with it was a twinge of dismay that he needed to be bolstered all the time. She couldn't help thinking of how differently Steven would have reacted, cursing up hill and down dale, never caring who knew his car had been stolen as long as he got it back fast. In fact, it was hard to picture anyone daring to steal Steven's car.

David had seemed very quiet that evening, but she'd put that down to tiredness and strain, for the trip had plainly taken a lot out of him. He'd excused himself from seeing her very much before the wedding, arguing that he had to work long hours at his business to get everything in shape before he left for their honeymoon. Jennifer had acquiesced with a feeling that she'd guiltily recognised as relief.

Since then they'd barely met or spoken, and she'd been left with a sensation of being in limbo, caught between the two men, but in touch with neither of them.

And in a few hours the day would be here when she must commit herself to a man she was fond of, but whom she did not love. David was charming and kindly, but he lacked the steel that her ideal man must possess. Not that the steeliest man she knew was in any way ideal. He was arrogant, overbearing, impatient, rude and unforgettable.

She didn't return to bed, not daring to risk another dream. Besides, it was already growing light. Maud would soon be here to help prepare the 'happy bride'. She pulled herself together, and by the time Maud arrived the tears had been washed away and Jennifer could manage a smile.

Maud was lightly tanned from her honeymoon. Her waistline was increasing rapidly now, and, as she happily confided, she was longing to wear her first maternity frock.

The bridal outfit was a short cocktail dress in cream silk, topped off by a small matching hat. Maud made up Jennifer's face expertly and stood back to admire her handiwork.

'You look lovely,' she said. She glanced out of the window. 'Barney's car has just arrived. Shall we go?'

'Just—just a moment,' Jennifer said. 'I'm not quite ready.' She needed a little more time, to ignore the pain in her heart, and force herself to go ahead with this.

But at last there was no delaying it any longer. She gave Maud's hand a squeeze, and went out to where Barney was waiting for her.

The three of them said little on the way to the register office. Jennifer covered her pain with a fixed smile, and the other two seemed strangely uneasy. Barney filled the awkward silence by chattering about his coming great grandchild.

'Are you sure you're taking care of yourself?' he asked Maud for the hundredth time. 'You still look as though a breath would blow you away.'

'Don't you worry about me,' Maud told him. 'I'm a lot stronger than I look.'

You're stronger than you know.

Jennifer sat up straight with shock. Maud's words had opened a door in her brain, and through it walked Steven, as he'd been when her father deserted her again.

'You're stronger than you know...stand up on your own...you don't need anyone as badly as you think you do. Not your father, not David, not me.'

It had taken until now, when it was almost too late, for her to see what was staring her in the face. Steven had wanted to detach her from David for his own unscrupulous reasons. Blinded by that, she'd overlooked the simple truth. Steven had always understood her better than anyone.

She couldn't marry David. She was too fond of him to do him such an injury. She must break off this marriage now, and then she must tell Barney she was withdrawing from the firm. If he demanded back the shares he'd once given her, she would return them with a light heart, and somehow she would make him understand that it was time she reclaimed her own life.

What that life would be, it was too soon to say. But she knew abandoned animals would come into it somewhere.

And Steven? She simply had no idea what would happen between them, but she would confront him as a free woman: free and strong, as he'd shown her how to be.

All this flashed through her mind with the speed of light, less conscious thoughts than a series of blinding images. The decision was taken before the others could ask her why she was staring into space.

'Barney, have you got your mobile?' she asked breathlessly.

'Of course not,' he spluttered. 'Not on my way to a wedding.'

'Stop the car!' Jennifer cried.

She bounded out and ran frantically to the nearest telephone box. She must try to catch David before he left home. But the phone was answered by his mother, just about to depart.

'David went out an hour ago,' she said. 'He said he'd catch up with me there.'

Jennifer dived back into the car. 'I can't tell you anything yet,' she told the others breathlessly. 'It's just—I just—can't tell you.'

It was David's right to hear it first. But if only it didn't have to be at the register office! She failed to see the quick glance between Barney and Maud, or the way they both crossed their fingers.

Jennifer's heart was beating hard when they arrived. The next half-hour was going to be difficult, but she wouldn't weaken. If only poor David wasn't too badly hurt.

Some of his family were there already, and soon his mother arrived, looking anxious. 'I thought he'd be coming in the car with me,' she explained. 'But suddenly he said he had something important to do first. Oh, dear, I do hope he gets here soon.'

There was a small commotion, and heads turned. But it was Steven who entered. His face was harsh and set, and for a moment Jennifer thought he would come to her. But then he turned away, and she knew that he wouldn't try to stop her marriage. And that refusal would colour all their future relationship. If any.

Then her head went up. Steven himself had said she was strong enough to do without him, and she would prove it true, no matter how much her heart ached.

The time of the wedding came and went. The next party was ushered in first. Jennifer looked around, baffled. Normally David was as punctual as clockwork. It was part of his soundness, the quality that he used instead of inspiration.

Suddenly there was a hum in the little crowd. Turning, Jennifer saw David standing in the doorway, but not as she'd expected him. He wasn't dressed for a wedding, and he wasn't alone. Penny was beside him, holding his hand.

Pale and tense, the bride and groom faced each other

in the middle of the room. Jennifer took a deep breath, but David spoke first.

'I'm sorry, Jennifer,' he said. 'I can't marry you. I'm in love with Penny.'

The words seemed to hang in the air. Jennifer stared at him, too astounded to take in the look of triumph that flashed between Steven and Barney.

'Jennifer,' David pleaded. 'Please say something.'

The town hall had witnessed jilted brides before, but never one who let out a shriek of delight and hugged her ex-groom with relief.

'I'm so glad,' she wept. 'Oh, David, I'm so glad.'

'You—you are?'

'I wasn't going to go through with it either,' she confessed. 'We should never have got engaged. It was all my fault. Try to forgive me.'

'You're the most splendid woman in the world,' he said in relief. 'Too splendid for me. I think I've been falling in love with Penny since the night of the gala, but at first I wasn't sure. Then we were stranded on the island together—'

'Penny was there with you?'

'Your grandfather forgot to give me some important files, so she had to follow me up there. The night she arrived the car was stolen, and she was a tower of strength—'

'Of course,' Steven murmured.

'And our feelings were just too strong for us. I—' He looked at Penny, who squeezed his hand encouragingly. 'We felt the best thing was to be open about it.'

'How wise!' Steven said sardonically. 'And there's nothing like leaving it to the last minute.'

'Will you hush?' Jennifer said, digging him in the ribs. She was full of relief, but her joy was tinged with disappointment. Steven hadn't tried to halt her marriage. In one sense, little had changed.

David turned away to explain to his mother, who was looking bewildered. Jennifer thought she would soon be glad of the change. She knew that the little woman was slightly alarmed by herself. Penny would suit her far better.

Trevor and Maud were hugging each other with glee, and Jennifer was baffled to see Steven and Barney shaking hands vigorously, and laughing.

'The fox hasn't lost his touch after all,' Barney declared triumphantly. 'I did it.'

'*We* did it,' Steven said, his eye on Jennifer. 'I'm going to need my share of the credit for this. Although I'll admit you were the brains.'

'What are you two talking about?' Jennifer demanded.

'I'm surprised you need to ask,' Steven said. 'Did you really think I wasn't going to sabotage this wedding?'

'But what did you do?' Jennifer begged, her heart leaping.

'We gave David the chance to discover that he really loved Penny,' Steven said.

Barney joined in. 'I sent him to Scotland on a wild-goose chase. And then I sent Penny after him. I wanted him to take her in the first place, but he wouldn't—'

'He was being noble on your account,' Steven said wryly.

'Something you wouldn't know anything about,' Jennifer said, indignant at his tone.

'Not a thing. You won't catch me being noble where my own interests are concerned.'

'Never mind that,' Barney said, quelling the squabble. 'I invented the story about the files, so she had to follow him.'

'But the stolen car—?' Jennifer said, bewildered.

'That was the easiest of all,' Steven said. 'The "thief" worked for me, and he was armed with Trevor's spare key, with Trevor's permission. So he simply drove it away without trouble. He took it the night Penny arrived, locked it up in a private garage, and left it there for a week. Then we just had to sit back and wait while your fiancé's feelings overcame his scruples.'

'Something else you wouldn't understand,' Jennifer said.

'I've never had any scruples about taking what I wanted,' he agreed. 'But you almost defeated me with your crazy obstinacy.'

'Me? If you think—'

'Be quiet, woman, and kiss me,' he said, firmly taking her into his arms.

Her heart sang with the kiss from the man she loved, a kiss she'd thought she would never know again.

'That's it!' David cried suddenly. 'Now I remember.'

Everyone turned to look at him.

'The night we got engaged, I saw you two together when I woke up, but I was half-blind from the headache and it didn't properly register. Next morning I knew I'd seen something important, but I couldn't remember what. It's been driving me crazy, and now it's come back to me.'

'It's a pity you didn't remember sooner,' Steven growled. 'You might have saved us all a lot of trouble. Now, push off, there's a good fellow, and get yourself engaged again.'

'Actually, I already have,' David said, with a proud look at Penny.

'Fine.' Steven confronted Jennifer. 'That just leaves

us. I have something to say to you, and listen well, for I may never manage to say it again.

'I nearly lost you because I didn't know how to tell you how much I love and need you. I can't imagine the rest of my life without you. But, thank God, that isn't going to happen. We found each other in time.'

It was the declaration of love she'd longed for, and her heart seemed to take wing and soar with joy. Yet even now his self-assurance was just a little too much. If they were to be happy she needed to stand her ground at the start.

'An affair, I think you said,' she challenged him.

'Never in a million years,' he said emphatically, 'will I have an affair with you. We are getting married. Otherwise you might try to marry some other man, and I couldn't stand the strain of all this again.'

'An affair is what you wanted,' Jennifer said, equally emphatically. 'And an affair is what I'm offering.'

'Excuse me,' the registrar interrupted them, 'but is the Norton-Conner wedding going ahead or not?'

'Not,' Steven said firmly.

'In that case, may I ask you all to leave?'

'Come on,' Barney said. 'We've got all that food laid out at home. We'll have a party.'

'But without us,' Steven said, looking at Jennifer. 'We're going to have a party of our own.' He took her hand. 'Come with me.'

He was striding from the room even as he spoke, cheered on by the others. By Jennifer stopped him in the doorway, just long enough to toss her bouquet to Penny.

'Invite us to your wedding,' she cried, laughing, just before Steven whisked her out of the door.

Before she knew it she was seated in his car, and he was out on the road, driving with fierce concentration.

'You've spent too long dithering,' he said. 'I told you the first time we met that you were disorganised, and, boy, was it true! From now on I'm taking charge.'

'Of me? Of my life?'

'Of our entire relationship. Never, never again will I let you put me through what you did today.'

When they reached his house he hurried her upstairs, keeping a firm grip on her hand, as if afraid she would vanish if he let go. When he'd shut his bedroom door behind them she demanded, 'Can I speak now?'

'Not while you're wearing *his* wedding dress.' He was fumbling at the tiny pearl buttons down the front.

'Careful, you'll tear it.'

'So what? You're never going to wear it again.' He gave a wrench and the buttons spilled all over the floor. Another wrench and the dress was in pieces. 'That's better.'

'What do you think you're doing?'

'What I've been wanting to do for weeks,' he said, tossing her slip away. The next moment he'd torn off his jacket and shirt, and pulled her hard against his bare chest. His hands fumbled in her hair, tumbling it down about her shoulders, then his mouth was on hers, hot, fierce and urgent.

'I've lain awake dreaming about this,' he said between kisses. 'Night after night—going mad—afraid I'd never have you in my arms again—and you didn't care! You were so cool and composed, and all the time I was in hell!'

His lips silenced her before she could answer, but she responded without words, opening her mouth for his deeply exploring tongue. They clung together, united as much by relief as by passion. They'd been to the edge of the abyss and looked over into a life without each

other. And they'd backed off from that life, in dread.
The deep, mutual love they'd discovered infused every
action with beauty.

Jennifer had often wondered how their first loving
would feel. Now she knew she needn't have worried.
What was happening now was truly lovemaking, as
she'd hardly dared to dream it could be.

Steven held and caressed her as though she were a
treasure he'd thought lost for ever. Once Jennifer even
thought she saw anxiety in his eyes, but she enfolded
him in her arms, laying her lips reassuringly on his, and
love cast out fear.

When at last they became one he made love to her
with every part of his body, with his loins, his hands,
his eyes that watched her with a possessive, brooding
passion.

'Is everything all right, my love?' he whispered.

'Everything,' she whispered back. 'Everything.'

Her words—or perhaps something he heard in her
tone—seemed to be what he was waiting for. He claimed
her more deeply, but with a tenderness that was heart-
stopping. She gave it back a thousandfold, and knew that
finally all was well between them.

Afterwards they didn't fall apart, but clung together
even more closely. Then Steven, the least poetical of
men, surprised her with a gesture of pure poetry. Taking
her hand, he lifted it high, intertwining his fingers among
hers and bending his own so that she was held fast.

'Two becomes one,' he said. 'Do you see?'

'Yes, I see,' she said in wonder.

It was the safety she'd dreamed of but thought Steven
could never give her. If she'd known then what she knew
now she would have realised that safety lay in the arms

of a man who loved you passionately and feared nothing so much as to lose you. The rest was talk.

They dozed for a while, and when they awoke he kissed her. 'Did I hear you tell Conner you wouldn't have gone through with it either, or did I imagine that?'

'No, I really said it. I made up my mind in the car. You were right. I'm stronger than I knew. I'm leaving Nortons too. I have to find out where my life is heading.'

'It's heading down the aisle, with me.'

'I said I wouldn't marry you. Weren't you listening?'

'I never listen to nonsense. I love you. How about in six weeks' time?'

'And I love you, too. But have you any idea how outrageously you've behaved? Moving people around like pawns, sending David and Penny here and there, getting them stranded just to suit yourself—'

'And aren't you just glad I did? Them too.'

'That's beside the point.'

As she spoke she was letting her fingers drift down his chest, across his flat stomach, and lower, to where she could already see the growing urgency of his need.

'If you imagine,' she purred, 'that I'm marrying a man whose idea of polite conversation is to give orders—'

'Orders? Me? I'm the soul of meekness.' Steven drew a shuddering breath, trying to control himself against what she was doing to him. He had something to say, and it was important to get it out before she drove him completely crazy, but Jennifer spoke first.

'Who told me—"I'll never go through this kind of fancy performance"?'

'Never mind what I said then,' he growled. 'Listen to what I'm saying now.'

'Who also told me that I was strong enough to stand

alone, because I didn't need anyone, including Steven
Leary?'

'I was a fool. Jennifer, you're winding me up—aren't
you?'

'Partly,' she mused. 'I know I can stand on my own
two feet now, and you did that for me.'

'Now get this into your head once and for all,' he said
raggedly. 'We are getting married. Not in a register office, but in a church. You're going to wear white satin,
carry flowers and look glorious. I shall wear a morning
suit and look sheepish and ridiculous, as befits a groom.
But it doesn't matter because nobody will be looking at
me. They'll be thinking how beautiful you are, and how
lucky I am.

'Trevor will be my best man, and he'll wear the smug
expression of a man who's already been through it and
is enjoying watching the other fellow suffer. It will be
a completely wonderful wedding. And afterwards—'

'Afterwards?' Jennifer asked, her heart beating at a
sudden new note in Steven's voice.

'Afterwards, I shall never, ever let you go again.' His
voice was husky. 'So now that's settled—'

'Is it settled?' she asked mischievously.

'Yes, it is—and do you know what you're doing to
me?'

She smiled, an ancient, mysterious smile. 'I know *exactly* what I'm doing to you.'

'It's very dangerous unless you mean it.'

'But I do mean it,' she said joyfully. 'I mean it with
all my heart.'

He abandoned the last of his control and took her
firmly into his arms. 'In that case…'

It was late evening before they got up, and the sun
was low in the sky.

'I'm hungry,' Jennifer murmured.

'Then I'll make you a feast. But first I want to take you outside and show you something.'

'But I haven't got any clothes or shoes here,' she protested, laughing.

He wrapped her in a huge bathrobe of his own, and carried her out into the grounds. The sunset drenched the land in a soft glow, and she snuggled against him blissfully, wondering where they were going, but content simply to be in his arms.

He carried her through the trees, to the place she'd seen on Maud's wedding day. The ground was completely cleared now, and more buildings had been outlined, but work seemed to have stopped.

'It couldn't go any further without you,' Steven explained, seating himself on a huge log, with her on his lap. 'I need your ideas before I start building.'

'My ideas about what?'

'Oh, didn't I mention that? It's going to be an animal sanctuary.'

'A what? *Steven!*'

'It's your wedding present. And in my usual arrogant, overbearing way, I started setting it up before you'd agreed to marry me.'

'A sanctuary,' she breathed in wonder.

'Well, I thought you'd like one. The thing is, I shall still need you at Nortons, at least for a while. But gradually you'll spend less time with the firm, and concentrate on running this place. Even when you give up your job you'll have the income from your shares, and you can use that to pay for the staff you'll need here. I thought one person to start with, but later—'

'Hey, hold on,' she protested. 'You've got it all

worked out, haven't you? What happened to giving me a say?'

'Did I get it wrong? All right, tell me how *you'd* like to manage things.'

'Well—actually—I'd like to do exactly what you've just described. And, Steven, if there's one thing about you that annoys me more than anything else it's the way you can read my mind, and anticipate what I want before I even want it. And cut that out.' For Steven had shouted with laughter.

'Sorry,' he said at last. 'My disgraceful habit of being right all the time is something you'll have to come to terms with.'

Jennifer kicked him with her bare foot, but not very hard.

'So what else am I going to want to do?' she asked. 'Tell me now, and save me the bother of thinking it out for myself.'

'Well, something tells me that you're going to expand the sanctuary until we have to move out to make room for the inmates—'

'Residents.'

'Residents. And don't worry about where they're coming from. There's a local animal charity that's got more waifs and strays than they know what to do with, and they're very anxious to meet you. When you've approved the plans I'll have the men start on the foundations, and then—'

His words were cut off by her mouth, clasped eagerly to his. He was the first person who had ever sympathised with this side of her life, and without words she tried to tell him of her passionate gratitude that he'd understood her needs and wanted to fulfil them.

'So this was the big secret you steered me away from at the wedding,' she said, when she could speak.

'I was going to enjoy surprising you, and you nearly spoiled everything by discovering this place. And by the way, I said it was your wedding present—'

'I'll marry you; I'll marry you,' she said at once.

He grinned. 'I thought this would do it. But actually, I have another present for you. He's just over there, coming to investigate us.'

Jennifer gave a cry of delight at the sight of a small black cat with white paws, bounding across the grass. He leapt into her lap and began nuzzling her.

'Is it really him?' she asked.

'The very same. I sought out that family and told them I wanted Paws Two as soon as he was old enough to leave.'

'But we were going to call him Steven.'

'Don't you dare call him after me,' Steven said severely. 'He's a total idiot. Since he moved in the place has been a shambles.'

She gave a sigh of contentment, and snuggled against him. 'Oh, everything's perfect. To think you started mapping this place out while you hated me.'

'I never hated you. I didn't like you pumping me for information for David, but when you said it was just a practical joke, I guess I always believed you. But my pride had got tangled up by then, and I couldn't think straight.

'It hurt, and that warned me that I was in deeper than I'd thought. So I did everything wrong. I tried to wrest you from Conner by force, instead of coming to you and saying I loved you, which is what I should have done. When my clumsiness had propelled you into that engagement I was nearly off my head.

'I started preparing this place for you as a way of reassuring myself that things would be all right. And all the time I blundered on, making things worse, and your wedding day got closer. I think I went a bit crazy. Luckily, Barney came to the rescue, and we thought up this scheme to throw Conner and Penny together.'

'But, darling, suppose David hadn't jilted me? Did you have a plan for that too? Or would you have just stood there and tamely watched me marry another man?'

Steven gave her his wickedest smile. He put Paws Two firmly on the ground and drew her very close, murmuring, 'My love—my dearest love—what do *you* think?'

Modern Romance™
...seduction and
passion guaranteed

Tender Romance™
...love affairs that
last a lifetime

Medical Romance™
...medical drama
on the pulse

Historical Romance™
...rich, vivid and
passionate

Sensual Romance™
...sassy, sexy and
seductive

Blaze Romance™
...the temperature's
rising

27 new titles every month.

Live the emotion

 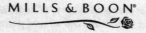

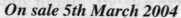

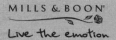

MILLS & BOON®

Live the emotion

Modern Romance™

HIS PREGNANT PRINCESS by Robyn Donald

Princess Lucia has never met anyone like millionaire Hunter Radcliffe and their mutual attraction is immediate. But then Lucia finds she's expecting Hunter's child and he insists they marry. Lucia has little choice – it's just another marriage of convenience for the royal house of Bagaton...

THE ITALIAN'S MARRIAGE BARGAIN by Carol Marinelli

Gorgeous Italian Luca Santanno needs a temporary bride – and sexy Felicity Conlon is the perfect candidate! Felicity hates Luca with a passion – but she can't refuse his marriage demand. And as soon as she shares his marriage bed she finds it impossible to leave...

THE SPANIARD'S REVENGE by Susan Stephens

The Ford family caused the death of Xavier Martinez Bordiu's brother – and now Sophie Ford works for him! He will take his revenge in the most pleasurable way... But as Xavier's practised seduction awakens Sophie's sensuality he finds the ice around his heart beginning to melt...

THE ITALIAN'S PASSION by Elizabeth Power

Mel Sheraton has her life under control. But a trip to Italy brings her face to face with the past, in the shape of gorgeous millionaire Vann Capella. Swept away in the Italian heat, Mel feels her life falling apart – if she spends time with Vann she risks him learning her deepest secret.

On sale 5th March 2004

Available at most branches of WHSmith, Tesco, Martins, Borders, Eason, Sainsbury's and all good paperback bookshops.

0204/01b

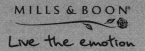

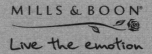

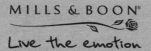

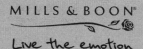